Marian Gruenfelde

30 Chalcot Crescent

London N. W. 1

CATALOGUE OF
RUBBINGS OF BRASSES
AND INCISED SLABS

VICTORIA AND ALBERT MUSEUM

CATALOGUE OF RUBBINGS OF BRASSES AND INCISED SLABS

BY

MURIEL CLAYTON, M.A.

LONDON
HER MAJESTY'S STATIONERY OFFICE
1968

PREFATORY NOTE

THE *List of Rubbings of Brasses*, published by the Museum in 1915, is now out of print. The present volume contains all the material of the previous one, considerably revised and enlarged. A generous gift of 2200 rubbings was made by the Society of Antiquaries of London in 1911. Of these, 1527 were included in the *List of Rubbings*, and the remaining 627 have been identified and are catalogued for the first time in this volume. This collection has since been supplemented by a later gift of 375 rubbings from Mr. J. S. M. Ward, besides large numbers from Mr. Mill Stephenson, Mr. Marcus Huish, Mr. Ernest W. Morley, Miss Frances Weale, and other donors.

It may be said here that a large collection of rubbings from heraldic medallions incised on stone has recently been presented by Mr. Nicolas Toke. Though these are closely associated with brasses, they represent a separate and later development of the sepulchral memorial, and are, therefore, not included here.

This Catalogue differs from other existing lists of brasses in that the rubbings are classified under Military Costume, Civil Costume, Ecclesiastical Costume, etc., and the arrangement is chronological, instead of topographical. The latter purpose is served by an index of place-names.

The Catalogue has been revised, and a new and fuller Introduction has been written by Miss Muriel Clayton, Assistant in the Department of Engraving, Illustration, and Design. The Index of Names and the Index of Place-Names have been compiled by Miss K. Sproule, of the same Department.

ERIC MACLAGAN.

October 1929.

This *Catalogue of Rubbings of Brasses and Incised Slabs* has long been out of print, and is now re-issued in its original form, without alterations or additions.

March 1968

TABLE OF CONTENTS

LIST OF ILLUSTRATIONS

NOTE.—*In some cases canopies, inscriptions, etc., are omitted.*

MILITARY COSTUME

CIVIL COSTUME

MALE

LIST OF ILLUSTRATIONS

INSCRIPTIONS

FOREIGN BRASSES AND INCISED SLABS

MILITARY COSTUME

CIVIL COSTUME

MALE

FEMALE

ECCLESIASTICAL COSTUME

SHROUDED EFFIGIES

INTRODUCTION

I. GENERAL HISTORY

IT is now well over a hundred years since the archæological and historical importance of the study of Monumental Brasses was recognised for the first time by Richard Gough in his work on the *Sepulchral Monuments in Great Britain*, and for a long time they have been regarded as one of the chief contemporary sources of evidence for the details of armour and costume, and the variations of palæography and heraldry. England still possesses a very large number of brasses, in spite of the spoliation of the religious houses at the time of the Dissolution and the subsequent havoc wrought during the Civil War and the Commonwealth. Unfortunately, the intrinsic value of the metal has often roused the crusading zeal of those whose religious prejudices alone would not have urged them to desecration, and the brasses we now have can only be a fraction of the original number. Nevertheless, there are still enough brasses in England to enable the course of their development to be traced clearly, while very few remain of the once numerous brasses on the Continent. In France those that survived the troubles of the sixteenth century were swept away in the Reign of Terror, and almost the only evidence of their existence is furnished by the collection of drawings bequeathed by Gough to the Bodleian Library at Oxford. Germany still possesses a fairly large number, including many that show striking beauty of design, such as those at Lübeck, and the series in the Cathedrals of Meissen and Freiburg, commemorating members of the royal house of Saxony. The Low Countries have many very fine examples, especially at Bruges, Brussels and Ghent, while Ringstead in Denmark has a splendid brass, dated 1319, to King Eric Menved and Queen Ingeborg. But although the best of these foreign brasses are finer than anything existing in England, they are too few in number to throw much light on the history of monumental brasses in general, which must be traced from the English brasses.

Incised slabs, of which the Continent has preserved more examples than England, preceded brasses in favour as sepulchral memorials. They evolved from the altar-tomb, which about the twelfth century was replaced by a bas-relief of the deceased on the lid of the coffin, and later by the incised slab. Early examples are the slabs of St. Piatus, c. 1142, at Seclin, near Lille, and of Bishop Barthelemy de Vir, 1158, at Laon, both in pontificals. The earliest represented in the Museum collection is the slab with an effigy of St. Helena, engraved about 1180, at Forêt, near Brussels. Among the few existing slabs in English churches are those in Salisbury Cathedral of Bishop Roger, 1139, and Bishop Jocelin, 1184, in which lines are incised on the relief figures, and the very interesting slab of Sir Walter de Bitton, 1227, Bitton, Gloucestershire, where the upper part of the body is in bas-relief, and the lower part is incised. Other English slabs are those of a knight, c. 1260, at Avenbury, Hereford-shire ; of Bishop St. William de Byttone, 1274, at Wells, and of William de Freney, Archbishop of Rages, c. 1290, at Rhuddlan, N. Wales, and later examples are the slabs of James Samson, 1349, Middleton, Essex, in mass vestments, and of John Cherowin, 1441, Brading, Isle of Wight, in armour. The transition from the incised slab to the engraved brass appears to have taken place at the beginning of the thirteenth century, after which the two methods existed side by side. In England the number of incised slabs was small compared with that of the brasses, but on the Continent the former retained an equal popularity for a considerable period.

The material used for brasses was an alloy of copper and zinc, and until the end of the sixteenth century the Continent had a monopoly of its production, and exported it to England. Cologne was the chief manufacturing centre for North Germany and Flanders, and in England brass was often known as " Cullen plate," though " latten " was the more usual term. In Dugdale's *Antiquities of Warwickshire* an extract is given from the contract made between the executors of Richard Beauchamp, Earl of Warwick, and the artisans employed for the con-struction of his great tomb in the Beauchamp Chapel, Warwick, and it is stated " that they shall make, forge and worke in most finest wise and of the finest Latten one large plate to be dressed . . . the large plate to be made of the finest and thickest Cullen plate," and further that " these 14 scutcheons and the Armes in them, the said Bartholomew shall make, repare, grave, gild, enamel and pullish as well as possible."

Traces can still be seen in many brasses of the colours which originally enlivened them. Heraldic shields were very often coloured, and tabards and heraldic mantles demanded similar treatment, as did the almuces of ecclesiastics, the sword-belts of knights and the linings of the mantles of ladies. It is not clear what substance was used. Enamel is found occa-sionally, and indeed the principle of inlaying probably derived from the Limoges enamels, but some kind of coloured composition was no doubt employed, of which the daily treading of many feet has left remaining only a few fragments. When enamel was used, it is still intact and clear, as in the blue shield of Sir John D'Aubernoun, 1277, at Stoke d'Abernon, Surrey. Occasionally separate shields of enamel were prepared, and let into the brass, as in the effigy of Margarete de Camoys, c. 1310, at Trotton, Sussex, where the indents for nine small shields can be seen in her gown.

Brasses in England are found most frequently in the eastern counties, especially in Kent, Essex, Suffolk and Norfolk. In the west and north they occur much more rarely, and Scotland and Ireland have only three and five respectively. The preponderance on the east coast is no doubt due to the natural facilities for intercourse with the Continent, and also to the great wealth of the merchant princes of Ipswich, Norwich, Lynn and Lincoln. In this part of England there are several brasses of foreign workmanship, but they are easily recognisable, for while English brasses have the figure cut out to the outline and inlaid in a setting of stone, in foreign brasses the figure is engraved in the centre of a large rectangular plate, and the background is as a rule completely filled in with diapered work of great minuteness and delicacy. The list of brasses of foreign workmanship in England is as follows :—

Elsing, Norfolk, 1347, Sir Hugh Hastyngs (PLATE 4).
King's Lynn, Norfolk, 1349, Adam de Walsokne.
St. Albans Abbey, c. 1370, Abbot Thomas de la Mare (PLATE 52).
Wensley, Yorks., c. 1375, Sir Simon de Wenslagh, priest (PLATE 54).
King's Lynn, Norfolk, 1364, Robert Braunche (PLATE 39).
North Mimms, Herts., c. 1370, a priest (PLATE 54).
Aveley, Essex, 1370, Ralph de Knevyngton (PLATE 5).
Newark, Notts., 1361, Alan Fleming.
Topcliffe, Yorks., 1391, Thomas de Topclyffe.

All Saints, Newcastle-on-Tyne, 1411, Roger Thornton.
St. Mary Quay, Ipswich, 1525, Thomas Pownder (PLATE 44).
Fulham, Middx., 1529, Margaret Svanders, wife of Gerard Horne-
    bolt.
All Hallows, Barking, London, 1533, Andrew Evyngar.
St. Nicholas, Aberdeen, 1613, Duncan Liddel, M.D.

The first group of these brasses are obviously all products of the same school of engraving, and are strikingly similar in manner to a group of fourteenth-century continental brasses. These are :—

Ringstead, Zealand, 1319, King Eric Menved and Queen Ingeborg.
Schwerin, Mecklenburg, 1339, Bishops Ludolph and Henry de
    Bulowe.

Lübeck, 1350, Bishops Burchard de Serken and John de Mul.

Stralsund, Pomerania, 1357, Albert Hovener.

Thorn, Poland, 1361, Johannes von Zoest.

Brussels, 1332, John and Gerard de Heere (PLATE 67).

Schwerin, Mecklenburg, 1375, Bishops Godfrey and Frederic de Bulowe.

These seven brasses are so precisely similar in details that, allowing for the differences in date of execution, it is impossible to resist the inference that they come from the same workshop, if indeed the first five are not actually the work of the same hand. Now the brasses in England of Adam de Walsokne and Robert Braunche, both of them merchants, bear an extraordinary resemblance to the brasses of the merchants Albert Hovener and Johannes von Zoest. A unique feature is the reservation of a narrow rectangular panel below the figures, which is filled with a delicate engraving of scenes of daily life. On the Stralsund brass there are represented a deer hunt and a boar hunt, and at Thorn a feast of the wild men of the woods, while the Walsokne brass shows a deer hunt and a boar hunt, and the Braunche represents the famous " peacock feast." A similar connection is clear between the brass of Thomas de la Mare at St. Albans, and the brasses of Bishops Ludolph and Henry de Bulowe, of Bishops Burchard de Serken and Johan de Mul, and of King Eric Menved. Later in date and similar to one another in treatment are the brasses of Alan Fleming at Newark and of Bishops Godfrey and Frederic de Bulowe at Schwerin. The remaining English brasses do not fall into groups so easily, but the Wensley brass is treated in much the same manner, and the North Mimms brass, though much inferior in execution, is similar in design. All these brasses must clearly have originated from the same centre. Where exactly this was situated is not known, and the brasses have always been called " Flemish," but Mr. H. W. Macklin makes out a good case for giving Lübeck the credit of their creation. Certainly the Hanseatic League, of which Lübeck was an important member, had affiliated houses in Ipswich, Lynn, Norwich and York, while the trade of Bruges and Ypres was mainly with London, and the brass of King Eric Menved, who was elected by the citizens Lord of Lübeck, undoubtedly originated in the same workshop as two of the brasses of bishops. It is a point upon which no certainty seems possible, but on the grounds of dissimilarity in style to any existing Flemish brasses, as well as of geographical distribution, " North German " might perhaps be a less controversial designation. The Aveley brass and the Topcliffe brass are rather different in handling, and the remaining foreign brasses in England are later in date and inferior in workmanship.

Thirteenth-century brasses are few in number. The earliest known is that at Verden of Bishop Yso von Wilpe, who became the thirty-first bishop of Verden in 1205, and died in 1231. It is engraved very much in the manner of the incised slabs of the period. Very similar in treatment is the brass of Bishop Otto de Brunswick, 1279, in Hildesheim Cathedral (PLATE 71). It is certain that there were many brasses laid down in England during this century, but the earliest which has survived is the brass of Sir John D'Aubernoun, 1277, Stoke d'Abernon, Surrey, in chain mail (PLATE 1). The series of military brasses in England, ranging from this to the brass of Nicholas Toke, 1680, Great Chart, Kent, is perhaps the most valuable and certainly the most interesting monumental record that we possess.

The fourteenth century is the best period of brass engraving. In the first half of the century brasses are laid down exclusively to knights and their ladies, and to ecclesiastics. The effigy is represented as recumbent, with the feet resting against a heraldic animal, and the features are conventionalised. The rise of the middle classes to prosperity is heralded by the brass at Taplow, Bucks., to Nichole de Aumberdene, fishmonger, c. 1350 (PLATE 40), and towards the end of the century small brasses are found commemorating the petty tradesmen. Brasses of this period are simple and dignified in treatment, with lines deeply incised into thick plates of metal. Canopies were often added, reflecting the architectural style prevailing at the time. There are six fourteenth-century canopies at Cobham, Kent, which possesses the finest series of brasses in England, and other good canopies are on the brasses of Alianore de Bohun, 1399, Westminster Abbey (PLATE 49), Walter Pescod, 1398, Boston, Lincs., and Laurence de St. Maur, 1337, Higham Ferrers, Northants (PLATE 53). Variations on the more usual type of monument are cross brasses, of which the religious troubles have left us very few examples, and bracket brasses. Cross brasses fall into three classes : floriated crosses with a long stem, enclosing within the head the figure of the deceased, for example, Nichol de Gore, priest, c. 1330, Woodchurch, Kent ; octofoil crosses with figures in the head, a good example being Nichole de Aumberdene, c. 1350, Taplow (PLATE 40); and crosses without human figures, such as that at Higham Ferrers, Northants, 1400, to Thomas Chichele (PLATE 62). Among the third class the variety is endless. Bracket brasses of this century survive only in a mutilated condition.

The fifteenth century, though producing in its first half many splendid brasses, yet shows the beginning of the decline. The finest examples reach the same high standard as before, but the use of brasses has now spread to all ranks and the total number laid down increases considerably. This naturally tends to inferior workmanship and indifferent design.

Canopies are still fine, a particularly graceful example being that of Thomas Nelond, 1433, Cowfold, Sussex (PLATE 59). Towards the end of the century the Perpendicular style of architecture is reflected in the heavier and coarser type of the canopies. Bracket brasses become fairly frequent, and a very fine example is at Upper Hardres, Kent, 1405, where John Strete kneels to a bracket supporting the figures of SS. Peter and Paul (PLATE 60). Usually, however, the deceased himself stood on the bracket, as in the brass of John Bloxham and John Whytton, c. 1420, Merton College, Oxford (PLATE 59). The fifteenth century falls naturally into two almost equal parts, and the brasses of the first half rank almost beside those of the fourteenth century in dignified treatment. Most of the military brasses of this period are very fine, especially perhaps the monuments of Thomas de Beauchamp, Earl of Warwick, 1406, St. Mary, Warwick (PLATE 13), and of Lord Thomas Camoys, 1419, Trotton, Sussex (PLATE 15). Many of the armed figures wear the collar of SS, the symbol of the supporters of the House of Lancaster. Sometimes a knight wears civilian costume, as in the brass of Sir Thomas Brook, 1437, Thorncombe, Devon, and often in place of the heraldic animal at the feet there is a lively portrait of a favourite dog, as the " Jakke " of Sir Brian Stapilton, 1438, now lost, but formerly at Ingham, Norfolk, or the " Terri " of Lady Cassy, 1400, Deerhurst, Gloucestershire (PLATE 61). The brasses of civilians in this period are of great interest. Many varieties of trade have their representatives, but by far the most important are the wool merchants of Gloucestershire and Lincolnshire. They were connected with the Staple of Calais, the most influential trade guild of the fifteenth century, and the arms of the Staple appear on the brass of a wool merchant in St. Olave's, Hart Street, London, dated 1516. The merchant was usually represented with his feet resting against two bales of wool, and sometimes a sheep is substituted for one of the bales. The most important series of these brasses is at Northleach, Gloucestershire, and others are at Chipping Campden, Cirencester, Stamford in Lincolnshire, and also in Hertfordshire and Bedfordshire. Other trades represented at this time are the vintners, the mercers and the haberdashers. " Merchants' marks " are generally shown. These may have originated as a sort of trade-mark, but since they were hereditary, the merchants soon came to regard them almost as their armorial bearings. Often the device is combined with the initials of the merchant.

The second half of the fifteenth century was a period of rapid deterioration. Few even of the military brasses have canopies, and all in general are smaller in size. Very often the figure is represented as standing on a ground of grass and flowers, although the great tilting helmet is still beneath the head, as if the attitude were recumbent. Children are frequently shown, generally as a group of diminutive figures below the effigies of their parents. Small scrolls bearing texts are sometimes found above the figures. Heraldic garments, in the shape of tabards for the knights and heraldic kirtles for their ladies, become frequent, and the collar of SS is replaced by the Yorkist collar of Suns and Roses. An innovation is the use of mural brasses, rectangular in shape, which were to become very common in the following century. Chalice brasses are often found commemorating a priest. The earlier brasses to priests frequently represent them with a chalice and wafer lying on their breasts, as in the brass of Robert Lond, 1461, St. Peter, Bristol (PLATE 54), and the custom appears to have originated in Yorkshire of engraving the chalice alone with an inscription. From Yorkshire the practice spread to Norfolk, which produced the majority of brasses of this type. Examples occur both with and without the wafer. Heart brasses are another new development of this century. In their simplest form the heart is shown with scrolls rising up from it, and the inscription below. Possibly the earlier examples indicate that the heart alone was buried beneath, a frequent custom in the days of foreign wars. A variation in form was the heart held by two hands issuing from clouds, and often a heart is found in a subordinate position in a figure brass.

A peculiar and unpleasant development of the later fifteenth century was the introduction of shroud brasses, which in the following century became extremely popular. They are usually quite small, and generally the shrouded figure appears alone, or in company with a second shrouded figure. But occasionally a husband is shown in a shroud, with a wife in ordinary costume, indicating that she survived him and that the brass was laid down in her lifetime. In a brass at Taplow, Bucks., 1455, to Richard Manfeld, his sister and his younger brother John (PLATE 42), the figure of John is in a shroud, and the others are in ordinary dress. Sometimes a skeleton takes the place of the shrouded figure, and occasionally a shrouded skeleton appears. A very impressive foreign example of shrouded effigies is the great brass in Bruges Cathedral to Joris de Munter and his wife, Jakemine van der Brucghe, 1439 (PLATE 72). The severe and simple drapery of the shrouds, completely concealing the bodies and pulled forward over the faces, and the dignity and restraint of the handling quite overshadow the unpleasantness of the subject. But the average English shroud brass expresses pure morbidity, without any redeeming features.

The sixteenth century carries on the characteristics of the previous century, until the end of the reign of Henry VIII. There are quantities of brasses belonging to this period ; they were more popular than ever before, but the deterioration in workmanship is very marked. Shading is freely introduced, to the detriment of the simple dignity afforded by the outline treatment.   A new departure is the frequent use of a rectangular mural brass, with the whole surface engraved, where the figures are generally shown kneeling at desks, with their children in rows behind them, and accessory figures of saints.   These were at first set into the wall above a high stone tomb, but the use was soon extended, and mural plates become very frequent.   In this century also the practice begins of laying down brasses to children, for example, the brass to Dorothy Alleine, aged three, Woodham Mortimer, Essex, 1584.   Often an infant is represented in a chrysom, as on the brass to Elyn Bray, 1516, Stoke d'Abernon, Surrey. Heraldic brasses become more frequent than before, and scrolls are almost the rule.   Religious subjects are popular, with or without the figure of the deceased.   The Trinity had long been a favourite subject, and the Virgin appears on the brass to Henry Porte, 1512, Etwall, Derbyshire.   The Annunciation, the Adoration of the Shepherds and the Resurrection also occur several times.

The most interesting of the Tudor brasses are perhaps those which illustrate the great Merchant Companies of England.   The Gloucestershire wool-staplers have been mentioned already, but it was not until the sixteenth century that the arms of the Staple of Calais appeared on a brass. Nearly all the companies are represented in this century.   Most frequent are the arms of the Merchant Adventurers, incorporated 1296, *e.g.* on the brass of Thomas Pownder, 1525, St. Mary Quay, Ipswich (PLATE 44). The arms are : Barry nebulée of six, argent and azure, a chief quarterly gules and or, on the 1st and 4th quarters a lion passant gardant or, on the 2nd and 3rd two roses gules barbed vert.   They are often combined with merchants' marks, and with arms of a trading company, such as the Mercers' or the Goldsmiths'.   All these companies had been incorporated some centuries before.   A list of examples of brasses showing the arms of the various companies may be of interest.

The Mercers' Company : Wm. Thorpe, 1504, Higham Ferrers, Northants.
The Goldsmiths' Company : Rich. Ballett, 1598, Ufford, Suff.
The Skinners' Company : Wm. Shosmyth, 1479, Mereworth, Kent.
The Grocers' Company : Thos. White, 1610, Finchley, Middx.
The Drapers' Company : Sir G. Monox, 1543, Walthamstow, Essex.
The Haberdashers' Company : Anon., c. 1580, Faversham, Kent.
The Merchant Taylors' Company (two grants) : remains of brass to Hugh Pemberton, 1500, St. Helen, Bishopsgate ; Rich. Fynche, 1640, Dunstable, Beds.

The Salters' Company : Andrew Evyngar, 1533, All Hallows, Barking (PLATE 46).

The Fishmongers' Company : Christ. (?) Grantham, c. 1520, Wooburn, Bucks.

The Ironmongers' Company : John Carre, 1570, Stondon Massey, Essex.

The Brewers' Company : Roger James, 1591, All Hallows, Barking, London.

The Stationers' Company : John Daye, 1584, Little Bradley, Suff.

The Carpenters' Company : Thos. Edmonds, 1619, Horsell, Surrey.

The Vintners and the Clothworkers do not appear to be represented.

The number of brasses laid down decreases enormously in the period between the death of Henry VIII. and the accession of Elizabeth. Figures in armour compose, as usual, the bulk of those existing, and the brasses are small and decadent in design. The reign of Elizabeth saw a great increase in quantity, though not in quality. The plates of brass were now manufactured in England, instead of being imported from the Continent, but unfortunately the plates were so thin that the later brasses are very battered and often almost obliterated. Only the increasing popularity of the mural brass has preserved intact any of the monuments of this period. Nor is there any distinction in the drawing, which is weak and uncertain, with a great deal of erratic shading, and the engraving is so shallow, especially in the later brasses, that the lines seem hardly more than scratched on the plate. There are no new developments of any interest ; the old traditions are continued, though there is a larger proportion of curious brasses, such as the series sometimes called " Bedstead Brasses," commemorating women who died in childbirth. The old use of religious symbols has, of course, disappeared under the influence of the Reformation, and the allegorical hour-glasses, skulls, etc., which take their place, do not contribute to the aesthetic result.

The Caroline brasses are even worse than the Elizabethan. Almost the only tolerable examples are the brasses of Samuel Harsnett, Archbishop of York, 1631, Chigwell, Essex, and of Sir Edward Filmer, 1629, East Sutton, Kent. Very few brasses seem to have been laid down in the seventeenth century, and none are of any interest. In the eighteenth century the brass seems to disappear. Either the engraving of brasses became a lost art after a period of decadence, or fashion began to demand a different type of memorial, whether the mural monument or the stone slab, usually with heraldic bearings, set into the floor of nave or chancel. For these reasons the eighteenth century appears to have only four brasses, of which the latest in date is that of Benjamin Greenwood and his wife Philadelphia, 1773, St. Mary Cray, Kent.

During the nineteenth century brasses appear with shields of arms and with inscriptions, usually in poor lettering. From about 1850 there was somewhat of a revival which has naturally increased since the war, but, except in a few cases of genuine artistic invention, has shown no new developments and is simply an archaistic imitation of older styles. The Museum has few examples of brasses after 1800, and more modern examples are therefore excluded from this Catalogue.

PALIMPSESTS

Many of the brasses of the sixteenth century are known as Palimpsests. The term is not strictly accurate, for a palimpsest brass is actually one which has been reversed and engraved on the back, not one in which the original engraving has been erased to accommodate a new design. Palimpsests fall into two main classes : (i) brasses which are engraved on their reverse side, and (ii) appropriated and converted brasses. Class (i) is the more numerous. From the earliest days of brass-engraving there had been a possibility of the occurrence of palimpsests, for very often the spoiled plates from a continental workshop would be exported to England, or an English spoilt plate would be used again. But the two main causes of the existence of so many palimpsests are the Dissolution of the monasteries under Henry VIII., and the sacking of the Netherland churches in 1566. The brasses looted from the monasteries and churches were either melted down or sold to the brass-workers and reissued as fresh plates. Often, of course, the original plate was very much cut about in the process. The whole original plate is simply reversed in the brass to Amphillis Peckham, 1545, Denham, Bucks., which has on the back a complete fifteenth-century figure, with inscription and shield, but much more frequently only fragments of the original can now be traced. A very interesting example is the palimpsest inscription on the brass to William Hyde, 1562, Denchworth, Berks., the back of which shows a complete inscription in French relating to the foundation of Bisham Priory by Edward III. (*see* p. 141 *and* PLATE 63). Another good example is the brass to Margaret Bulstrode, 1540, Hedgerley, Bucks., where the effigy of the lady, the inscription, a group of children, and a shield are all cut out of brasses plundered from the great abbey at Bury St. Edmunds. Very frequently the reverse shows that the original was Flemish ; for example, the mutilated inscription at Sall, Norfolk, to Geoffrey Melman (?), c. 1580, has on the reverse part of the head of a lady with braided hair, of undoubted Flemish workmanship. A very curious palimpsest is the brass of John Laurence of Wardeboys, Abbot of Ramsey, at Burwell, Cambs., which was engraved during the Abbot's lifetime and represented him in full pontificals, but after the suppression of the Abbey in 1539 the effigy was reversed and the lower part re-engraved with cassock and surplice, a new plate being used for the upper part of the body. The total number of palimpsests among Elizabethan brasses is fairly large, and wherever a brass of Elizabethan date is engraved on a thick and solid piece of metal instead of on a flimsy sheet, the existence of a palimpsest is practically certain.

Appropriated and converted palimpsests form a much smaller class. A " palimpsest by appropriation," to use the technical term, is one which by the addition of a fresh inscription and new shields of arms has been made to do duty as a memorial to a later owner. There are several examples of this, a good one being at Bromham, Bedfordshire, where the brass was originally laid down in 1435 to Thomas Widville and his two wives, and was appropriated in 1535 to Sir John Dyve, his wife and his mother. A " converted " brass is an appropriated one which has been reworked to some extent to suit the later date. There are not very many of these, but a good example is at Waterperry, Oxfordshire, where the effigies of a man and wife of about 1440 have been extensively altered in accordance with the fashions of about 1540, and a new inscription assigns the brass to Walter Curson and his wife Isabel Saunders.

INSCRIPTIONS

The inscriptions attached to brasses constitute in themselves a field of great interest. Quite apart from their obvious historical importance, they present a perfect survey of·the different types of lettering used, a dictionary and grammar of the changing language, and an unfailing guide to the prevailing popular taste. The earliest inscriptions were placed round the edge of the slab in which the brass was set and each letter was cut separately out of the brass, and sunk in the stone, but this method was not very satisfactory, and at an early date the letters were cut on a narrow border of brass. In later brasses the inscription is on a small rectangular plate below the figures. In the thirteenth and fourteenth centuries the language is French, and a few French inscriptions are found in the early fifteenth century. As a rule throughout the fifteenth century Latin was employed, while in the sixteenth English takes its place, except in inscriptions to ecclesiastics, which are in Latin at all periods. The earliest type used was Lombardic, but at the beginning of the fourteenth century it gave way to early Black-Letter, which in turn was replaced in the fifteenth century by straight Black-Letter, and in the sixteenth by Tudor Black-Letter. In the seventeenth century Roman capitals were generally used. The early inscriptions are very simple, and are typified by the inscription to Sir John D'Aubernoun : " SIRE : IOHN : DAVBERNOVN : CHIVALER : GIST : ICY : DEV : DE : SA : ALME : EYT : MERCY." The Latin inscriptions of the fifteenth century are more difficult to decipher, owing to the frequent contractions employed, somewhat similar to those found in classical manuscripts. Inscriptions begin with " Hic jacet," or " Orate pro anima," and usually end with " cujus anime propitietur deus, Amen." Often a set of verses is added. The earliest English inscriptions are in the language of the *Canterbury Tales*, and usually begin with " Of your charity pray for the soul of . . ." or simply, " Pray for the soul of . . ." and end with " On whose soul Jesus have mercy." Verses often occur, commemorating the merits of the deceased, as at Holme-next-the-Sea, Norfolk, on the brass to Herry Notingham, c. 1405 :—

> " Herry Notyngham & hys wyffe lyne here
> yat maden this chirche stepull & quere
> two vestments & belles they made also
> Crist hem saue therfore ffro wo
> ande to bringe her saules to blis at heven
> sayth pater & aue with mylde steuen."

After the Reformation the invocatory phrases at the beginning and end of an inscription were often erased. Sixteenth-century inscriptions have to a large extent lost the dignified restraint of epitaphs of the early tombs, though they have not yet fallen into the degradation of the fulsome and moralising eulogies of the seventeenth century, of which a typical example is from Headcorn, Kent, dated 1636 :—

" Here lyeth the body of John Byrd sonn of William Byrd of this parish of Headcorn, who was borne the 10th of May 1629, and in the time of his sicknesse delivered many godly exhortations to his parents, taking his leave of them with such unexpected expressions as are not common in so young a child he departed this life on the 31st of January, anno 1636."

II. COSTUME ON BRASSES

A. MILITARY COSTUME

The incised slab of Sir John de Bitton, 1227, Bitton Church, Somersetshire, is a good example of the type of armour in force in the period immediately preceding that of the earliest brasses. Sir John wears a complete suit of chain mail, with a long surcoat, and has a large shield and a long, broad sword. The mail was composed of small metal rings, each ring interlinking with four others. The pot-helmet which was worn over the mail hood is not shown in this slab, but appears on the slab of Georges de Niverlée, 1262, Niverlée, Belgium (PLATE 66). But there are too few illustrations of this period for a detailed discussion to fall within the limits of this Introduction, and also its principal features were carried on into the next period, when the brasses begin. The development of armour as shown on Brasses falls into very distinct divisions.

I. *The Reinforced Chain Mail, or Surcoat Period*, 1250-1325.

The earliest example of this type is the life-sized brass of Sir John D'Aubernoun, 1277, Stoke d'Abernon, Surrey (PLATE 1). The armour consists of *hauberk* (shirt), mail *coif*, *chausses* (stockings), and gloves of mail, every link of which is accurately shown. Secondary defences are represented by knee-cops of steel or *cuir-bouilli*,[1] strapped over the mail. The plain surcoat falls to below the knees, and is fastened by a cord at the waist. It was divided at back and front, for the purpose of riding. The shield is small, flat and heater-shaped, and bears the arms in coloured enamel (*azure*, a chevron *or*). It is suspended by a *guige* passing over the right shoulder, and ornamented with roses and swastikas. The sword is long and straight, and hangs diagonally in front of the body, gripped by the sword-belt in two places. Short prick spurs are strapped to the feet, and the lance, which is not represented elsewhere on brasses, is held in the crook of the right elbow. The brass of Sir Roger de Trumpington, 1289, Trumpington, Cambs. (PLATE 1), is similar in its main features, but the head is resting on the great conical tilting helm, the weight of which was chiefly taken by the shoulders. It is secured by a chain fastened to the cord confining the surcoat. This is one of the few brasses showing *ailettes*, which were small shields fastened at right angles to the shoulders, to lessen the force of a sweeping blow. In brasses they are turned at right angles to their real position to display heraldic bearings. The shield is larger, and is concave to the body. The brass of Sir Robert de Bures, 1302, Acton, Suffolk (PLATE 1), may be considered the finest military brass in existence. It shows the same equipment as the Stoke d'Abernon and Trumpington brasses, but above the knee-cops and beneath the skirt of the hauberk can be seen the padded and quilted trews, which covered the chausses from the knees upward. In the brass of Sir Robert de Setvans, 1306, Chartham, Kent (PLATE 1), the mail coif is lying on the shoulders, leaving the head bare, and below the edge of the hauberk appears the padded *haqueton*. The knight wears ailettes, which are

---

[1] *cuir-bouilli* = boiled leather.

charged with his device of a winnowing-fan, as is his surcoat.   His knee-cops are of plate.

A half-effigy at Croft, Lincolnshire, c. 1300, illustrates the use of banded mail, an innovation of this period.   It was formed of small metal disks, sewn on to leather so as to overlap in rows, and was very flexible and almost impervious to arrows.

Two brasses illustrate the transition to the succeeding style.   The figures of Sir — Bacon, c. 1320, Gorleston, Suffolk, and of Sir William Fitzralph, c. 1323, Pebmarsh, Essex (PLATE 2), show a great advance in the plate defences.   Steel straps fasten plates of steel round the back of the upper arms from shoulder to elbow, and the front of the arms from elbow to wrist.   These are known as *demi-brassarts* and *demi-vambraces*. The elbows are covered by elbow-cops of plate, and roundels of plate appear at the shoulder and elbow bends.   The legs are protected by greaves of plate strapped to the shins, and the Pebmarsh knight has *sollerets*, or lames of plate riveted together and strapped over the feet.   The Gorleston brass shows ailettes and a heater-shaped shield, while Sir William Fitz-ralph has no ailettes and his shield is concave.   The Gorleston knight is in banded mail.

II. *The Cyclas Period*, 1325-1335.
A typical figure of this period is Sir John de Creke, c. 1325, Westley Waterless, Cambs. (PLATE 2).   Below his hauberk can be seen the padded haqueton, reaching nearly to the knees, and the hauberk itself terminates in a point in front.   It is made of banded mail, which seems to be the favourite in this period.   The breastplate was worn over the hauberk, but is hidden by the *cyclas*.   Over breastplate and hauberk was the *gambeson*, another padded and quilted garment, and over this the cyclas, which differs from the surcoat in being laced at the sides, cut very short in front, and reaching to the knees behind.   A narrow belt held it round the waist. Sir John has a fluted bascinet to which is attached the *camail* of banded mail, which protected the neck, and covers part of the cyclas.   It was fastened by a cord running through staples called *vervelles*.   His demi-brassarts and elbow-cops show nothing new, but his forearms have complete vambraces, which pass below the sleeve of the hauberk.   His knee-cops, *demi-jambarts* and sollerets are as before.   He has rowel, not prick, spurs, but the brass of Sir John D'Aubernoun the younger, 1327, Stoke d'Abernon, Surrey (PLATE 5), whose armour is substantially the same as that of Sir John de Creke, shows prick spurs.   The brass of Sir John de Northwood, c. 1330, Minster, Sheppey (PLATE 3), differs in many curious details.   The upper arms are protected only by roundels and elbow-cops, while the vambraces on the forearms are of scale-like steel plates.   The

bascinet is pointed but not fluted, and of the swelling shape which was fashionable on the Continent. The chain of the tilting helm is fastened to an ornamental staple on the left side of the breastplate, and the small concave shield is hung at the left hip, suspended by a long narrow guige passing over the right shoulder. It has been thought that these peculiarities may be due to French influence, a theory which is supported by the fact that the costume of Lady de Northwood is very similar to that in fashion at the French court of the period. It should be noted that the figure from the knees downward is a later and incorrect restoration.

III. *The Studded and Splinted Period*, 1335-1360.

There is no uniformity in the armour of this period, for under the stress of Edward III.'s French wars every device was attempted which might give additional safety. Mail, plate and cuir-bouilli share the honours almost equally, and the combination of all three in what was perhaps the most effective armour of the time has given it its name. Persistent features in all the variety were the surcoat, which fitted closely to the waist above a full short knee-length skirt, the hauberk of varied types of mail, the globular breastplate, and the mail chausses. Only three brasses illustrate this period, but one of these is the famous brass of Sir Hugh Hastyngs, 1347, Elsing, Norfolk (PLATE 4), which is a mine of information. The effigy of Sir Hugh stands beneath an elaborate canopy, and the side-shafts consist of four panels, each containing an armed figure. Six of these remain : Edward III., Thomas de Beauchamp, and Roger Lord Grey of Ruthyn on the dexter side ; and on the sinister side, Henry Plantagenet Earl of Lancaster, Ralph Lord Stafford, and Almeric Lord St. Amand. All these figures show the shortened surcoat, with the upper part emblazoned with the wearer's arms, but otherwise differ considerably in detail. Sir Hugh wears a rounded bascinet with a raised visor, and a gorget of plate encircles his neck over the camail. His arm and leg defences are much as in the preceding period, but thigh-pieces of *studded pourpoint* appear for the first time. This material was cuir-bouilli studded with small metal disks, and was used extensively. The legs from the knees down are missing, but an old rubbing in the British Museum shows that mail chausses were worn. EDWARD III. and Henry Earl of Lancaster both have laminated *pauldrons* but no roundels, and have plate defences covering the shins. Thomas de Beauchamp, Earl of Warwick, and Ralph Lord Stafford both wear pointed bascinets with huge visors and dependent guards for the neck. Roger Lord Grey of Ruthyn, who leans on a large pole-axe, is armed similarly to the others, except for his complete brassarts of plate. Almeric Lord St. Amand presents the most peculiar helmet shown on a brass. On top of his globular bascinet he wears a *chapelle-de-*

fer, in shape something like a "tin hat" with a very wide brim. He also wears a gorget similar to that of Sir Hugh. The only other brasses of this period are those of Sir John de Wautone, 1347, Wimbish, Essex, and of Sir John Gifford, 1348 (?), Bowers Gifford, Essex, and neither throws any additional light.

IV. *The Camail and Jupon Period*, 1360-1410.

In this period there are for the first time a really large number of fine effigies in armour. They all display a remarkable uniformity, and slight deviations in detail alone can be noted. The characteristic feature is the *jupon*, which was a sleeveless outer garment reaching halfway down the thighs. It fitted very closely, and was made of several layers of material, the outer layer being of silk or velvet, and often bearing the wearer's arms. The skirt was usually scalloped, and the jupon was laced at the sides. Sometimes the skirt was cut into the form of leaves, as in the brass of Sir Nicholas Dagworth, 1401, Blickling, Norfolk (PLATE 13). Beneath the jupon was the globular breastplate, which gives the knights of the period such a curious contour, and beneath the breastplate the hauberk of banded or linked chain mail. The bascinet was tall and pointed. The camail was at first made of banded mail, but by 1380 some variety of chain mail was frequently used instead. It was fastened to the bascinet by a cord running through staples, but after about 1387 these were hidden by a rich border. The camail gradually increased in size until it protected the shoulders and the upper part of the arms. The plate defences are more extensive than in the preceding period. Complete brassarts and vambraces protected the arms, with pauldrons of overlapping plates, and hinged elbow-cops. The legs were completely cased in plate, though often studded pourpoint was used for the thigh-pieces, and sometimes the jambarts protecting the shins are splinted, *i.e.* are vertical bands of steel fastened with studs to cuir-bouilli or pourpoint, as in the brass of Thomas Cheyne, 1368, Drayton Beauchamp, Bucks. (PLATE 6). The sollerets were long and pointed, made of jointed plate, and rowel spurs were the rule. A feature of the period was the magnificent jewelled sword-belt, which was fastened round the hips, holding the sword at the left side. In early effigies the belt is fastened by a buckle and the hanging piece is looped through itself, as in the brass of Sir John de Cobham, 1354, Cobham, Kent (PLATE 5). The later effigies occasionally show the great hip-belt used merely as an ornament, while the sword is suspended from a separate diagonal belt, as in the brass of an anonymous knight, c. 1400, Laughton, Lincs. (PLATE 10). The shield never appears. The gauntlets were of leather and steel, with steel plates, called *gadlings*, on the knuckles.

Several brasses illustrate the transition to the succeeding style, of which a good example is the brass of William d'Eresby, c. 1400, Spilsby, Lincs. (PLATE 11). The jupon is discarded, revealing the breastplate and the skirt of *taces*, or overlapping plates, and the camail is partly covered by a gorget of steel. This knight wears the *orle* or wreath round his bascinet ; a rare feature on brasses. Other examples of the transition are John Hauley, 1408, Dartmouth, Devon (PLATE 14), and Sir Peter Courtenay, 1409, Exeter Cathedral (PLATE 15).

V. *The Surcoatless, Complete Plate or Lancastrian Period,* 1410-1430.

In this period armour consisted of a complete suit of plate, with no surcoat of any description, and practically no chain mail. The camail was superseded by the gorget of plate, and the rounded bascinet was made to rest on the gorget, relieving the head of the weight. The chin was protected by the chin-piece riveted to the bascinet. Breastplate and back-plate are globular in form, and the short skirt of taces is fixed to a leather lining. In early effigies the edge of the hauberk appears under the taces, but after about 1420 the hauberk seems to have been discarded altogether. Laminated pauldrons protected the shoulders, with roundels to guard the arm-pits, but often the roundels were replaced by *palettes*, which were oblong in shape, as on the brass of Sir Symon Felbrygge, 1416, Felbrigg, Norfolk (PLATE 17). The elbow-cops are sometimes fan-shaped, and sometimes roundels. The arm and leg defences are practically the same as in the preceding period. During the early part of the period the hip-belt is worn over the taces, but usually the sword was simply hung at the left side by a narrow belt passing diagonally from the right hip, and the *misericorde*, or dagger, is fastened to the taces on the right side. The brass of John Leventhorpe, 1437, Sawbridgeworth, Herts., shows the earliest development of the *tuilles* of the following period. The lowest tace is divided into two plates, and attached by buckles.

VI. *The Yorkist or Tabard Period,* 1430-1485.

The armour of this period shows no radical change, but the experiences of the Wars of the Roses caused many readjustments. The breastplate was generally reinforced by an additional plate, rising from the waist to halfway up the chest, but as a rule this is not seen very clearly on brasses, owing to the position of the arms. The laminated pauldrons of the preceding style are replaced or covered by large single plates shaped to the shoulder, and often deeply ridged to intercept sword-cuts. They seem to be a natural development of the palettes. The elbow-cops, frequently of the butterfly pattern, grow larger and larger, especially after 1450, when the shield was finally abandoned and the elbow-cop on

RB C

the left arm took its place.   Early examples of this period show the globular bascinet, but the majority of the effigies are bareheaded, often with the head resting on the great tilting helm.   After about 1450 the *sallet* became popular.   It apparently evolved from the old chapelle-de-fer and was like a wide-brimmed " tin hat," having a projecting brim at the back to guard the neck, and a falling visor in front.   It was worn in combination with a chin-piece.   A typical example of armour of this time is the brass of Robert Staunton, 1458, Castle Donington, Leicestershire (PLATE 21), which shows the sallet, and is also a good illustration of extravagant elbow-cops.   The skirt of taces tended to grow shorter, with a corresponding increase in the size of the tuilles, which were pointed plates concave to the thighs, and fastened with straps to the lowest tace. The succeeding style is often foreshadowed by the fringe of mail attached between the tuilles to the lowest tace.   About 1460 it became the custom to wear the sword in front of the body, instead of at the left side, as in the brass of Thomas Sherneborne, 1458, Shernbourne, Norfolk (PLATE 22).

The tabard is by no means an invariable feature of this period.   In its earliest form it had already appeared on the brass of John Wantele, 1424, Amberley, Sussex (PLATE 11).   It was a short, sleeved surcoat, reaching to the middle of the thighs and charged with the wearer's arms. It was slit at the sides and sometimes loosely fastened, sometimes left hanging free.   A fine early tabard appears on the brass to William Fynderne, 1444, Childrey, Berks.   The colouring of the arms was achieved by various compositions sunk into the plate, which was cut away to receive them, lead being used where a white field was required.   In the following period the tabard became extremely popular.

VII. *The Early Tudor, or Mail Skirt Period*, 1485-1558.

In this period the extravagances characteristic of the Yorkist period have vanished.   The arm defences are moderate in size, and more or less laminated.   The pauldrons are made of overlapping lames of steel, with the upper lame projecting at right angles to the shoulder to form a *pass-guard*.   The leg defences are practically unchanged, but the pointed sollerets are replaced by the clumsy, square-toed *sabbatons*, which appear on the brass of Peers Gerard, 1492, Winwick, Lancs. (PLATE 24).   The mail skirt reached almost to the knees, and was sometimes slit up for convenience in riding.   It was partly covered by the short skirt of taces, from which depended two tuilles of very varying size.   The sword and misericorde are sometimes slung diagonally across the body at the back, as in the brass of Peers Gerard.   The tabard frequently appears.   The general effect of armour of the period is heavy and uncouth, in marked contrast to the Gothic grace of the earlier styles.   There are few variations to be noted in the effigies illustrating the period, none of which is of any great interest.

VIII. *The Elizabethan and Jacobean Period*, 1558-1625.

The style of this period lasted until the final disuse of armour, which was rendered superfluous by the change of military tactics and the development of firearms. Naturally the abandonment was gradual, and the armour of this period anticipates its own extinction in the manner in which it conforms to the fashions of civilian dress. The effigies of the first years of Elizabeth's reign illustrate a transitional style, well shown in the brass of Sir Henry Sacheverell, 1558, Morley, Derbyshire (PLATE 35). The tuilles are replaced by very small *tassets*, which were defences for the front of the thigh, consisting of rows of hinged plates, and strapped in this instance to the lowest tace. But very soon armour was altered to conform to the current civilian fashion of long doublet and puffed trunk hose, and the mail skirt and the skirt of taces both disappear, while the tassets are lengthened and enlarged and buckled to the projecting edge of the pointed breastplate. The pauldrons are very large, often almost meeting in front, and are made of several plates. Both pauldrons and tassets are generally lined with leather, which is carried beyond the edge of the plates and cut into a scalloped edging. The ruff is always worn, and usually frills at the wrists also. The sword has a basket-hilt, and the dagger is suspended by a small sash. The head is nearly always bare, but when a helmet is shown it is small and close-fitting. The leg defences are much as before, but the sabbatons are less clumsy. Occasionally the puffed breeches were not worn, and the leg defences could be made continuous from the breastplate to the knee-cops, as in the brass of Thomas Hawkins, 1587, Boughton-under-Blean, Kent (PLATE 34). The effigy is usually represented as standing on a small pedestal or on a chequered ground.

On Caroline brasses the armour shown is generally a demi-suit, with large jack-boots. But the variations range from the complete suit of Sir Jarrate Harvye, 1638, Cardington, Beds. (PLATE 38), to the steel gorget which is the only relic retained by George Hodges, c. 1630, Wedmore, Somerset. The last military figure known, that of Nicholas Toke, 1680, Great Chart, Kent, which shows Jacobean armour with tassets, was probably copied from an earlier brass.

B. CIVIL COSTUME

(I) MALE

Fourteenth-century brasses show three varieties of civilian dress. The earliest fashion consists of a long *cote-hardie* or tunic, which reaches almost to the ankles and is slit up in front. The sleeves reach to the elbows, and then extend as hanging lappets, known as *liripipia*. The forearms are covered by the tight-fitting sleeves of the under tunic, which have a row of buttons extending from wrist to elbow. Over the shoulders is worn the close-fitting *chaperon*, which was a tippet with a hood attached. Tight hose are worn, and long pointed shoes. This costume is shown on the brass of Robert Braunche, 1364, King's Lynn, Norfolk (PLATE 39). Sometimes the cote-hardie was very close-fitting and did not reach to the knees, as on the brass of Robert de Paris, 1408, Hildersham, Cambs. (PLATE 40). Occasionally a perfectly plain, long loose tunic and hood is worn, without belt or buttons, as on the brass of Richard Torrynton, 1356, Great Berkhampstead, Herts. (PLATE 40). The third type of dress, which seems to belong more to the close of the century, shows a long full tunic, nearly ankle-length, fastened by a girdle from which hangs the *anelace*, a short, broad sword. The tunic is usually buttoned down the front, and over it is worn a loose, full mantle, buttoned on the right shoulder and flung over the left shoulder. The chaperon is apparently worn under the mantle. This costume is worn by Walter Pescod, 1398, Boston, Lincs., and by John Curteys, 1391, Wymington, Beds. (PLATE 40). Sometimes the mantle is not worn, as in the brass of John Corp, 1391, Stoke Fleming, Devon (PLATE 40).

The change that took place at the beginning of the fifteenth century is illustrated in the brass of Richard Martyn, 1402, Dartford, Kent (PLATE 40). His tunic reaches to his ankles, and is slit up a little way at the bottom, and the very full sleeves are gathered in tightly at the wrists. He wears a mantle fastened on his right shoulder, and looped over his left arm. Very often the mantle does not appear, and the hood alone is worn. The belt and anelace were usual with this dress, and the hair is short.

This is substantially the costume that continues to be worn until almost the end of the century. The tunic grows shorter, coming to just below the knees, and the sleeves are less full, while the mantle and hood are not often seen. The anelace, too, is seldom worn, and often a short rosary appears instead. A typical example is the brass of Richard Manfeld, 1455, Taplow, Bucks. (PLATE 42). Sir Thomas Brook, 1437, Thorncombe, Devon (PLATE 41), wears a long, fur-lined tunic with a belt and loose hanging sleeves, which is probably the *houppelande*.

About 1475 the short tunic gave way to a long gown, lined and edged with fur, and open in front. The sleeves are wide, and round the waist is a girdle, from which hangs the *gypcière* or purse, and frequently a rosary. When the hood appears it is worn on the shoulder, usually the right shoulder, though the brass of a notary, c. 1475, St. Mary Tower, Ipswich (PLATE 43), shows it on the left. The anelace very seldom appears, but it is worn by William Maynwaryng, 1497, Ightfield, Salop (PLATE 43). A few years later the gown acquires a broad collar and cuffs of fur, and the fronts are turned back to show the fur lining. Sometimes a belt is worn, but it is quite usual for the gown to hang loose, as in the brass of Andrew Evyngar, 1533, All Hallows, Barking, London (PLATE 46). William Norwiche, 1472, St. George Colegate, Norwich, wears the mantle with this dress. It was probably the official attire of civic dignitaries.

The next change, which took place about 1525, is that the gown is invariably unbelted, and long hanging false sleeves appear. Under the gown is worn the skirted doublet. The shoes are square in shape, like the sabbatons of the contemporary military dress, and the hair is generally long. Examples are the brass of Thomas Pownder, 1525, St. Mary Quay, Ipswich (PLATE 44), and of Sir Thomas Nevell, 1542, Mereworth, Kent (PLATE 43).

This style persisted until the early years of the reign of Elizabeth. Then the skirted doublet became shorter, and was worn with trunk hose, which were later replaced by stuffed breeches. But on brasses the long gown is nearly always worn, completely hiding the costume underneath. The hair is cut short again and pointed beards appear. Ruffs come into fashion, and little frills at the wrists. There are any number of examples, of which Thomas Noke, 1567, Shottesbrooke, Berks. (PLATE 45), is very typical. The brass of Robert Whalley, 1591, Queen's College, Cambridge (PLATE 47), shows the doublet and breeches worn under the gown. The gown, however, was confined to men of mature years, and young men and boys wear a short, full cloak. Sons depicted on the brasses of their parents usually wear the cloak, while their father wears the gown, as in the brass of William Dunche, c. 1585, Little Wittenham, Berks.

Under Charles I. ruffs and frills were replaced by collars and cuffs. The breeches are smaller, and jack-boots are frequently worn. Both the long gown with false sleeves and the short cloak appear, the latter on the brass to George Coles, 1640, St. Sepulchre, Northampton (PLATE 48).

Eighteenth-century costume is illustrated only by the brass of Benjamin Greenwood, 1773, St. Mary Cray, Kent.

(II) FEMALE

The earliest female effigy is that of Margarete de Camoys, c. 1310, Trotton, Sussex. She wears a long loose cote-hardie, the short sleeves of which reveal the close-fitting buttoned sleeves of her kirtle, and her hair is bound by a narrow fillet across the forehead. A *wimple* completely conceals her throat, and a *covrechef*, or veil, over her head falls on her shoulders. Jone de Kobeham, c. 1320, Cobham, Kent, wears exactly the same dress. Lady de Creke, c. 1325, Westley Waterless, Cambs. (PLATE 2), has a sleeveless cote-hardie of great length, with its folds caught up and held by the left arm, revealing the skirt of the kirtle. Over this she wears a mantle, which is fastened by a cord across the breast, and covrechef and wimple cover her head. Margaret de Walsokne, 1349, King's Lynn, Norfolk, wears the same costume, but her kirtle is richly embroidered. Lady de Northwood, c. 1330, Minster, Kent (PLATE 3), wears an unusual dress which is similar to that in fashion at the French court of the period. It has already been pointed out that this brass shows French influence. She wears the kirtle and sleeveless cote-hardie gathered up under her arm, and two curious triangular pieces hang down from the neck in front, which, like the cote-hardie, are lined with fur. Her neck and chin are concealed by a large gorget, and her braided hair has no covering.

The second half of the fourteenth century presents a good deal of variety in fashion. The plain, buttoned kirtle fitting closely to the waist is often worn simply with the mantle, which is invariably fastened by a short cord across the breast, as in the brass of Lady Dallingridge, c. 1380, Fletching, Sussex (PLATE 8). Frequently the kirtle was *heraldic*, emblazoned with the arms of the lady's husband impaled with those of her own family, as in the brass of Lady Harsick, 1384, Southacre, Norfolk (PLATE 9), or the kirtle shows the lady's arms and the mantle those of her husband, as in the brass of the Countess of Warwick, 1406, St. Mary, Warwick (PLATE 13). A frequent costume of this period was a cote-hardie similar to that worn by the men, with short tight sleeves and hanging liripipes. The two wives of Robert Braunche, 1364, King's Lynn, Norfolk (PLATE 39), wear embroidered kirtles and long cote-hardies caught up in the bend of the elbow, with liripipes lined with vair. Another favoured costume was the *sideless cote-hardie*, in which the sides of the garment are cut away as far as the hips, leaving only a narrow piece up the front of the body and two strips over the shoulders. It was usually edged with fur, as in the brass to John Hauley and two wives, 1408, Dartmouth, Devon (PLATE 14). Another variety is the long plain cote gathered into a round neck-band and buttoned all the way down the front, which appears in the brass to Reginald de Malyns and two wives, 1385, Chinnor, Oxon. The kirtle alone is worn by the granddaughter of John Corp, 1391, Stoke Fleming, Devon (PLATE 40).

The head-dresses of this period present a great deal of variety. They fall into three main classes : (i) *braided*, (ii) *veiled*, (iii) *zigzag*, *nebulé* or *reticulated*. In the first the hair is plaited at the sides of the face, and fastened by a jewelled fillet. This style is worn by Lady Harsick, 1384, Southacre, Norfolk (PLATE 9). The veiled head-dress consisted of two kerchiefs, one bound tightly round the head enclosing the forehead and the sides of the face, and the other falling loosely over it.   An example of this style is the brass of Eleanor de Paris, 1408, Hildersham, Cambs. (PLATE 40).   In the third type of head-dress, the hair is plaited and gathered tightly in a net to frame the face, and there is little difference between the three varieties.   The nebulé head-dress is worn by Joan de Cobham, wife of Sir John de la Pole, c. 1380, Chrishall, Essex (PLATE 6), and its later form, which does not enclose the sides of the face, appears on the brass to Lady de Redford, c. 1390, Broughton, Lincs. (PLATE 7).   A tress of hair usually falls on each shoulder, with its end rolled up and netted into a ball. Reginald de Malyns, 1385, Chinnor, Oxon., is shown with two wives, one of whom wears nebulé head-dress and the other zigzag.

The first half of the fifteenth century saw no striking change of fashion. The kirtle and mantle and the sideless cote-hardie continue to be worn extensively, the latter either with or without the mantle.   Sometimes a long loose robe appears, with wide pointed sleeves reaching nearly to the ground, a broad turned-down collar, and a high girdle.   This is worn by Joan Peryent, 1415, Digswell, Herts. (PLATE 16), and her head-dress is quite unique on brasses.   A somewhat similar robe appears on the brass of Claricia de Frevile, c. 1410, Little Shelford, Cambs. (PLATE 12), but it has a high collar buttoned up the throat and standing out round the face. This dress seems to have been exclusive to ladies of rank.   Another variety of gown, mainly worn by those of lesser position, was a long full dress girded at the waist, with very wide sleeves gathered in at the wrist. This is illustrated on the brass of — Martyn, 1402, Dartford, Kent (PLATE 40).

To the head-dresses already mentioned which still appear occasionally, there must now be added the *crespine*.   In this the hair is gathered into jewelled nets on each side of the face, level with the top of the head, and a veil is pinned on top and falls on to the shoulders behind.   The earlier form of this head-dress appears on the brass of Margaret, wife of Sir S. Felbrygge, 1416, Felbrigg, Norfolk (PLATE 17), and its later form in the brass of Lady Camoys, 1419, Trotton, Sussex (PLATE 15).   Gradually the nets of hair curve upwards to make the *horned* head-dress, sometimes called the *hennin*.   The wife of Peter Halle, c. 1430, Herne, Kent (PLATE 16), wears an early type of horned head-dress, and Jamon de Cherneys, wife of T. Sherneborne, 1458, Shernbourne, Norfolk (PLATE 22), has the later or mitred variety.

A new style of gown, which came into fashion about 1460 and remained for a very long time, consisted of a long full robe worn over the kirtle.   It was cut very low at the neck and bordered with fur, and it had either long tight sleeves with cuffs covering the hand to the knuckles and sometimes turned back to show a fur lining, or wide fur-lined sleeves. It was close-fitting to the waist and fastened with a girdle. The wide-sleeved gown appears on the brass to Jane Keriell, 1455, Ash-next-Sandwich, Kent (PLATE 50), whose horseshoe-shaped head-dress is quite unique. Shortly after the appearance of this style of gown, the mitred head-dress gave way to the brief fashion of the *butterfly*. In this the nets of hair of the preceding style are moved to the back of the head, and the hair is dragged back from the forehead. Upon the nets is erected a large framework of wire, covered by a light gauze veil. No doubt the effect was very attractive, although it looks particularly clumsy when represented on brasses, where the exigencies of the medium make it appear as a solid mass. The head was always shown in profile, to display this head-dress.

Shortly after the accession of Henry VII. the butterfly head-dress was replaced by the *pedimental*. In this style the face was framed by stiff embroidered bands which met in a sharp angle in the middle of the forehead, and hung down to the shoulders on each side. The hair was drawn into a sort of cap at the back of the head, and sometimes covered with a veil. The brass of Thomas Pownder, 1525, St. Mary Quay, Ipswich (PLATE 44), shows the wife wearing a pedimental head-dress with a veil, while the six daughters have no veils. Lady Elizabeth Scroope, wife of John de Vere, Earl of Oxford, 1537, Wivenhoe, Essex (PLATE 50), wears a heraldic mantle with a pedimental head-dress surmounted by a coronet. Occasionally the veiled head-dress appears, instead of the pedimental, as in the brass to Jacquette Widville, wife of John Lord Strange, 1509, Hillingdon, Middlesex (PLATE 26). The gown of the period remains very much the same, but the neck is usually cut square, and a rich girdle is worn, with a long end hanging almost to the ground at the side or in front. Sometimes a long chain hangs from the girdle and supports an ornament or perfume box.

About 1525 the gown changed slightly, and the sleeves became very wide and reached only to just below the elbows, where they were finished with a deep band of fur. Beneath were full sleeves gathered at the wrists. The square opening at the neck was filled in by the *partlet*, made of pleated linen and fitting to the neck. The hanging lappets of the pedimental head-dress were doubled up and pinned in front. This dress is shown on the brass to Elizabeth Perepoynt, 1543, West Malling, Kent (PLATE 51).

During the reign of Edward VI. this fashion begins to be superseded, and the pedimental head-dress gives way to the *Paris head* or *French hood*. This was often called the Mary Queen of Scots head-dress, and consisted of a close-fitting cap with a curved border coming over the ears in front and a veil hanging behind. The brass to Sir Henry Sacheverell and his wife, 1558, Morley, Derbyshire (PLATE 35), shows the fashionable dress that went with this cap. Substantially the gown is the same as before, but from the waist downwards it is open in front to show the petticoat. The partlet is finished with a small frill, which later developed into the Elizabethan ruff. The sleeves of the dress are short and puffed, and the striped sleeves of the under-dress are edged at the wrist with a small frill. Sometimes the dress has false sleeves hanging down, as in the brass to Jane Downe, wife of William Foxe, 1554, Ludford, Hereford (PLATE 34), where the pedimental head-dress also appears.

This attire develops into the familiar Elizabethan dress. About 1570 the petticoat becomes elaborately embroidered and is more exposed. The over-gown is fastened at the waist by a small sash, and the sleeves of the over-gown disappear. The characteristic ruff comes into fashion, and the dress is distended at the hips by a wired farthingale. Sometimes the wheel-farthingale appears, as on the brass to Radcliff, wife of Sir T. Wingfield, 1601, Easton, Suffolk. The Paris head is still worn, but the lappet hanging at the back is turned up on top of the cap. Hats are often worn, as on the brass to Thomas Inwood and three wives, 1586, Weybridge, Surrey (PLATE 46).

The costume of the time of Charles 1. is very badly reproduced on brasses, the most satisfactory example being the brass of Sir Edward Filmer, 1629, East Sutton, Kent (PLATE 37). The portraits of Van Dyck have made familiar the charming fashions of the period, with the broad falling collar of fine lace, the short vandyked bodice and full sleeves. For some time the ruff still held its own, as in the brass to G. Coles and two wives, 1640, St. Sepulchre's, Northampton (PLATE 48), and Lady Filmer wears a ruff while her daughters wear falling collars.

Later costume is even more sketchily illustrated. A brass at Great Chart, Kent, to Nicholas Toke and three daughters, dated 1680, but probably engraved earlier, shows the dress of the Lely pictures, and eighteenth-century costume is represented only by the very poor brass of Philadelphia Greenwood, c. 1773, St. Mary Cray, Kent.

Brasses of very varying dates are found with effigies of women with long flowing hair, sometimes bound by a fillet or a garland. As a rule such effigies are those of girls or unmarried women, and occur at all times from the fourteenth to the seventeenth century. Very occasionally a married woman is shown with flowing hair, as in the brass to Nicholas Kniveton and his wife Joan, c. 1475, Mugginton, Derbyshire (PLATE 22).

Widows wear a dress which for almost three centuries remain unchanged. In the fourteenth century it consisted of the kirtle, mantle and veil head-dress, with a plaited *barbe* or gorget of finely pleated linen fitting closely to the chin. A very fine example is the brass of Alianore de Bohun, 1399, Westminster Abbey (PLATE 49). In the fifteenth century the kirtle is covered by a long tight-sleeved dress and a mantle. The veil head-dress and the barbe are the same as before. The traditional costume survives into the sixteenth century in many instances, but the habit was steadily increasing of indicating the widowed state simply by a long veil.

C. ECCLESIASTICAL COSTUME

It is not possible to date the brasses of ecclesiastics by means of the variations in their dress, for the vestments had remained unchanged for four hundred years before the time of the earliest brasses, and no change took place up to the time of the Reformation and the consequent disappearance of ecclesiastical brasses. Unidentified brasses can only be dated by such details as the treatment of the hair or the variations in the designs of the embroideries, or by those general changes in design and execution which have already been pointed out.

The majority of the brasses of priests that have been preserved illustrate the eucharistic vestments, in which the average parish priest was usually represented. These consisted of *amice*, *alb*, *stole*, *maniple* and *chasuble*, and are well shown in the fine brass to Laurence de St. Maur, 1337, Higham Ferrers, Northants (PLATE 53). The *amice* had originally been a hood, but had become a sort of kerchief, with long strings attached to hold it in position. Along one edge was an embroidered border, which was turned down to give the appearance of a collar. This border was called an *apparel*, a general term for any piece of embroidery applied to the amice or the alb. The embroidered strips which adorned the other vestments, such as the chasuble or the cope, were called *orphreys*. The *alb* was a long linen vestment reaching to the feet and with long sleeves, and was adorned with six apparels, one on the breast, one on the back, one on each wrist, and one sewn to the lower edge of the garment at front and back. White linen was the customary material for the alb, but it was sometimes coloured or of rich materials. An inventory mentions twenty silk albs at Westminster Abbey in 1388. The *stole* was a long embroidered strip, a few inches wide, which was worn round the neck, crossed on the breast, and held by the cincture confining the alb. Only the fringed ends are visible below the chasuble. The *maniple*, which was originally a napkin, had become, like the stole, a strip of embroidered silk, about three feet in length and hung over the left arm. The *chasuble* covered the other vestments, and was a large oval vestment put on over the head and hanging down so as to cover the upper part of the arms. It was always made of the richest possible materials : velvet or cloth of gold with orphreys embroidered in coloured silks, gold thread and pearls.

Sometimes it is quite plain, but more often it has an ornamented border, and in the case of the higher dignitaries a broad orphrey runs down the centre of the front and of the back. Occasionally, as in the brass of Thomas de la Mare, c. 1370, St. Albans Abbey (PLATE 52), two strips called humeral orphreys pass over the shoulders.

Bishops and mitred abbots wore the vestments described, with the addition of others peculiar to their rank. The *tunicle* was a plain vestment slit up at each side and with fringed edges. It was much shorter than the alb over which it was worn, and was usually of linen, though sometimes of rich material. Over the tunicle was worn the *dalmatic*, a vestment of similar shape to, but shorter than, the tunicle. It was generally made of the same material and colour as the chasuble, which was worn immediately over it. *Gloves* of white netted silk and *sandals* of silk with three orphreys completed the vestments of a bishop. The insignia of his rank consisted of the ring, the mitre and the crozier. The ring was worn on the middle finger of the right hand above the lower finger-joint, and was a plain circlet set with an unengraved precious stone, frequently a sapphire. The mitre in the fourteenth century was comparatively low, with plain edges, as in the brass to Archbishop Grenefeld, 1315, York Minster : a form which was retained in the much later brass to Robert Pursglove, Bishop of Hull, 1579, Tideswell, Derbyshire (PLATE 54). Gradually the mitre grew in height, and the edges acquired crockets. Two *infulae*, or strips of silk, were attached to the back of the mitre and hung behind the ears. They are shown in the brass to John Bowthe, Bishop of Exeter, 1478, East Horsley, Surrey. Finally the mitre acquired a curved and swelling shape, as in the brass to Archbishop Harsnett, 1631, Chigwell, Essex (PLATE 57). Mitres were made in three degrees of splendour for use on varying occasions. The *mitra simplex* was of white linen or silk, without much ornament ; the *mitra auri frigiata* had orphreys embroidered in gold, and the *mitra pretiosa* was set with plates of gold and studded with gems. The crozier is usually shown as a long staff with the end curved in a heavy volute carved with foliage, and often enclosing a religious symbol, such as the Agnus Dei. A little scarf, called a *vexillum*, was often attached to the knot below the crook.

Archbishops usually, though not always, hold the cross-staff instead of the crozier, as in the brass to Thomas Cranley, Archbishop of Dublin, 1417, New College, Oxford (PLATE 53). It was possible for an archbishop to have both, as appears from the brass to Archbishop Albrecht von Brandenburg, 1545, Mayence. In addition to the full vestments of a bishop, archbishops wear the *pall*, which was a strip of white wool adorned with crosses, and encircling the shoulders, while a long end hung down in front and behind. The brass of Archbishop Cranley is an illustration.

The pall was worn over the chasuble, and must carefully be distinguished from the central orphrey with humeral branches.

The choir and processional vestments consisted of *cassock, surplice, almuce* and *cope*. The cassock was the ordinary dress of the priest, and was in fact worn with the eucharistic vestments beneath the alb, by which it is completely hidden. Occasionally the brass of a priest represents him in cassock alone ; for example an anonymous brass, c. 1480, Cirencester, Gloucestershire. The surplice was much as it is to-day, with long hanging sleeves. Over the surplice was worn the *almuce*, which was a large cape lined with fur turned down over the shoulders so as to show the lining, and with two long ends of fur hanging down in front. Many brasses show priests in the almuce, without the cope. The fur is represented by cutting away the surface of the brass and inlaying with lead or coloured composition. When the cope appears it is worn over the almuce which produces the effect of a fur collar. The *cope* was a large semi-circular cloak, made of very rich material, and fastened at the throat by a large jewelled brooch, called a *morse*. Sometimes the whole surface of the cope was richly diapered, as in the brass to John Blodwell, 1462, Balsham, Cambs. (PLATE 55), but more often the material was plain, though rich, and two broad orphreys ran down the straight edges in front. These orphreys were frequently embroidered with the figures of saints ; for example, John Sleford, 1401, Balsham, Cambs. (PLATE 55).

The mantle of the Order of the Garter was worn instead of the cope by Canons of Windsor. It was of plain purple material, with a small cross set in a circular badge on the left shoulder. It is illustrated in the brass to Roger Lupton, 1540, Eton College Chapel (PLATE 58).

There are a few brasses of priests wearing neither mass nor processional vestments, and their costume is often difficult to distinguish from academical dress. The cassock is of course the basis of all clerical dress, but when, as in the brass to John Strete, 1405, Upper Hardres, Kent (PLATE 60), the cassock is supplemented by a tippet and hood, it is almost similar to academic dress, and may bear some connection with it. Thomas Awmarle, c. 1400, Cardynham, Cornwall, might almost be a civilian, with his buttoned cassock and anelace. At the beginning of the sixteenth century a small scarf often appears, fastened to the cassock by a rosette on the left shoulder and flung round the back of the neck to fall over the right shoulder. It is shown in the brass of John Yslyngton, c. 1520, Cley, Norfolk.

Very few brasses commemorating members of the religious orders survived the disturbances of the Dissolution. Only about thirty exist, apart from the brasses of mitred abbots who wear the usual episcopal vestments. The majority of the monastic brasses illustrate the Benedictine habit, which consisted of a cassock and a loose gown with hanging sleeves and a hood. The Benedictine Abbey of St. Albans has preserved, in addition to the brass of Abbot de la Mare, brasses to a sub-prior, a third prior and two others. Geoffrey Langeley, Benedictine Prior of Horsham St. Faith, 1437, St. Laurence, Norwich, wears the same dress, and since the Cluniac was an adaptation of the Benedictine Order, the same dress appears on the brass to Thomas Nelond, Cluniac Prior of Lewes, 1433, Cowfold, Sussex (PLATE 59). The dress of the Canons Regular of St. Austin is shown on the brass to John Stodeley, 1502, Over Winchendon, Bucks. He wears a cassock, white rochet belted at the waist, and a plain cope. Richard Bewfforeste, c. 1510, Abbot of the same Order, wears the plain cope over the usual choir vestments of cassock, surplice and almuce.

The costume of nuns is almost identical with that of widows, who formed a large proportion of the population of a convent. The dress seems to have consisted of a long white gown, with a black mantle, veil head-dress and plaited barbe. This is worn by the two Abbesses, Dame Elizabeth Herwy, c. 1520, Abbess of the Benedictine Abbey of Elstow, Elstow, Beds., and Dame Agnes Jordan, c. 1540, Abbess of the Bridgetine Convent of Syon, Denham, Bucks. Margaret Dely, 1561, Treasurer of Syon, wears the same dress without the mantle. Among the few brasses of nuns there are four to members of the Order of Vowesses, who were widows who had vowed never to remarry. They wear the traditional costume of widows.

After the Reformation the clergy are generally represented as wearing the ordinary civil dress of the period ; doublet and hose and the gown with false sleeves, or the Geneva preaching gown. Some exceptions are the brasses of Dr. William Bill, Dean of Westminster, 1561, Westminster Abbey, which shows a long gown with a doctor's hood ; of Leonard Hurst, 1561, Denham, Bucks., in cassock and surplice ; and of William Dye, 1567, Westerham, Kent, in cassock, surplice and scarf. Post-Reformation bishops wear the *rochet* and *chimere*, the former of which was a sort of alb of white linen, with sleeves which gradually increased to an enormous size. Over this was worn the chimere, a sleeveless gown of silk or satin, usually black, but sometimes scarlet. It was open in front, and with it was worn a long stole-like scarf, with the ends hanging down in front. Examples are the brasses of Edmund Geste, 1578, Bishop of Salisbury, Salisbury Cathedral (PLATE 58), and of Henry Robinson, 1616, Bishop of Carlisle, Queen's College, Oxford.

D. ACADEMICAL COSTUME

The question of the representation of academic costume on brasses is beset by many thorny problems. As at the present time, the distinction between the costumes appropriate to the different degrees was indicated by the colour and material and not by the shape of the dress, so that it is impossible to ascertain the exact degree of the person represented if it is not mentioned in the inscription. It is probably unnecessary to point out that in mediæval times the connection between the Church and the University, which still lingers on, was so close that most of the colleges both at Oxford and Cambridge were under ecclesiastic or monastic rule, and that consequently in almost all cases the wearers of academic costume on brasses are also priests. The cassock, then, was the basis of academic as of ecclesiastic dress, and over it was worn a gown, which appears to have varied in shape to some extent according to the degree of the wearer. Doctors in Divinity wear a full sleeveless gown, unbelted and with a slit in front through which both arms appear. This is the *cappa clausa*, and over it is worn a tippet of fur and a skull cap or a doctor's cap. The brass of Thomas Hylle, D.D., 1468, New College, Oxford (PLATE 60), illustrates this gown. In the brass of John Argentein, D.D., 1507, King's College, Cambridge, the belted cassock can be seen through the opening in the cappa clausa. Another type of gown has two slits for the arms (*taberdum talare*), and is worn with the tippet and hood. There are not many examples of this, and its significance is uncertain. It appears on the brass of John Bloxham, B.D., c. 1420, Merton College, Oxford (PLATE 59), and also on that of John Lowthe, Professor of Civil Law, 1427, New College, Oxford. A third dress, which may perhaps be associated with the M.A. degree, was the *sleeved tabard*, a loose gown shorter than the cassock, with full, short, pointed sleeves. The tippet worn with this was usually of cloth edged with fur. This costume is worn by Eudo de la Zouch, 1414, St. John's College, Cambridge (PLATE 60), and we know that his degree was that of LL.D. It also appears in the brass to John Kyllyngworth, M.A., 1445, Merton College, Oxford. Another variety was a similar gown, but without sleeves, and called the *sleeveless tabard*. The two gowns last mentioned seem to be worn indifferently by those holding the degrees of M.A., B.A., and LL.B. There is only one example of what may have been the regular dress of the mediæval undergraduate. Thomas Baker, student of Civil Law, on the brass to David Lloyde, LL.B., 1510, All Souls College, Oxford, wears a belted tunic, a fur-sleeved gown, a mantle fastened on the left shoulder and thrown over the right arm, and a hood.

E. LEGAL COSTUME

Members of the legal profession represented on brasses are for the most part judges. They wear a long plain gown reaching to the ankles, a long mantle lined with minever, fastened on the right shoulder and caught up over the left arm, and a hood. The distinctive mark of their rank was the *coif*, a small close-fitting cap of white silk or linen tied under the chin. It was made in two parts and joined with a band down the middle. Its use was confined to Justices, Serjeants-at-law, and the Chief Baron of the Exchequer. This dress is shown in the brass of Sir John Cassy, Chief Baron of the Exchequer, 1400, Deerhurst, Gloucestershire (Plate 61), and that of Sir John Juyn, Chief Justice of the King's Bench, 1439, St. Mary Redcliffe, Bristol (Plate 61). Sir William Laken, Justice of the King's Bench, 1475, Bray, Berks. (Plate 61), wears a belted gown with a rosary and an anelace. Serjeants-at-law wear the long gown, tippet, hood, and coif, but Thomas Rolf, 1440, Gosfield, Essex, wears a tabard over his long robe, and but for his coif would be difficult to distinguish from a Master of Arts.

BOOKS OF REFERENCE

THE following are the principal authorities which have been consulted in the compilation of this Catalogue.

(i) GENERAL.

Haines, H., 1861 . . A Manual of Monumental Brasses.

Waller, J. G. and L. A. B., 1864   A Series of Monumental Brasses.

Macklin, H. W., 1890. 6th   Monumental Brasses.
ed., 1913.

Macklin, H. W., 1907 . . The Brasses of England.

Stephenson, Mill, 1926 . A List of Monumental Brasses in the British Isles.

(ii) COSTUME.

Druitt, H., 1906 . . A Manual of Costume as Illustrated by Monumental Brasses.

Ashdown, C. H., 1909 . . British and Foreign Arms and Armour.

(iii) ENGLISH COUNTIES.

Bedfordshire . . . Isherwood, Grace, 1906. Monumental Brasses in Bedfordshire Churches.

Sanderson, H. K. The Brasses of Bedfordshire, in the "Transactions of the Monumental Brass Society," Vol. II.

Berkshire . . . . Morley, T. H., 1924. Monumental Brasses of Berkshire.

Cambridgeshire . . . Transactions of the Monumental Brass Society, Vols. II., III., IV., V.

Cheshire . . . . Thornely, J. L., 1893. Monumental Brasses of Lancashire and Cheshire.

Cornwall . . . . Dunkin, E. H. W., 1882. Monumental Brasses of Cornwall.

Derbyshire . . . Field, H. E. The Monumental Brasses of Derbyshire, in the "Transactions of the Monumental Brass Society," Vols. III., V.

Devonshire . . . Rogers, W. H. H., 1877. Ancient Sepulchral Effigies and Monumental and Memorial Sculpture of Devonshire.

Essex . . . . Chancellor, F., 1890. The Ancient Sepulchral Monuments of Essex.

Gloucestershire . . . Davis, C. T., 1899. Monumental Brasses of Gloucestershire.

Herefordshire . . . Davis, C. T. The Monumental Brasses of Herefordshire and Worcestershire, in the "Transactions of the Birmingham and Midland Institute (Archæological Section)," 1884-5.

Havergal, F. T., 1881. Monumental Inscriptions in the Cathedral Church of Hereford.

Hertfordshire . . . Andrews, W. F., 1903. Memorial Brasses in Hertfordshire Churches, 2nd ed., 1903.

Page, W. The Brasses and Indents in St. Albans Abbey, in the " Home Counties Magazine," Vol. I., 1899.

Huntingdonshire . . . Macklin, H. W. The Brasses of Huntingdonshire, in the " Transactions of the Monumental Brass Society," Vol. III.

Kent . . . . Belcher, W. D. 2 vols., 1888, 1905. Kentish Brasses.

Griffin, R., and Stephenson, Mill, 1922. List of Monumental Brasses remaining in the County of Kent in 1922.

Lancashire . . . . Thornely, J. L., 1893. The Monumental Brasses of Lancashire and Cheshire.

Lincolnshire . . . Jean, G. E., 1895. A List of the Existing Brasses in Lincolnshire.

Norfolk . . . . Cotman, J. S., 1839. Engravings of Sepulchral Brasses in Norfolk and Suffolk.

Farrer, E., 1890. A List of Monumental Brasses remaining in the County of Norfolk.

Farrer, E., 1887-93. The Church Heraldry of Norfolk.

Northampton . . . Hudson, F., 1852. The Brasses of Northampton.

Nottingham . . . Briscoe, J. P., and Field, H. E., 1904. Monumental Brasses of Nottinghamshire.

Oxfordshire . . . Oxford Journal of Monumental Brasses, 1897-1912.

Oxford Portfolio of Monumental Brasses, 1898-1901.

Suffolk . . . . Cotman, J. S., 1838. Engravings of Sepulchral Brasses in Suffolk.

Farrer, E., 1903. A List of Monumental Brasses remaining in the County of Suffolk.

Sussex . . . . Woodman, T. C., 1903. The Sussex Brasses.

Warwickshire . . . Badger, E. W., 1895. The Monumental Brasses of Warwickshire.

Dugdale, Sir William, 2nd ed. by W. Thomas, 1730. Antiquities of Warwickshire.

Wiltshire . . . . Kite, E., 1860. The Monumental Brasses of Wiltshire.

Yorkshire . . . . M'Call, H. B., 1910. Richmondshire Churches.

(iv) FOREIGN.

Creeny, The Rev. W. F., 1891   Illustrations of Incised Slabs on the Continent of Europe.

Creeny, The Rev. W. F., 1884   A Book of Facsimiles of Monumental Brasses on the Continent of Europe.

Brussels : Musées Royaux . Frottis de Tombes Plates. Catalogue Descriptif, par Henry Rousseau.

ABBREVIATIONS

B.   =Brass.
I.S.   =Incised Slab.
br.   =bracket brass.
ca.   =canopy.
ch.   =children.
cha.   =chalice.

hf-eff. =half-effigy.
ins.   =inscription.
kng.   =kneeling effigy.
w.   =wife.
wid.   =widow.

Details of Design or Ornament

A.   =The Annunciation.
AA.   =Angels.
Arm.   =Arms on dresses worn over armour.
Armf.   =Arms on mantle (female).
B.V.   =The Blessed Virgin.
C.   =St. Christopher.
C.B.V. =The Coronation of the Blessed Virgin.
Cx.   =The Crucifixion.
D.   =The Figure of Death.
E.S.   =The Evangelistic Symbols.

Fn.   =Figures in niches, etc., of canopies other than saints.
G.d.   =St. George and the Dragon.
H.T.   =The Holy Trinity.
J.B.   =St. John the Baptist.
L.   =Our Lord.
R.   =The Resurrection.
SS.   =Figures of Saints on orphreys, in niches of canopies, etc.

BRITISH BRASSES

For List of Abbreviations, see p. 34.

Ref.—M.S.=Mill Stephenson: *A List of Monumental Brasses in the British Isles,* 1926.

NOTE.—*The Numbers given under the heading M.S. refer to the Order of the Brasses in the Series under the PLACE-NAMES in Mill Stephenson's List.*

ROYAL COSTUME

Date.	Name, Description, Place and Emblems, etc.	M.S.
c. 1440	St. Ethelred, King of the West Saxons, martyr, hf-eff. ins., Wimborne Minster, Dorset	I.

MILITARY COSTUME

13TH CENTURY

1277	Sir John D'Aubernoun, Stoke d'Abernon, Surr. PLATE I	I.
1289	Sir Roger de Trumpington, Trumpington, Cambs. PLATE I	I.
c. 1300	Anon., hf-eff., Croft, Lincs.	I.

14TH CENTURY

1302	Sir Robt. de Bures, Acton, Suff. Plate I	I.
1306	Sir Robt. de Setvans, Chartham, Kent. Arm. PLATE I	I.
c. 1310	Sir Richard de Boselingthorpe, hf-eff., Buslingthorpe, Lincs. (Holding heart.)	I.
c. 1320	Sir — de Bacon, Gorleston, Suff.	I.
c. 1323	Sir Wm. Fitzralph, Pebmarsh, Essex. PLATE 2	I.
c. 1325	Sir John de Creke, w., Westley Waterless, Cambs. PLATE 2	I.
1327	Sir John D'Aubernoun, ca., Stoke d'Abernon, Surr. PLATE 5	II.
c. 1330	? Sir John de Northwood, w., Minster, Sheppey. PLATE 3	I.
1347	Sir Hugh Hastyngs, ca., Elsing, Norf. Arm. C.B.V. G.d. Fn. PLATE 4	I.
1347	Roger Lord Grey of Ruthyn : panel from the brass of Sir H. Hastyngs, Elsing, Norf.	I.
1347	Sir John de Wautone, w., Wimbish, Essex. (Formerly in head of cross.)	I.
1348 ?	Sir John Gifford, Bowers Gifford, Essex	I.

Date.	Name, Description, Place and Emblems, etc.	M.S.
1354	Sir John de Cobham, ca. ins., Cobham, Kent. PLATE 5	II.
c. 1360	Wm. de Aldeburgh, br. ins., Aldborough, near Boroughbridge, Yorks. (N. and W.R.). Arm. (Holding heart.) PLATE 3	I.
c. 1360	John (?) Bodyham, Bodyham, Suss. Arm.	I.
1361	Sir Philip Peletoot, ca. ins., Watton-at-Stone, Herts.	I.
1365	Wm. de Audeley, Horseheath, Cambs.	I.
c. 1365	Anon., Great Berkhampstead, Herts.	II.
c. 1365	Sir John de Cobham, ins., Cobham, Kent. (Holding church.) PLATE 6	III.
c. 1365	— de Compton, Freshwater, Isle of Wight. Arm.	I.
c. 1366	Sir John de Mereworth, ca. ins., Mereworth, Kent	I.
1367	Sir Thos. de Cobham, ins., Cobham, Kent	IV.
1367	Sir Adam de Clyfton, ca., Methwold, Norf.	I.
1368	Thos. Cheyne, shield-bearer to Edward III., Drayton Beauchamp, Bucks. PLATE 6	I.
1370	Ralph de Knevynton, ca. ins., Aveley, Essex. PLATE 5	I.
c. 1370	Edmund Flambard, ca., Harrow, Middx.	I.
c. 1370	Anon., Ticehurst, Suss. (The two female effigies, and the inscription to John Wybarne (d. 1490) and his wives, were added in 1503.)	I.
1371	Thos. Stapel, Shopland, Essex	I.
1375	Wm. Cheyne, ins., Drayton Beauchamp, Bucks.	II.
1378	Richard Charlis, ins., Addington, Kent. E.S.	I.
1378	Sir John de Foxle, ws. (2) br., Bray, Berks. Arm. Armf.	I.
c. 1380	Anon., Calbourne, Isle of Wight	I.
c. 1380	Sir John de la Pole, w. ca. ins., Chrishall, Essex. PLATE 6	I.
c. 1380	Symond de Felbrig, w., and Roger de Felbrig, w. ins., Felbrigg, Norf.	I.
c. 1380	Sir — Dallingridge, w. ca., Fletching, Suss. Arm. PLATE 8	I.
c. 1380	— Peacock, St. Michael, St. Albans	II.
1381	Richard de Feversham, ins., Graveney, Kent	II.
1382	Sir Nich. Burnell, ca. ins., Acton Burnell, Salop	I.
1384	Sir John Harsick, w. ins., Southacre, Norf. Arm. Armf. PLATE 9	I.
1385	Sir Thos. de Audeley, ca. ins., Audley, Staffs.	I.
1385	Sir Renald de Malyns, ws. (2) ins., Chinnor, Oxon.	III.
c. 1385	Sir Esmoun de Malyns, w. hf-effs. ins., Chinnor, Oxon.	IV.
1387	Sir Aymer de Athol, w. ca. ins., St. Andrew, Newcastle-on-Tyne.	
1387	Sir Robt. de Grey, ca. ins., Rotherfield Greys, Oxon.	I.
1388	Sir Wm. de Echingham, ins., Etchingham, Suss.	I.
1389	Sir John de Wyngefeld, Letheringham, Suff. Arm.	I.
1390	Robt. Albyn, w. ins., Hemel Hempstead, Herts.	I.
1390	Sir Andrew Loutterell, ca., Irnham, Lincs. PLATE 7	I.
c. 1390	? Sir — de Redford, w. ca., Broughton, Lincs. (Holding hearts.) PLATE 7	I.

Date.	Name, Description, Place and Emblems, etc.	M.S.
c. 1390	John Flambard, ins., Harrow, Middx.	II.
c. 1390	Robt. Russell, ins., Strensham, Worc.	I.
1391	Sir Wm. de Kerdeston, w. ca., Reepham, Norf.	I.
1392	John Cray, Chinnor, Oxon.	VII.
1392	Thos. Lord Berkeley, w., Wotton-under-Edge, Glos.	I.
1393	Sir Thos. Walsch, w. ins., Wanlip, Leic. E.S.	I.
1393	Hen. Englisshe, w., Wood Ditton, Cambs.	I.
1394	Sir Rich. Attelese, w. ca. ins., Sheldwich, Kent. PLATE 10	I.
1395	Sir Robt. Bardolf, ca. ins., Mapledurham, Oxon.	I.
1395	Sir Wm. de Bryene, ins., Seal, Kent. E.S.	I.
1400	Sir John Mauleverere, w. ins., Allerton Mauleverer, Yorks (W.R.). Arm.	I.
1400	Sir Ingram Bruyn, ca., South Ockendon, Essex	I.
1400	Sir Geo. Felbrigg, ins., Playford, Suff. Arm. PLATE 7	I.
c. 1400	— Massynberde, w. ca., Gunby, Lincs. (Appropriated to Sir Thos. Massyngberde, 1552, and w. Joan Bratoft.)	I.
c. 1400	? — Dalison, ca., Laughton, Lincs. (Appropriated to Wm. Dalison, 1549.) PLATE 10	I.
c. 1400	Wm. Baron Willoughby d'Eresby, w. ca., Spilsby, Lincs. PLATE 11	II.

15TH CENTURY

Date.	Name, Description, Place and Emblems, etc.	M.S.
1401	Sir Nich. Dagworth, ins., Blickling, Norf. PLATE 13	II.
1401	Sir Morys Russell, w. ca. ins., Dyrham, Glos.	I.
1401	Thos. de Braunstone, ins., Wisbech, Cambs.	I.
1402	Rauf de Cobham, hf-eff. ins., Cobham, Kent	IX.
1402	Sir Wm. Fienlez, ca. ins., Hurstmonceaux, Suss. PLATE 10	I.
1403	Sir Reginald Cobham, ins., Lingfield, Surr.	II.
1404	Sir Wm. (?) Moyne, w. ins., Sawtrey, Hunts.	I.
1405	Sir Reginald Braybrok, ch. ca. ins., Cobham, Kent. H.T. PLATE 14	X.
1405	Sir Roger Drury, w. ins., Rougham, Suff. PLATE 12	I.
1405	Sir John Russel, ca. ins., Strensham, Worc.	II.
1406	Thos. de Beauchamp, Earl of Warwick, w., St. Mary, Warwick. Arm. Armf. PLATE 13	I.
1407	Sir Wm. Bagot, w. ins., Baginton, Warw. Arm.	I.
1407	Sir Nich. Hauberk, ch. ca. ins., Cobham, Kent. B.V. H.T. G.d. PLATE 14	XI.
1408	John Hauley, ws. (2) ca. ins., St. Saviour, Dartmouth, Devon. PLATE 14	I.
1408	Thos. Seintlegier, ins., Otterden, Kent	I.
1408	Sir Wm. Tendring, Stoke-by-Nayland, Suff. PLATE 13	II.
1409	Wm. Snayth, w. ca. ins., Addington, Kent	II.
1409	Sir Wm. de Burgate, w. ca. ins., Burgate, Suff.	I.

Date.	Name, Description, Place and Emblems, etc.	M.S.
1409	Sir Peter Courtenay, K.G., ca. ins., Exeter Cathedral. PLATE 15	I.
1410	Thos. de Frevile, wid., Little Shelford, Cambs.	II.
1410	Robt. Morle, ins., Stokenchurch, Bucks.	I.
c. 1410	Sir Thos. Burton, w. ins., Little Casterton, Rutland	I.
c. 1410	Anon., Holbeach, Lincs.	I.
c. 1410	Rich. Hansard, w. ins., South Kelsey, Lincs.	I.
c. 1410	Robt. de Frevile, w., Little Shelford, Cambs. PLATE 12	I.
c. 1410	Wm. Loveney, Wendens Ambo, Essex	I.
1411	Thos. de Cruwe, w. ca. ins., Wixford, Warw.	I.
1412	Sir Robt. Swynborne and son Sir Thos., ca. ins., Little Horkesley, Essex. PLATE 15	I.
1413	Robt. Lord Ferrers of Chartley, w., Merevale, Warw.	I.
1414	John Cressy, w. ins., Dodford, Northants	I.
1414	Geoff. Fransham, ca. ins., Great Fransham, Norf.	I.
1414	Sir Ivo Fitzwaryn, ins., Wantage, Berks.	II.
1415	John Skypwyth, ins., Covenham St. Bartholomew, Lincs.	I.
1415	John Peryent, esquire for the body and pennon-bearer to Rich. II., esquire to Hen. IV. and Hen. V., w. ins., Digswell, Herts. PLATE 16	I.
1415	Walter Cookesey and Sir John Phelip, w. ca. ins., Kidderminster, Worc.	I.
1415	Robt. Morle, ins., Stokenchurch, Bucks.	II.
c. 1415	? John Northwood, Addington, Kent	III.
c. 1415	Anon., Barsham, Suff.	I.
c 1415	Walter Roland, ins., Cople, Beds.	II.
c. 1415	Sir John de Erpingham, ins., Erpingham, Norf.	I.
c. 1415	Anon., ins., Felsted, Essex	I.
1416	Matthew Swetenham, ins., Blakesley, Northants. PLATE 17	I.
1416	Sir Symon Felbrygge, K.G., w. ca. ins., Felbrigg, Norf. PLATE 17	III.
1416	Sir Thos. de Skelton, ws. (2) ins., Hinxton, Cambs.	I.
1417	Sir John Drayton, Dorchester, Oxon.	I.
1417	John Hadresham, ins., Lingfield, Surr. PLATE 17	III.
1418	John Fossebrok, w. ins., Cranford St. Andrew, Northants	I.
1418	Thos. Lathe, ins., Stradsett, Norf.	I.
1419	Thos. Baron Camoys, w. ch. ca. ins., Trotton, Suss. PLATE 15	II.
1419	Wm. Maydestone, ca. ins., Ulcombe, Kent	I.
1420	Sir Arnold Savage, ca. ins., Bobbing, Kent	II.
1420	John Doreward, w., Bocking, Essex	I.
1420	Sir Wm. Calthorp, ca. ins., Burnham Thorpe, Norf. E.S.	I.
1420	Nich. Maudyt, ins., Wandsworth, Surr.	I.
1420	John Chetewode, ins., Warkworth, Northants	II.
c. 1420	Sir Arnold Savage, wid. ins., Bobbing, Kent	I.
c. 1420	? Sir John Holt, w. ca., Brampton-by-Dingley, Northants	I.
c. 1420	Barth. Lord Bourchier, ws. (2) Halstead, Essex	I.

Date.	Name, Description, Place and Emblems, etc.	M.S.
c. 1420	Thos. Quatremayn, w. and son Thos., wid. ins., Thame, Oxon.	I.
c. 1420	? John Harvey, Thurleigh, Beds.	I.
c. 1420	? John de Boys, w., Tolleshunt Darcy, Essex	II.
c. 1420	Thos. Walysch, w. ins., Whitchurch, Oxon.	I.
c. 1420	? John Hampden, Nether Winchendon, Bucks.	I.
1421	Thos. Coggeshall, Springfield, Essex	I.
1422	Wm. Wylde, wid. ins., Dodford, Northants	II.
1422	Sir Thos. Dymoke, w. ca., Scrivelsby, Lincs. Now lost	
1422	Thos. Salle, ins., Stevington, Beds.	I.
1424	John Wantele, ins., Amberley, Suss. Arm. PLATE 11	I.
1424	John Compton, w. ch. ins., Dinton, Bucks.	I.
1424	John Bedgebery, Goudhurst, Kent	I.
1424	John Poyle, w. ins., Hampton Poyle, Oxon.	I.
1424	Nich. Paris, Linton, Cambs.	I.
1424	Robt. Hayton, ins., Theddlethorpe All Saints, Lincs.	I.
1425	Sir Baldwin Seyntgeorge, ins., Hatley St. George, Cambs.	I.
1425	Sir Wm. Molyns, wid. ins., Stoke Poges, Bucks.	I.
c. 1425	? John Framlingham, w. hf-eff., Debenham, Suff.	I.
c. 1425	? John Brook, Easton, Suff.	I.
c. 1425	Sir John Lysle, ca. ins., Thruxton, Hants	I.
1426	John Cosyngton, w. ins., Aylesford, Kent	I.
1426	John Lowe, ins., Battle, Suss.	I.
1426	John Cely, w. ins., Sheldwich, Kent	II.
1426	Sir Thos. le Strange, Constable of Ireland, ins., Wellesbourne Hastings, Warw.	I.
1426	Sir John de Brewys, ins., Wiston, Suss. PLATE 18	I.
1427	Henry Paris, w., Hildersham, Cambs. PLATE 19	II.
1427	Rich. Leverer, w. ch., Weston Colville, Cambs.	I.
1428	Sir John Reynes, ins., Clifton Reynes, Bucks.	I.
1428	John Norwiche, w., Yoxford, Suff.	I.
1429	Roger Isly, ins., Sundridge, Kent	I.
1430	Reginald Malyns, ins., Chinnor, Oxon.	XII.
1430	Sir Thos. Brounflet, ins., Wymington, Beds.	III.
c. 1430	Harry Hawles, ins., Arreton, Isle of Wight	I.
c. 1430	? John Cockayne, Hatley Cockayne, Beds.	I.
c. 1430	Anon., w., Harlow, Essex	I.
c. 1430	Peter Halle, w. ins., Herne, Kent. PLATE 16	I.
c. 1430	— Warrene, St. Michael, Lewes, Suss.	I.
c. 1430	Anon., Victoria and Albert Museum	I.
1431	Thos. Bekingham, Northleigh, Oxon.	I.
1433	Wm. Scott, ca., Brabourne, Kent	I.
1433	Wm. Harwedon, wid. br. ins., Great Harrowden, Northants. E.S.	I.
1433	Wm. Rickhill, w., Northfleet, Kent	III.
1435	Wm. Arnold, hf-eff. ins., Battle, Suss.	III.

Date.	Name, Description, Place and Emblems, etc.	M.S.
1435	Thos. Widville of Grafton, ws. (2) ca., Bromham, Beds. (Appropriated to Sir John Dyve, 1535.) PLATE 18	I.
1435	John Launcelyn, w. ins., Cople, Beds.	III.
1435	Rich. Delamare, w. ca. ins., Hereford Cathedral	IX.
1436	Thos. Chaucer, wid. ins., Ewelme, Oxon.	I.
1437	Roger Elmebrygge, ins., Beddington, Surr.	V.
1437	Thos. Brokhill, w. ins., Saltwood, Kent	II.
1437	John Leventhorpe, wid., Sawbridgeworth, Herts.	I.
1438	Rich. Dixton, ca. ins., Cirencester, Glos.	II.
1438	Sir John Harpeden, Westminster Abbey. PLATE 21	VIII.
1439	Rich. Fox, Arkesden, Essex	I.
1440	John Weston of Weston, ins., Albury (old church), Surr.	I.
1440	John Mepertyshale, ins., Mepshall, Beds.	I.
1440	Rich. Malemayns, ins., Pluckley, Kent	II.
c. 1440	Anon., w., Ashen, Essex	I.
c. 1440	Anon., Irnham, Lincs.	II.
c. 1440	Thos. de Mohun, ins., Lanteglos-near-Fowey, Cornwall	I.
c. 1440	Sir Laur. Pabenham, ws. (2) ins., Offard Darcy, Hunts.	I.
1441	Reginald Barantyn, ins., Chalgrove, Oxon.	II.
1441	Sir Hugh Halsham, w. ca., West Grinstead, Suss. PLATE 20	II.
1441	John Boteler, w. ins., Mepshall, Beds.	II.
1441	Rich. Trevet *alias* Hasylwode, ins., Stratfield Mortimer, Berks.	I.
1442	Sir Thos. Chedder, Cheddar, Som.	I.
1442	John Peryent, ins., Digswell, Herts.	II.
1442	Valentine Baret, w. ins., Preston-by-Faversham, Kent	I.
1442	Thos. Torrell, Willingale Doe, Essex	I.
1443	Thos. Faryndon, w. ins., Faringdon, Berks.	II.
1444	Wm. Fynderne, w. ca. ins., Childrey, Berks. Arm. Armf.	II.
1444	Sir Wm. Echyngham, w. and son Sir Thos. ca. ins., Etchingham, Suss. PLATE 20	II.
1444	Wm. Burys, ins., Halstead, Kent	I.
1444	Nich. Manston, ins., St. Laurence, Thanet	I.
1444	John Frogenhall, Teynham, Kent	I.
1445	John Throckmorton, wid. ins., Fladbury, Worc.	I.
1445	Thos. de St. Quintin, ins., Harpham, Yorks. PLATE 19	II.
1445	John Daundelyon, ins., St. John, Margate	V.
c. 1445	? Robt. Watton, Addington, Kent	IV.
c. 1445	Anon., Sharrington, Norf.	I.
1446	Drew Barantyn, ws. (2) ins., Chalgrove, Oxon.	III.
1446	Wm. Whappelode, steward to Hen. Beaufort, Cardinal of England, w. ins., Chalfont St. Peter, Bucks.	II.
c. 1446	Wm. Whappelode, w. ins., Chalfont St. Peter, Bucks.	I.
1447	John Maltoun, ins., Little Waltham, Essex	II.
1450	John Gaynesford, ins., Crowhurst, Surr. PLATE 19	I.

Date.	Name, Description, Place and Emblems, etc.	M.S.
c. 1450	? Geoff. Goodluck, Isleworth, Middx.	I.
c. 1450	? Jas. Montague, Luddesdown, Kent	I.
1451	Sir John Bernard, w. ca. ins., Isleham, Cambs.	I.
1451	Thos. Reynes, wid. ch. ins., Marston Mortaine, Beds.	II.
1452	Hen. Rowdell, ins., Northolt, Middx.	I.
1454	John Stathum, w. kng. ins., Morley, Derb. C.	V.
c. 1455	? John Digges, w., Barham, Kent	II.
c. 1455	? Wm. Browning, w., Wytham, Berks.	I.
1456	Walter Grene, ins., Hayes, Middx.	III.
1458	Robt. Staunton, w. ch. ca. ins., Castle Donington, Leic. PLATE 21	I.
1458	Wm. Stapilton, w. ins., Edenhall, Cumb. Arm.	I.
1458	Thos. Shernborne, Chamberlain to Queen Margt. of Anjou, w., Shernbourne, Norf. PLATE 22	I.
1459	Sir John Langton, wid. ins., St. Peter, Leeds, Yorks.	I.
1459	Wm. Mareys, ins., Preston-by-Faversham, Kent	II.
1460	John Gaynesford, ins., Crowhurst, Surr.	II.
1460	John Jenney, w. ins., Knodishall, Suff.	I.
1460	Sir John Byron, wid., Manchester Cathedral	II.
1460	John Ansty, ch. kng. ins., Stow-cum-Quy, Cambs.	I.
1460	Sir Robt. del Bothe, w. ca. ins., Wilmslow, Ches.	I.
c. 1460	Anon., w., Adderbury, Oxon. PLATE 21	I.
c. 1460	John Bartelot, w. ch. ins., Stopham, Suss. (Children added c. 1630, and both figs. partly recut c. 1670-80.)	II.
c. 1460	Rich. Quatremayn, w., Thame, Oxon.	II.
c. 1460	Anon., Wappenham, Northants	I.
1461	Wm. Brome, ins., Holton, Oxon.	I.
1462	Wm. Prelatte, ws. (2) ins., Cirencester, Glos.	VI.
1462	Sir Thos. Grene, wid. ch. ins., Green's Norton, Northants	I.
1462	John Tothyll, w. ins., Swaffam Prior, Cambs.	I.
1463	Robt. Eyr, w. ch. ins., Hathersage, Derb.	I.
1465	John Threel, ins., Arundel, Suss.	VII.
1465	Thos. Cobham, wid. ins., Hoo St. Werburgh, Kent	V.
1466	Rich. Ask, wid. ins., Aughton, Yorks.	I.
1466	Hen. Parice, ca., Hildersham, Cambs. PLATE 26	III.
1467	Hen. Grene, wid. ins., Lowick, Northants. Arm. E.S.	I.
1467	Roger Bothe, w. ch. ins., Sawley, Derb.	I.
1467	Sir Wm. Vernon, wid. ch. ins., Tong, Salop	I.
1468	Barth. Halley (or Halsey), w., St. Albans Abbey	VII.
1469	Nich. Carew, ins., Haccombe, Devon	I.
1470	Robt. Watton, w. ins., Addington, Kent	VI.
1470	Sir Thos. Stathum, ws. (2) ins., Morley, Derb. B.V. C.	VI.
1470	Hen. Unton, kng. ins., Sculthorpe, Norf.	I.
1470	Hen. Rochforth, ins., Stoke Rocheford, Lincs.	I.
1470	Ralph St. Leger, w. ins., Ulcombe, Kent. PLATE 23	III.

Date.	Name, Description, Place and Emblems, etc.	M.S.
c. 1470	Anon., Milton-next-Sittingbourne, Kent	I.
c. 1470	John Croston, ws. (3) ch. ins., Swinbrook, Oxon.	I.
c. 1470	Ralph, Baron Cromwell, ins., Tattershall, Lincs.	III.
1471	Sir John Cursun, w. ins., Bylaugh, Norf.	I.
1471	Thos. Colte, w. ins., Roydon, Essex	I.
1471	Rich. Wylloughby, w. ins., Wollaton, Notts.	I.
1472	Sir Wm. Yelverton, w., Rougham, Norf. (Judge's costume over armour.).	I.
1472	Robt. Ingylton, ws. (3) ch. ca. ins., Thornton, Bucks.	I.
1473	Sir John Say, w. ins., Broxbourne, Herts. Arm. Armf.	II.
1474	Wm. Fitz William, wid. ins., Sprotborough, Yorks.	I
1474	Wm. Rokewood, ins., Warham All Saints, Norf.	I.
1475	Philip Mede, ws. (2) kng. ins., St. Mary Redcliffe, Bristol. Arm. Armf. L.	II.
1475	Ralph Blenerhaysett, ins., Frenze, Norf.	I.
c. 1475	John Weddeot, w. ch. ins., Aldington, Kent	I.
c. 1475	Nich. Kniveton, w. ch. ins., Mugginton, Derb. PLATE 22	I.
1476	Barth. Bolne, w. ins., West Firle, Suss.	I.
1477	John Feld, ch. and father John Feld, in civil dress, ins., Standon, Herts. Arm. PLATE 42	III.
1478	Sir Robt. Clyfton, ins., Clifton, Notts.	I.
1478	John Fastolff, w. ins., formerly Oulton, Suff. Now lost.	
1478	John Welbek, ins., Putney, London	I.
1478	Roger Bothe, wid. ch. ins., Sawley, Derb.	II.
1479	Francis Hetht, ins., Feltwell, Norf.	I.
1479	Thos. Playters, w. ins., Sotterley, Suff.	II.
1480	John Fitz-Geffrey, w. ch. ins., Sandon, Herts.	I.
1480	Sir Anth. Grey, son of Edm., Earl of Kent, St. Albans Abbey. PLATE 26	XI.
c. 1480	Anon., Balsham, Cambs.	III.
c. 1480-90	Nich. Gaynesford, esquire for the body to Edw. IV. and Hen. VII., w. ch. ins., Carshalton, Surr.	I.
c. 1480	John Yerde, w., Cheam, Surr.	V.
c. 1480	Anon., wid., Grendon, Northants	II.
c. 1480	Anon., w., Harpsden, Oxon.	II.
c. 1480	? John Whichcote, w., Harpswell, Lincs.	I.
c. 1480	Anon., w., Helmsley, Yorks.	II.
c. 1480	Anon., ch., Holbrook, Suff.	I.
c. 1480	Anon., Howden, Yorks.	II.
c. 1480	Anon., Sawston, Cambs.	III.
c. 1480	? Robt. or John Bomsted, Sotterley, Suff.	III.
c. 1480	Anon., Swaffham, Norf.	I.
c. 1480	Anon. In the possession of the Society of Antiquaries	III.
1481	Robt. Herward, Aldborough. Norf.	II.

Date.	Name, Description, Place and Emblems, etc.	M.S.
1481	Hen. Stathum, ws. (3) ch. ins., Morley, Derb. **PLATE 27**	VII.
1482	Wm. Robins, Clerk of the Signet to Edward IV., w. ch., St. Stephen, St. Albans	I.
1482	Thos. Wayte, ins., Stoke Charity, Hants	I.
1483	Hen. Bourchier, K.G., Earl of Essex, w., Little Easton, Essex. (With garter and mantle.) Arm. Armf. **PLATE 25**	II.
1483	John Weston, w. ins., Ockham, Surr.	III.
1483	Sir Thos. Vaughan, ins., Westminster Abbey	X.
1484	Edm. Molyneux, w. ca. ins., Chenies, Bucks.	II.
1484	Thos. Peyton, ws. (2) ca. ins., Isleham, Cambs.	III.
1484	John Teringham, ins., Tyringham, Bucks. Arm.	I.
1484	Thos. Gybon, ins., Whissonsett, Norf	II.
1485	John Seyntmour, w. ins., Beckington, Som.	I.
1485	John Estbury, ins., Lambourne, Berks. Arm.	III.
1485	Thos. Halle, ins., Thannington, Kent	I.
c. 1485	Anon., w. ch., Little Hadham, Herts.	II.
c. 1485	Anon., Heacham, Norf.	I.
c. 1485	Wm. Bozon, Whissonsett, Norf.	I.
1487	Sir Walter Mauntell, w. ins., Nether Heyford, Northants. **PLATE 25**	II.
1487	Sir Wm. Peeche, ins., Lullingstone, Kent	II.
1487	Sir Robt. Strelly, w. ins., Strelley, Notts.	I.
1488	Edw. Peytoo, ins., Fladbury, Worc.	IV.
1488	Hen. Covert, North Mimms, Herts.	III.
1488	John Eveas, w. ch. ins., Murston, Kent	I.
1488	Bernard Brocas, kng. ins., Sherborne St. John, Hants. Arm.	II.
1488	Edm. Clere, w. ins., Stokesby, Norf.	II.
1488	John Brecknock, ca., Wraysbury, Bucks.	I.
1489	Wm. Brewes, w. ins., Fressingfield, Suff.	I.
1490	Thos. Andrewe, w. ch. ins., Charwelton, Northants	I.
1490	Thos. Caple, ins., Ledbury, Hereford	II.
c. 1490	Anon., Chedzoy, Som.	I.
c. 1490	Anon., w., Goring, Suss.	I.
c. 1490	? Sir John Culpeper, ca., Goudhurst, Kent	II.
c. 1490	Wm. Berdewell, w. ins., West Harling, Norf.	II.
c. 1490	Wm. ? Harper, w. ch., Latton, Essex	II.
c. 1490	? Wm. Wyngefeld, Bodleian Library, Oxford. From Letheringham, Suff.	I.
c. 1490	Anon. Said to be from Myddle, Salop.	
c. 1490	Anon., Wath, Yorks.	II.
1491	Sir Gervis Clyfton, ins., Clifton, Notts.	II.
1491	Roger Salisbury, ws. (2) ins., Horton, Northants	I.
1491	Paul Dayrell, w. ins., Lillingstone Dayrell, Bucks.	I.
1492	John Brocas, ws. (2) ch., Sherborne St. John, Hants	III.
1492	John Brocas, kng. ins., Sherborne St. John, Hants. H.T.	IV.

Date.	Name, Description, Place and Emblems, etc.	M.S.
1492	Geoffrey Sherard, w. ch. ins., Stapleford, Leic.	I.
1492	Peers Gerard, ch. ca., Winwick, Lancs. Arm. PLATE 24	I.
1493	Ralph Eyre, w. ins., Hathersage, Derb.	II.
1493	John Conquest and son Rich., w. ch. ins., Houghton Conquest, Beds.	I.
1493	John Southill, wid., Stokerston, Leic.	II.
1494	Walter Duredent, ws. (2) ch. ins., Denham, Bucks.	I.
1495	Wm. de Grey, ws. (2) ch., Merton, Norf. Arm.	III.
1496	Rich. Curzon, w. ch., Kedleston, Derb.	I.
1496	Nich. Parker, ins., Honing, Norf.	I.
1496	John Payne, w. ch. ins., Hutton, Som.	I.
1497	Rich. Rysle, w. ins., Great Cressingham, Norf.	I.
1497	John Trenowyth, ins., St. Michael Penkivel, Corn.	I.
1498	Thos. Karesburght, w. ins., Floore, Northants	I.
1498	Thos. Huntingdon, w., Hempstead, Essex	III.
1498	John Newdegate, ins., Merstham, Surr.	III.
1499	Sir John Fogge, ins., Ashford, Kent. (Head only.)	III.
1499	Thos. Hevenyngham, w. ch. kng. ins., Ketteringham, Norf. Arm. Armf.	II.
1500	John Tame, w. ins., Fairford, Glos.	I.
1500	Rich. Conquest, w. ins., Houghton Conquest, Beds.	II.
c. 1500	? Geo. Catesby, kng., Ashby St. Legers, Northants. Arm.	IV.
c. 1500	Anon., w., Assington, Suff.	I.
c. 1500	Anon., Caius Coll., Camb.	I.
c. 1500	John Samwell, w. ch. kng., Cottisford, Oxon.	I.
c. 1500	Robt. Eyre, w. ch. kng. ins., Hathersage, Derb. Arm. Armf.	III.
c. 1500	? John Norwood, w., Milton-next-Sittingbourne, Kent. Arm.	II.
c. 1500	— Scarisbrick, Ormskirk, Lancs. Arm.	I.
c. 1500	Sir Hugh Johnys, w. ch. ins., Swansea, Glam.	I.
c. 1500	? Thos. Lovett, w., Wappenham, Northants	IV.
c. 1500	Thos. Lovett, w. ins., Wappenham, Northants	V.
c. 1500	— Bedell, w. ch., Writtle, Essex	I.
c. 1500	? Compton, w. kng. ins. In possession of the Surrey Archæological Society, Guildford. PLATE 27	I.

16TH CENTURY

1501	Robt. Baynard, w. ch. ins., Lacock, Wilts. Arm. Armf.	I.
c. 1501	Sir John Guise, Aspley Guise, Beds.	II.
1502	Wm. Poyntz, w. ch. ins., North Ockendon, Essex	I.
1502	John Aucher, ins., Otterden, Kent	III.
1502	Robt. Russell, w. ins., Strensham, Worc.	III.
1503	Roger Wake, w. ch. ins., Blisworth, Northants	I.
1503	John Covert, ca. ins., Slaugham, Suss.	I.
1503	Robt. Borrow, w. ins., Stanford Rivers, Essex	II.

Date.	Name, Description, Place and Emblems, etc.	M.S.
1503	Oliver St. John, w. ch. ins., Stoke Rocheford, Lincs.	II.
1504	Rich. Culpepyr, w. ca. ins., Ardingly, Suss.	II.
1505	Sir Thos. Grey and Rich. Lewkener, ins., East Grinstead, Suss.	I.
1505	John Burgoyn, w. ch. ins., Impington, Cambs. Arm. Armf. E.S.	I.
1505	Morys Denys and son Sir Walter Denys, kng. ins., Olveston, Glos. Arm.	r.
1505	Sir Humph. Stanley, ins., Westminster Abbey	XII.
1505	John Harewell, w. ch. ins., Wooton Wawen, Warw.	I.
1506	Sir Roger le Strange, ca. ins., Hunstanton, Norf. PLATE 29	II.
1507	Jas. Rolleston, w. ch. ins., Ashover, Derb.	II.
1507	Anth. Hansart, w. kng. ins., March, Cambs. Arm. Armf. A.	II.
1507	Thos. Elmebrygge, w. ins., Merstham, Surr.	IV.
1507	Wm. Viscount Beaumont and Lord Bardolf, ca. ins., Wivenhoe, Essex. PLATE 29	I.
c. 1507	Thos. Gray, w. ch. ins., Cople, Beds.	IV.
1508	Sir Robt. Clyfford, knight for the body to Hen. VII., and master of his ordnance, w. ch. kng. ins., Aspenden, Herts. Arm. Armf.	II
1508	Wm. Roberts, ws. (2) ch. ins., Little Braxted, Essex	I.
1508	Wm. Berdewell, w. ins., West Harling, Norf.	III.
1508	Rich. Blount, w. ch. ins., Iver, Bucks.	I.
1508	Jas. Aucher, ins., Otterden, Kent	IV.
1509	John le Strange, Lord Strange of Knockyn, Mohun, Wassett, Warnell, Lacy and Colham, w. ch. ca., Hillingdon, Middx. PLATE 26	I.
1509	Sir Wm. Ayscugh, w. ins., Stallingborough, Lincs. Arm. Armf.	I.
1510	Nich. Culpepyr, w. ch. ins., Ardingly, Suss.	III.
1510	Robt. Pecke, w. ins., Cookham, Berks. H.T.	IV.
1510	Hen. Michell, w. ins., Floore, Northants	II.
1510	John Blenerhaysett, ins., Frenze, Norf.	II.
1510	Thos. Ramsey, w. ch. ins., Hitcham, Bucks.	I.
1510	John Leventhorp, ins., St. Helen, Bishopsgate, London	VII.
1510	Anth. Fetyplace, ins., Swinbrook, Oxon. Arm.	II.
c. 1510	Anon., British Museum.	I(8).
c. 1510	? Sir Rich. Ashton, w. ch., Middleton, Lancs.	I.
c. 1510	Hugh Starky, ins., Over, Ches.	I.
c. 1510	Wm. Yelverton, w. ch. ins., Rougham, Norf.	III.
1511	Rich. Quadryng, ins., Outwell, Norf.	II.
1511	Rich. Gyll, ins., Shottesbrooke, Berks.	III.
1512	Thos. Pekham, w. ch. ins., Wrotham, Kent	IV.
1513	John Toke, ws. (2) ins., Great Chart, Kent	V.
1513	John Sylam, ws. (2) ins., Luton, Beds.	VIII.
1513	John Acworth, ws. (2) ins., Luton, Beds.	IX.
1513	Rafe Dellvys, w. ins., Wybunbury, Ches.	I.
1514	John Kyngeston, w. ins., Childrey, Berks. H.T.	VII.

Date.	Name, Description, Place and Emblems, etc.	M.S.
1514	Sir John Danvers, w. ins., Dauntsey, Wilts.	I.
1514	Sir Rich. Delabere, ws. (2) ch. ins., Hereford Cathedral	XVIII.
1514	Robt. Rochester, ins., St. Helen, Bishopsgate, London	VIII.
1514	Wm. Aucher, ins., Rainham, Kent	III.
1514	John Butler, Watton-at-Stone, Herts.	VI.
1515	Edm. Cockayne, w. ch. ins., Hatley Cockayne, Beds.	V.
1515	Raffe Caterall, w. ch. kng. ins., Whalley, Lancs.	I.
c. 1515	? — Latton, ws. (2) ch., Blewbury, Berks.	IV.
1516	Hen. Palgrave, w. ch. ins., Barningham Norwood, Norf.	II.
1516	Olyver Hyde, w. ins., Denchworth, Berks.	II.
1516	Thos. Knyghtley, ins., Fawsley, Northants. Arm.	I.
1516	Sir Wm. Huddesfeld, w. ch. kng. ins., Shillingford, Devon. Arm. Armf.	I.
1517	Hen. Leynham, Tidmarsh, Berks. Arm.	II.
1517	Edw. Bulstrode, ws. (2) ch., Upton, Bucks.	II.
c. 1517	John Dering, ins., Pluckley, Kent. (A 17th-century restoration.)	III.
1518	Thos. Broke, w. ins., Ewelme, Oxon.	XII.
1518	Robt. Newport, w. ch. kng., Furneux Pelham, Herts.	II.
1518	Thos. Isley, w. ch., Sundridge, Kent	III.
1519	Sir Lionel Dymoke, ch. kng. ins., Horncastle, Lincs.	I.
1520	Sir Rich. Carew, w. ins., Beddington, Surr. Arm. Armf. (A modern restoration from an old print of the original.)	VII.
1520	Hen. Pudsey, w. kng. ins., Bolton-by-Bowland, Yorks. (W.R.). Arm. Armf.	I.
1520	John Goring, kng. ins., Burton, Suss.	I.
1520	Gerard Danet, w. ch. ins., Tilty, Essex	II.
c. 1520	Anon., w., Bishop's Sutton, Hants	I.
c. 1520	Thos. Fowler, w. ins., Christ's Coll., Cambridge	I.
c. 1520	— Culpeper, Goudhurst, Kent	III.
c. 1520	Anon., ch. kng., East Horndon, Essex	II.
c. 1520	John White (d. 1567, date added), w. (d. 1548), ch. ins., Southwick, Hants. (Appropriated effigies.)	I.
c. 1520	Anon., w. ch. kng., Theydon Gernon, Essex. PLATE 28	II.
c. 1520	Anon., w., Little Thurlow, Suff.	I.
c. 1520	Anon., with tabard with Filliol quartering Brewes. In the possession of Dr. H. N. Diamond about 1860.	
1521	Rich. Grey, ins., Eton Coll., Bucks.	VI.
1521	John Colt, ws. (2) ch. ins., Roydon, Essex. Arm. Armf. E.S.	II.
1522	Robt. Thornburgh, ws. (2) ch. kng. ins., Kimpton, Hants :	I.
1523	Sir John Daunce, w. ch. ins., Blewbury, Berks. Arm. Armf.	V.
1523	Wm. Brugge, w. ins., Longdon, Worc.	I.
1523	Roger Porter, ins., Newent, Glos.	I.
1524	Sir Wm. Scott, ins., Brabourne, Kent	III.
1524	Hen. Norris, w. ins., Childwall, Lancs. Arm. Armf.	I.

Date.	Name, Description, Place and Emblems, etc.	M.S.
1524	Hen. Everard, w., Denstone, Suff. Arm. Armf.	I.
1524	John Fetyplace, w. ch. kng. ins., Little Shefford, Berks.	I.
1525	Meredith ap Ivan ap Robert Wynne, kng. ins., Dolwyddelan, Carn.	I.
1525	Thos. Englysche, w. ins., Ipsden, Oxon.	I.
1525	John Sacheverell, killed at Bosworth Field, w. ch. kng. ins., Morley, Derb. H.T.	VIII.
1525	Reynold Pekham, w. ins., Wrotham, Kent. Arm. Armf.	V.
c. 1525	Anon., Great Barford, Beds.	I.
c. 1525	John Hampden, w. ch. ins., Great Hampden, Bucks.	I.
c. 1525	Anon., w. ch., Hutton, Essex	I.
c. 1525	Sir John Towchet, Lord Audley, ins., Shere, Surr.	VI.
1526	John Shelley, w. ins., Clapham, Suss. Arm. Armf. H.T. PLATE 31	IV.
1526	Rich. Verney, w. ch. ins., Compton Verney, Warw.	II.
1527	Rich. Babham, w. kng. ins., Cookham, Berks.	V.
1527	Sir John Ratclif, w. ins., Crosthwaite, Cumb.	I.
1527	Sir Peter Legh, w. ins., Winwick, Lancs. Armf. E.S. (Knight and priest, in armour with chasuble.) PLATE 30	II.
1528	Hen. Bures, Acton, Suff.	III.
1528	John Fysher, w. ins., Clifton, Beds.	I.
1528	Hen. Stanley, Hillingdon, Middx.	II.
1528	Thos. Payne, w. ch. kng. ins., Hutton, Som.	II.
1528	Sir Rich. Clement, ins., Ightham, Kent. Arm.	I.
1528	Sir Rich. Fitzlewes, ws. (4), Ingrave, Essex. Arm. Armf. PLATE 28	II.
1528	Sir Edw. Grey, ws. (2) ch. ins., Kinver, Staffs.	I.
1528	Rich. Rowthall, w., Moulsoe, Bucks.	I.
1528	Edw. Whyte, w. ins., Shotesham St. Mary, Norf.	I.
1529	Sir Edw. Wotton, w. ins., Boughton Malherbe, Kent	II.
1529	Sir Godfrey Foljambe, w. ch. ins., Chesterfield, Derb. Arm. Armf.	III.
1529	Sir Thos. Brooke, w. ch. ins., Cobham, Kent. PLATE 30	XIX.
1529	Sir Robt. Clere, ins., Great Ormesby, Norf.	II.
c. 1530	Thos. Knighton, ch., Little Bradley, Suff.	II.
c. 1530	— Rokewood, w., Euston, Suff.	IV.
c. 1530	John Wodehows, w. ins., Kimberley, Norf.	I.
c. 1530	Anon. Formerly in possession of — Edlin, Cambridge. Sold at Puttick and Simpson, Nov. 1903.	
1531	John Borrell, serjeant-at-arms to Hen. VIII., Broxbourne, Herts.	IV.
1531	John Lawrence, Rich. Radclyffe and Thos. Bothe, w. ins., Middleton, Lancs.	III.
1531	John Horsey, w. ins., Yetminster, Dorset. PLATE 32	I.
1532	Sir Nich. Harve, ins., Ampthill, Beds.	V.
1532	John Scott, w. ch. kng. ins., Camberwell, Surr.	III.

Date.	Name, Description, Place and Emblems, etc.	M.S.
1532	James Pekham, Wrotham, Kent	VI.
1534	Sir Edm. Tame, ws. (2) ch. ins., Fairford, Glos. Arm. Armf. .	II.
1534	Sir Edm. Tame, ws. (2) ch. kng. ins., Fairford, Glos. Arm. Armf. H.T.	III.
1534	Sir Wm. Fitzwilliams, w. kng. ins., Marholm, Northants. Arm. Armf.	I.
1535	John Brampton, ws. (2) ch. ins., Brampton, Norf. . . .	IV.
1535	Sir John Dyve, mother and w. ca. ins., Bromham, Beds. (Appropriated brass, originally of Thos. Widville of Grafton, 1435.) PLATE 18	I.
c. 1535	Sir Geo. Throkmorton, w. ch. ins., Coughton, Warw. . .	I.
1537	Edw. Hawte, w. ins., Erith, Kent	VII.
1537	Wm. Assheby, w. ch. ins., Harefield, Middx.	V.
1538	Francis Cockayne, w. ca. ins., Ashbourne, Derb. Arm. .	II.
1538	Sir Thos. Bullen, K.G., Earl of Wiltshire and Ormond, ins., Hever, Kent. (In full insignia of the Order of the Garter.) PLATE 29	II.
1539	Sir John Basset, ws. (2) ch., Atherington, Devon . . .	I.
1539	Sir John Clerk, kng. ins., Thame, Oxon. Arm. . . .	VIII.
1540	Thos. Hatteclyff, ins., Addington, Surr.	I.
1540	Sir Wm. Gascoigne, comptroller of the household to Cardinal Wolsey, ws. (2), Cardington, Beds. Arm. Armf. PLATE 33	I.
1540	Robt. Fowler, w., St. Mary, Islington, London . . .	I.
1540	Edm. Fetyplace, w. ch. kng. ins., Marcham, Berks. . . .	I.
1540	Thos. Manfeld, ws. (2) ins., Taplow, Bucks.	VI.
1540	Anth. Darcy, ins., Tolleshunt Darcy, Essex	IV.
c. 1540	— Hutton, w., Dry Drayton, Cambs.	I.
c. 1540	Anon., Odiham, Hants	VI.
c. 1540	Wm. Brocas, kng. ins., Sherborne St. John, Hants . .	V.
c. 1540	Walter Curson, w. ins., Waterperry, Oxon. (Effigies of c. 1440, altered and adapted to the later date.) . . .	II.
1541	Thos. Andrewes, w. ins., Charwelton, Northants . .	III.
1542	Roger Gyffard, w. ch. ins., Middle Claydon, Bucks. . .	III.
1544	Thos. Heron, w. ch., Croydon, Surr.	IV.
1545	Harry Gray, ins., Flitton, Beds.	III.
1545	John Lymsey, w. ch. ins., Hackney, London. (The male eff. is a re-used figure of c. 1510-20.)	II.
1545	Gregory Lovell, w. ins , Harlington, Middx. . . .	II.
1545	Laur. Saunders, w. ch. kng. ins., Harrington, Northants . .	I.
1545	Thos. Clere, St. Mary, Lambeth, Surrey	II.
1545	John Spelman, ins., Narborough, Norf.	III.
1545	Sir Geo. Cotton, ins., Nettleden, Bucks.	I.
1545	Sir Robt. Demoke, ins., Scrivelsby, Lincs.	I.
1545	Sir John Arundell, K.B., w. ins., St. Columb Major, Corn. .	I.

Date.	Name, Description, Place and Emblems, etc.	M.S.
c. 1545	? John Knighton, w., Bayford, Herts.	I.
c. 1545	Rich. Dering, ca., Pluckley, Kent	VI.
1546	Wm. Thynne, master of the household to Hen. VIII., w. ins., All Hallows, Barking, London	X.
1546	Hen. Savill, w. ins., St. Mary, Islington, London	II.
1546	Sir John Greville, ins., Weston-on-Avon, Glos. Arm.	I.
1547	Sir Ralph Verney, w. ch., Aldbury, Herts. Arm. Armf. PLATE 31	II.
1547	Rich. Covert, ws. (3) kng. ins., Slaugham, Suss. R.	II.
1548	Sir Humf. Stafford, esquire for the body to Hen. VIII., w. ch. ins., Blatherwyck, Northants	I.
1548	John Latton, w. ch. ins., Blewbury, Berks. Arm.	VI.
1549	Thos. Fyndarne and John Lord Marnay, w. ins., Little Horkesley, Essex. Arm. Armf. PLATE 33	IV.
1550	John Shelley, w. ch. kng. ins., Clapham, Suss.	V.
1550	Thos. Giffard, ins., Twyford, Bucks.	II.
c. 1550	Anon., Cobham, Surrey. PLATE 32	II.
c. 1550	Anon., w. ch., Margaretting, Essex	I.
1551	Thos. Grenewey, w. ins., Dinton, Bucks.	IV.
1551	Rich. Grenewey, w. ins., Dinton, Bucks.	V.
1551	Nich. Clarke, ins., Hitcham, Bucks.	II.
1552	Robt. Cheyne, w. ins., Chesham Bois, Bucks.	I.
1552	Rich. Fermer, mcht. of the Staple of Calais, w. ins., Easton Neston, Northants	I.
1552	Wm. Fermoure, w. ins., Somerton, Oxon.	I.
1553	Sir John Hampden, ws. (2) ch. ins., Great Hampden, Bucks.	II.
1554	Wm. Foxe, w. ch. ins., Ludford, Hereford. PLATE 34	I.
1554	Christ. Lytkott, w. ch. ins., Swallowfield, Berks.	II.
1556	Robt. Bulkeley, w. ch. kng. ins., Cople, Beds.	VII.
1557	Sir John Porte, ws. (2) ch. kng. ins., Etwall, Derb. Arm. Armf.	II.
1557	Humf. Cheynie, ins., West Hanney, Berks. E.S.	II.
1557	Sir Wm. Drury, ws. (2) ins., Hawstead, Suff.	VI.
1557	Guy Wade, ins., Standon, Herts.	V.
1558	Wm. Gardyner, w. ch. ins., Chalfont St. Giles, Bucks.	VII.
1558	Anth. Cave, w. ins., Chichley, Bucks.	I.
1558	Thos. Engeham, w. ch. ins., Goodnestone-next-Wingham, Kent	IV.
1558	Edw. Shurley, w. ins., Isfield, Suss.	II.
1558	Sir Hen. Sacheverell, w. ins., Morley, Derb. PLATE 35	IX.
1558	John Parker, ins., Willingdon, Suss.	I.
1558	Thos. Harlakynden, ws. (2) ch. kng. ins., Woodchurch, Kent	III.
1559	John Colby, ins., Brundish, Suff.	II.
1559	Erasmus Forde, w. ch. kng. ins., Thames Ditton, Surr.	I.
1559	Sir Edw. Greville, ins., Weston-upon-Avon, Glos. Arm.	II.
1560	John Colby, w. ch. ins., Brundish, Suff.	III.
1560	John Gyfforde, w. ch. ins., Northolt, Middx.	II.

Date.	Name, Description, Place and Emblems, etc.	M.S.
1560	Sir Rich. Rede, w. ch. kng., Redbourn, Herts.	III.
c. 1560	Rich. Lytleburye, w. ch. ins., Ashby Puerorum, Lincs.	I.
c. 1560	Anon., Ashby Puerorum, Lincs.	II.
c. 1560	Anon., Upper Hardres, Kent	IV.
c. 1560	Sir Arthur Eyre, w. kng. ins., Hathersage, Derb. Arm. Armf.	IV.
c. 1560	Anon. Said to be from Ketteringham, Norf.	
c. 1560	Rich. Butler, w. ins., North Mimms, Herts.	V.
1561	Hen. Hobart, ins., Loddon, Norf. Arm.	VII.
1561	John Eyer, w. kng. ins., Narborough, Norf.	VI.
1561	Sir John Arundell, ws. (2) ch. ins., Stratton, Cornw.	I.
1562	Rich. Calthorp, ch. ins., Antingham, Norf.	III.
1562	Wm. Heron, w. ins., Croydon, Surr.	V.
1562	Thos. Boys, kng. ins., Upper Deal, Kent	II.
1562	Wm. Hyde, w. ch. ins., Denchworth, Berks.	III.
1562	Arthur Dericote, ws. (4) ch. kng. ins., Hackney, London	III.
1562	Sir Gyles Strangways, ins., Melbury Sampford, Dorset. Arm.	V.
1562	Thos. de Greye, ins., Merton, Norf.	VI.
1562	Sir John Russell, w. ch. kng. ins., Strensham, Worc. Arm. Armf.	IV.
1562	Geo. Medeley, w. ch. ins., Tilty, Essex	III.
1563	John Gyfford, ch. ins., Crondall, Hants	II.
1565	John Toke, w. ch. ins., Great Chart, Kent	VI.
1565	Sir Edw. Warner, ins., Little Plumstead, Norf.	IV.
1566	John Mayne, w. ch. kng. ins., Biddenden, Kent	II.
1566	Thos. Gascoign, Burgh Wallis, Yorks. PLATE 34	I.
1567	Wm. Hyde, w. ins., Denchworth, Berks.	IV.
1568	Nich. Williams, ws. (2) ins., Burghfield, Berks.	I.
1568	Peter Rede, ins., St. Peter Mancroft, Norwich. (A copy of an earlier figure, c. 1470.)	III.
1568	Sir Rich. Molyneux, ws. (2) ch. ins., Sefton, Lancs.	III.
1569	Alex. Newton, ins., Braiseworth, Suff. PLATE 36	I.
1570	Sir Clement Heigham, chief baron of the exchequer to Queen Mary, w. ch. kng. ins., Barrow, Suff.	II.
1570	Thos. Fletewoode, ws. (2) ch. kng. ins., Chalfont St. Giles, Bucks.	VIII.
c. 1570 ?	Sir Wm. Molineux, ws. (2) ins., Sefton, Lancs.	II.
1572	Anth. Forster, w. ch. kng. ins., Cumnor, Berks.	I.
1572	Raphe Jenyns, w. ins., Churchill, Som.	I.
1572	Thos. Playters, ins., Sotterley, Suff.	VI.
1573	Sir Wm. Harper, w. ins., St. Paul, Bedford	I.
1573	Clement Throkmorton, w. ch. ins., Haseley, Warw.	I.
1573	Rainold Holingworth, w. ins., Stondon Massey, Essex	II.
1574	Rich. Twedye, ins., Stock, Essex	I.
1575	John Cosowarth, w. ch. ins., Colan, Cornw.	II.
1576	Rich. Tomynw, ins., Boxley, Kent	II.
1576	Rowland Shakerley, ins., Ditton, Kent	II.

Date.	Name, Description, Place and Emblems, etc.	M.S.
1576	Hen. Fortescue, ch. ins., Faulkbourne, Essex	II.
1576	Thos. Higate, w. ch. ins., Hayes, Middx.	IV.
1576	Rich. Faldo, w. ch. ins., Maulden, Beds.	I.
1576	Edm. Tyrell, w. kng. ins., Rawreth, Essex	II.
1577	Alan Bellingham, ins., Kendal, Westmorland	I.
1577	Francis Clopton, Long Melford, Suff. PLATE 36	VII.
1578	Wm. and Rich. Disney, w. ch. hf-eff. ins., Norton Disney, Lincs.	I.
1579	Wm. Wightman, w. ins., Harrow, Middx.	IX.
1579	Thos. Shurley, w. ins., Isfield, Suss.	III.
1579	Humf. Clarke, w. ch. ins., Kingsnorth, Kent	II.
1580	Simon Malory, ins., Woodford-near-Thrapstone, Northants	I.
1581	John Spelman, ins., Narborough, Norf.	VII.
1582	Roland Lytton, ws. (2) ins., Knebworth, Herts.	III.
1583	Hercules Raynsford, w. ch. ins., Clifford Chambers, Glos.	I.
1584	Sir Edm. Brudenell, ws. (2) ch. hf-eff. ins., Dene, Northants	I.
1584	John Wingfield, ins., Easton, Suff.	II.
1584	Edm. Shorditche, w. ch. ins., Ickenham, Middx.	III.
1584	Edm. Wiseman, w. ch. ins., Steventon, Berks.	II.
1585	Edm. Bockinge, ws. (2) ch. ins., Ash Bocking, Suff.	I.
1585	John Copledike, w. kng. ins., Harrington, Lincs.	III.
1585	Edm. Roberts, ws. (2) ch. ins., Willesden, Middx.	IV.
1586	Sir Thos. Brudenell, w. ins., Dene, Northants	II.
1586	Thos. Carewe, ins., Haccombe, Devon	II.
1586	Nich. West, ch. ins., Marsworth, Bucks.	III.
1587	Thos. Hawkins, ins., Boughton-under-Blean, Kent. PLATE 34	III.
1587	Eustace Sulyard, w. kng. ins., Runwell, Essex	I.
1588	John Barnes, kng. ins., Little Wittenham, Berks.	VII.
1589	Hen. Bowyer, Cuckfield, Suss.	III.
1589	John Eyston, w. ch. ins., East Hendred, Berks.	III.
1589	John Pettie, w. ins., Stoke Talmage, Oxon.	II.
1590	Wm. Butler, w. ins., Coates-by-Stow, Lincs.	II.
1590	Thos. Nevynson, w. ins., Eastry, Kent	I.
c. 1590	John Walsingham, w. ins., Exhall, Warw.	I.
c. 1590	? Wm. Cleybrooke, St. John, Margate	X.
1591	Thos. Stoughton, ins., St. Martin, Canterbury	III.
1591	Thos. Maryet, ins., Remenham, Berks.	I.
1591	Geerardt Dewes, ins., Upminster, Essex	V.
1592	John Scrogs, w. ch. ins., Albury, Herts.	IV.
1592	John Shellee, w. ch. kng. ins., Clapham, Suss.	VI.
1593	Christ. Dawbeney, w. ch. kng. ins., Sharrington, Norf.	VII.
1593	Humph. Brewster, ins., Wrentham, Suff.	II.
1594	John Clippesby, w. ch. ins., Clippesby, Norf.	III.
1594	Wm. Copinger, kng. ins., Hoo All Hallows, Kent	II.
1595	John Gage, ws. (2) ins., West Firle, Suss.	VI.

Date.	Name, Description, Place and Emblems, etc.	M.S.
c. 1595	Sir Edw. Gage, w. ins., West Firle, Suss.	III.
c. 1595	Thos. Gage, w. ch. ins., West Firle, Suss.	IV.
c. 1595	Nich. Garneys, w. ch. kng. ins., Ringsfield, Suff. Arm. Armf.	
	(A copy of the brass at Kenton, Suff., to John Garneys, 1524.)	I.
1597?	John Browne and sister, ins., St. John Sepulchre, Norwich	III.
1597	John Pen, w. ch. ins., Penn, Bucks.	II.
1599	Sir Christ. Lytcot, ins., West Hanney, Berks.	IV.
1599	Edw. Bulstrode, w. ch. ins., Upton, Bucks. PLATE 36	III.
c. 1600	Edw. Leventhorp, w. ins., Sawbridgeworth, Herts.	VIII.

17TH CENTURY

1601	Hen. Bowyer, w. ch. kng. ins., Cuckfield, Suss.	IV.
1602	Christ. Septvans *alias* Harflete, w. ins., Ash-next-Sandwich, Kent	VI.
1602	Chas. Butler, w. ch. kng. ins., Coates-by-Stow, Lincs.	III.
1602	Francis Wellesborne, w. ch. ins., West Hanney, Berks.	V.
1603	Robt. Mohun, w. ch. kng. ins., Fleet, Dorset	I.
1603	Jas. Bassett, w. ch. ins., Illogan, Cornw.	I.
1605	— Mynto, kng. ins., Glasgow Cathedral	I.
1606	John Brudenell, w. ins., Dene, Northants	III.
c. 1608	Thos. Windham, ins., Felbrigg, Norf.	V.
1609	Nich. Poulett, w. ch. kng. Minety, Wilts.	I.
1611	Ambrose Duke, w. ins., Benhall, Suff.	III.
1611	Wm. Clerke, w. ch. ins., Wrotham, Kent	VII.
1612	Thos. Soame, w. ch. kng. ins., Little Bradley, Suff.	V.
1612	Thos. Heydock, ins., Broad Blunsden, Wilts.	II.
1612	Maximilian Mohun, w. ch. kng. ins., Fleet, Dorset	II.
1614	John Hayward, ins., Ledbury, Hereford	V.
1618	Sir Hen. Warner, ins., Mildenhall, Suff.	III.
1618	Edm. West, w. ch. ins., Marsworth, Bucks. D.	V.
1620	Sir Hen. (?) Cholmeley, w., Burton Coggles, Lincs.	II.
1622	Sir Clement Edmonds, w. ins., Preston Deanery, Northants	I.
1625	Sir Arthur Gorges, w. ch. kng., Chelsea, London	II.
1628	Simon Mayne, w. ch. ins., Dinton, Bucks.	VII.
1629	Sir Edw. Filmer, w. ch. ins., East Sutton, Kent. PLATE 37	I.
1630	Edm. Sawyer, w. kng. ins., Kettering, Northants	I.
1630	Hen. Brockman, w. ch. ins., Newington-next-Hythe, Kent	XI.
c. 1630	? John Knighton, Bayford, Herts.	II.
c. 1630	Geo. Verney, ins., Compton Verney, Warw.	III.
c. 1630	Christ. Playters, ins., Sotterley, Suff.	IV.
c. 1630	Rich. Barttelot, ws. (2) ch. ins., Stopham, Suss.	VII.
1633	Sir John Arundel, w. ch. ins., St. Columb Major, Cornw.	II.
1633	John Arundel, w. ch. ins., St. Columb Major, Cornw.	III.
1634	John Boscawen, kng. ins., St. Michael Penkivel, Cornw.	
1636	Rich. Bugges, ws. (2) ins., Harlow, Essex	XI.

Date.	Name, Description, Place and Emblems, etc.	M.S.
1638	Sir Jarrate Harvye, w. ch. ins., Cardington, Beds. PLATE 38	II.
1638	Wm. Pen, w. ch. ins., Penn, Bucks.	III.
1641	John Pen, w. ch. ins., Penn, Bucks.	V.
1650	Ralph Assheton, w. ch. ins., Middleton, Lancs.	V.
1656	Thos. Carew, w. ch. kng. ins., Haccombe, Devon. PLATE 38	V.
1680	Nich. Toke, ch. kng. ins., Great Chart, Kent.	VII.

CIVIL COSTUME

MALE

14TH CENTURY

c. 1325	John de Bladigdone, w. hf-eff. ins., East Wickham, Kent. (In the head of a cross.)	I.
1349	Adam de Walsokne, w. ca. ins., St. Margaret, Lynn, Norf. SS.	I.
c. 1350	Nichole de Aumberdene, ins., Taplow, Bucks. (In the head of a floriated cross.) PLATE 40	I.
c. 1350	Anon. w. hf-eff. ins., Upchurch, Kent	I.
1356	Rich. Torryngton, w. ins., Great Berkhampstead, Herts. PLATE 40	I.
c. 1360	John de Walden, hf-eff. ins., Ashbury, Berks.	I.
c. 1360	Anon., hf-eff., Blickling, Norf.	I.
c. 1360	John de Feversham and mother, hf-eff. ins., Graveney, Kent	I.
c. 1360	Anon., Hampsthwaite, Yorks. (W.R.). (On it has been scratched an inscription to Ad. Dyxon, 1570.)	I.
c. 1360	Beneit Engliss, hf-eff. ins., Nuffield, Oxon.	I.
c. 1360	Raulin Brocas and sister, hf-eff. ins., Sherborne St. John, Hants	I.
1364	Robt. Braunche, ws. (2) ca. ins., St. Margaret, Lynn, Norf. SS. PLATE 39	II.
c. 1370	Anon., Barham, Kent	I.
c. 1370	Anon., hf-eff., Deddington, Oxon.	I.
c. 1370	Rich. de Heylesdone, w. hf-eff. ins., Hellesdon, Norf.	I.
c. 1370	John de Kyggesfolde, w. hf-eff. ins., Rusper, Suss.	I.
c. 1370	Anon., ca., Shottesbrooke, Berks.	I.
c. 1380	Roger de Felbrig, w. ins., Felbrigg, Norf.	I.
c. 1380	John Pecok, w. ins., St. Michael, St. Albans	I.
c. 1390	Anon., Cheam, Surr.	I.
c. 1390	Anon., hf-eff., Cheam, Surr.	II.
c. 1390	Robt. de Brantyngham, hf-eff., East Horsley, Surr.	I.
1391	John Corp and grand-dau., ca. ins., Stoke Fleming, Devon. PLATE 40	I.
1391	Thos. de Topclyff, w. ca. ins., Topcliffe, Yorks. (N.R.). SS.	I.
1391	John Curteys, Mayor of the Staple of Calais, wid. ca. ins., Wymington, Beds. E.S. PLATE 40	I.

Date.	Name, Description, Place and Emblems, etc.	M.S.
1394	Anon., Hereford Cathedral. (Formerly in the head of a cross.)	IV.
1398	Walter Pescod, ca., Boston, Lincs. SS.	I.
1398	Wm. Groby, hf-eff. ins., High Halstow, Kent	I.
1400	John Mulsho, w. kng. ins., Newton-by-Geddington, Northants. (Kneeling to a cross with St. Faith in the head. Restored in 1858.)	I.
c. 1400	Anon., hf-eff. ins., Temple Ch., Bristol	I.
c. 1400	Anon., w. ca., Cirencester, Glos.	I.
c. 1400	? John Petle, w., Downe, Kent	I.
c. 1400	John Covesgrave, w. ins., Eaton Socon, Beds.	I.
c. 1400	Thos. Somer, w. hf-eff. ins., Ickleford, Herts.	I.
c. 1400	Wm. Overbury, w. hf-eff. ins., Letchworth, Herts.	I.
c. 1400	Anon., w. ins., Northleach, Glos.	I.
c. 1400	Anon., w. ca., Ore, Suss.	I.
c. 1400	Anon., St. Michael, St. Albans. (In the head of a cross.)	III.
c. 1400	Anon., w., Tilbrook, Beds.	I.

15TH CENTURY

1401	Wm. Grevel, w. ca. ins., Chipping Campden, Glos.	I.
1402	Rich. Martyn, w. ca. ins., Dartford, Kent. PLATE 40	I.
1404	John Rede, ca. ins., Checkendon, Oxon.	I.
c. 1405	Herry Notingham, w. ins., Holme-by-the-Sea, Norf.	I.
1406	John de Estbury, w. hf-eff., Lambourne, Berks. E.S.	I.
1408	Robt. de Paris, w. kng., Hildersham, Cambs. H.T. (Kneeling to a floriated cross with Trinity in the head.) PLATE 40	I.
1409	Edm. Cook, ins., Great Berkhampstead, Herts. Now lost.	
1409	Robt. de Haitfeld, w. ins., Owston, Yorks.	I.
c. 1410	Nich. atte Heelde, ins., Chinnor, Oxon.	XI.
c. 1410	Nichol Roland, serjeant-at-law, w. ins., Cople, Beds.	I.
c. 1410	John Estbury and son Thos., hf-eff. ins., Lambourne, Berks.	II.
1411	John Barstaple, ins., Trinity Almshouse Chapel, Bristol	I.
1411	Roger Thornton, w. ch. ca. ins., All Saints, Newcastle-on-Tyne, Northumb. SS. B.V. J.B.	I.
1411	Thos. Fayreman, w. ins., St. Albans Abbey, Herts.	III.
1411	Hugh de Gondeby, ins., Tattershall, Lincs.	I.
1412	Walter Moneslee, w. ins., St. John Maddermarket, Norwich	I.
1415	Wm. West, w. ch. ins., Sudborough, Northants	I.
c. 1415	Hugh atte Spetyll and son John, ins., Luton, Beds.	I.
c. 1415	John Kent, w. hf-eff. ins., St. Laurence, Reading, Berks.	I.
1416	Thos. Stokes, w. ch. ca. ins., Ashby St. Legers, Northants	I.
1417	Geoff. Barbur, hf-eff. ins., St. Helen, Abingdon, Berks.	I.
1418	John Fildyng, w. ins., Lutterworth, Leic.	I.
1418	Thos. Polton, w. ins., Wanborough, Wilts.	I.
1419	John Lyndewode, w. ch. ca. ins., Linwood, Lincs.	I.

Date.	Name, Description, Place and Emblems, etc.	M.S.
1419	John Sprunt, ins., St. Peter-le-Bailey, Oxford	I.
1420	John Urban, w. ins., Southfleet, Kent. PLATE 42	II.
1420	— Waltham, mother and sister, hf-eff. ins., Waltham, Lincs.	II.
c. 1420	? Wm. Vynter, w., Baldock, Herts. (In huntsman's dress.)	II.
c. 1420	Thos. Petle, ins., Downe, Kent	II.
c. 1420	Anon., w., Dunton, Bucks.	I.
c. 1420	Anon., wid. ca., Furneux Pelham, Herts.	I.
c. 1420	Anon., Hitchin, Herts.	I.
c. 1420	? Thos. Clopton, Long Melford, Suff.	II.
c. 1420	Anon., hf-eff., Sall, Norf.	I.
c. 1420	Anon., Sawston, Cambs.	I.
c. 1420	Wm. Barton, w. ins., Thornborough, Bucks.	I.
1421	John Pulter, w. ins., Hitchin, Herts.	II.
1421	John Lyndewode, ca. ins., Linwood, Lincs.	II.
1425	Roger Sencler, ins., Erith, Kent	II.
1425	Wm. Chichele, w. ca. ins., Higham Ferrers, Northants	III.
1429	John Thomas, ins., Lydd, Kent	II.
1430	Hen. Brudenell, w. ins., Amersham, Bucks.	I.
1430	Thos. Godefray, w. ca. ins., Lydd, Kent	III.
c. 1430	? Thos. Carew, and sister Isabel, w. of Brian Harsick and Robt. Buckton, Beddington, Surr.	IV.
c. 1430	Anon., Hoo St. Werburgh, Kent	III.
c. 1430	Anon., w. ca., Melton, Suff.	I.
1431	Nich. Canteys, ins., St. John, Margate	I.
1432	Nich. Carrew, w. ca. ins., Beddington, Surr. E.S.	III.
1432	Robt. Baxter, wid. ins., St. Giles, Norwich	I.
1433	Simon Seman, ins., Barton-on-Humber, Lincs. E.S.	I.
1435	John Ailemer, w. ins., Erith, Kent	III.
1435	John Henege, w. ins., Hainton, Lincs.	I.
1435	Rich. Adane, w. ins., Kelshall, Herts.	I.
1436	Rich. Purdaunce, wid. ins., St. Giles, Norwich	II.
1436	John Asger, ins., St. Laurence, Norwich	VI.
1437	John Spycer, w. br. kng. ins., Burford, Oxon. E.S.	I.
1437	Robt. Skern, w. ins., Kingston-on-Thames, Surr.	I.
1437	John Bacon, w. ins., All Hallows, Barking, London. (With scrolls encircling a heart.)	II.
1437	Sir Thos. Brook, w. ins., Thorncombe, Dorset. PLATE 41	I.
1439	Thos. Carbonell, w. ins., Amersham, Bucks.	II.
1439	Hen. and Roger Eldysley, ins., East Hendred, Berks.	I.
1439	Wm. Markeby, w. ins., St. Bartholomew-the-Less, London	I.
1439	Edm. Forde, ins., Swainswick, Som.	I.
1440	Robt. Pagge, w. ch. ca., Cirencester, Glos.	III.
1440	Geoff. Boleyn, w. ins., Sall, Norf.	II.
c. 1440	Anon., Newport Pagnell, Bucks.	I.

Date.	Name, Description, Place and Emblems, etc.	M.S.
c. 1440	Anon., Winchelsea, Suss.	I.
c. 1440	John Andrew and Thos. Palmere, w. ch. ins., Wye, Kent	I.
1441	John Parker, w. ins., St. John, Margate	III.
1441	Thos. Roose, w. ch. br. ins., Sall, Norf.	III.
1441	John Brigge, ins., Snodland, Kent	I.
1442	Reginald Spycer, ws. (4) ins., Cirencester, Glos.	IV.
1442	Peter Stone, ins., St. John, Margate	IV.
1443	Thos. Berwyck, ins., Easthampstead, Berks.	I.
1445	Ralph Coppyn, w., Aston Rowant, Oxon.	I.
1446	John Olyver, wid., Naseby, Northants	I.
1446	Stephen and Richard Charlis, ins., Hoo St. Werburgh, Kent	IV.
1447	Wm. Scors and Thos. Fortey, w. ch. ca. ins., Northleach, Glos.	II.
1449	Wm. Halsted, w. ins., Biggleswade, Beds.	I.
1449	John Quek, ch. ins., Birchington, Kent	I.
1449	Wm. Pyke, w. ins., Cheshunt, Herts.	II.
1449	John Arderne, w. ch. ins., Leigh, Surr.	I.
1450	Wm. Hicchecok, wid. ins., Ampthill, Beds.	I.
1450	Wm. Welley, w. ins., Chipping Campden, Glos.	II.
1450	Laur. Pygot, w. ins., Dunstable, Beds.	I.
c. 1450	Anon., Amersham, Bucks.	IV.
c. 1450	Wm. Fyge, ins., Borden, Kent	I.
c. 1450	John Stokes, w. ins., Chipping Norton, Oxon.	I.
c. 1450	Anon., Cley, Norf.	I.
c. 1450	? — Treffry, w., Fowey, Cornw.	I.
c. 1450	? John Townsend, w., Lechlade, Glos.	I.
c. 1450	John Todenham, ins., St. John Maddermarket, Norwich	II.
c. 1450	Edw. Courtenay, ins., Christ Church Cathedral, Oxford	I.
c. 1450	? John Barrington, w., Rayleigh, Essex	I.
c. 1450	Anon., w., New Shoreham, Suss.	I.
c. 1450	Hugh Bostok, w. ins., Wheathampstead, Herts.	I.
1451	John Yonge, w. ins., Chipping Norton, Oxon.	II.
1451	Rich. Byll, w. hf-eff. ins., Holy Trinity, Hull, Yorks. E S.	I.
1452	Wm. Joye, ch. ins., Bramley, Hants	I.
1452	Anon., w. ch. ins., Hitchin, Herts.	III.
1452	John Fitzaleyn, ins., Christ Church Cathedral, Oxford	II.
1452	Edm. Mille, w. ins., Pulborough, Suss.	II.
1453	Rich. and John Haddok, w. ch. ins., Leigh-on-Sea, Essex	I.
1454	John Felde, ins., Birchington, Kent	II.
1454	Roger Felthorp, w. ch. ins., Blickling, Norf.	III.
1454	John Godfrey, w. ins., Haddenham, Cambs.	II.
1454	David Kidwelly, porter of the palace to Hen. VI., ins., Little Wittenham, Berks.	II.
1455	Rich. Manfeld, sister Isabel and brother John in shroud, ins., Taplow, Bucks. PLATE 42	II.

Date.	Name, Description, Place and Emblems, etc.	M.S.
1456	Wm. Anabull, w. ins., Harpenden, Herts.	I.
1457	John Smyth, w. hf-eff. ins., Shorne, Kent	I.
1458	John Compton, w. hf-eff. ins., Cheam, Surr.	III.
1458	John Babham, ins., Cookham, Berks.	I.
1458	John Fortey, ca. ins., Northleach, Glos.	III.
1459	Wm. Lovelace, ins., Bethersden, Kent	I.
1459	Wm. Wodeward, hf-eff. ins., Cheam, Surr.	IV.
1459	Wm. Tabard, w. ins., Walton, Suff.	I.
1460	Thos. Bokenham, St. Stephen, Norwich	II.
1460	John Browne, w. ins., All Saints, Stamford, Lincs. PLATE 41	I.
1460	Thos. Harecourt and Nich. Atherton, ch. ins., Stanton Harcourt, Oxon.	I.
c. 1460	? — Pigott, ch., Abington Pigotts, Cambs.	I.
c. 1460	Anon., Chipping Norton, Oxon.	III.
c. 1460	Anon., ch., Cley, Norf.	II.
c. 1460	Anon., Corringham, Essex	III.
c. 1460	Thos. Clarell, w. ch. ins., Lillingstone Lovell, Bucks.	II.
c. 1460	Anon., w. hf-eff., Monks Risborough, Bucks.	II.
c. 1460	? John Curteys, Standon, Herts.	II.
c. 1460	John Bartelot, treasurer of the household to Thos., Earl of Arundel, w. ch. ins., Stopham, Suss. (Children added in 1630, new head added to man, and both figures partly recut c. 1670-80.)	I.
c. 1460	Anon., Sundridge, Kent	II.
c. 1460	Wm. Lucas, w. ch. ins., Wenden Lofts, Essex	I.
1461	John Edward, ins., Rodmarton, Glos.	I.
1462	John Frankeleyn, w. ch. ins., Chearsley, Bucks.	I.
1462	Rich. Bertlot, marshall of the hall to the Earl of Arundel, w. ch. ins., Stopham, Suss.	III.
1463	Wm. Aldewyncle, ins., Aldwincle All Saints, Northants	I.
1463	John Ballard, w. ins., Merstham, Surr.	I.
c. 1465	Anon., w., St. Helen, Bishopsgate, London	II.
c. 1465	Wm. Graffton, w. ins., Nutfield, Surr.	I.
c. 1465	Anon., St. Albans Abbey, Herts.	VIII.
c. 1465	Wm. Browne, w. ca. ins., All Saints, Stamford, Lincs.	II.
1467	Edm. Bryghtye, hf-eff. ins., Barnham Broom, Norf.	I.
1467	John Lethenard, w. ins., Chipping Campden, Glos.	III.
1467	Symon Snelling, w. ins., Iwade, Kent	I.
1467	Thos. Elyot, w. ins., Wonersh, Surr.	I.
1468	John Canon, w. ch. ins., Long Crendon, Bucks.	I.
1469	John Waliston, ws. (2) ins., Chenies, Bucks.	I.
1469	Gauwyn More, marshall of the king's hall, w. ch. ins., Tilehurst, Berks.	I.
1470	John Wynter, ins., St. Margaret, Canterbury	I.
1470	Geoff. Joslyne, ws. (2) ins., Sawbridgeworth, Herts.	II.

Date.	Name, Description, Place and Emblems, etc.	M.S.
c. 1470	? John Wattis, formerly Great Bircham, Norf. Now lost.	
c. 1470	Anon., Great Chart, Kent. (A notary.)	I.
c. 1470	Wm. Notyngham, w. ins., Cirencester, Glos.	VII.
c. 1470	Anon., ws. (2) Fakenham, Norf.	II.
c. 1470	Anon., w. ch., Flamstead, Herts.	II.
c. 1470	Anon., ch., Leatherhead, Surr.	II.
c. 1470	? John Renolds, w., Lutterworth, Leic.	II.
c. 1470	Anon., St. Albans Abbey, Herts.	IX.
c. 1470	Anon., Victoria and Albert Museum	II.
c. 1470	Wm. Pyrry, w. ch. ins., Ware, Herts.	III.
c. 1470	Anon., Watton-at-Stone, Herts.	V.
1472	Wm. Norwiche, w. ch. br. ins., St. George Colegate, Norwich. PLATE 42	I.
1472	Ralph Segrym, w., St. John Maddermarket, Norwich	III.
1473	Wm. Turnor, w. ins., Berden, Essex	I.
1473	Roger Hunt, w. ins., Great Linford, Bucks.	I.
1474	Robt. Parnell, w. ch. ins., Spratton, Northants	I.
1475	Wm. Style, w. ins., St. Nicholas, Ipswich	I.
1475	John Browne, wid. ins., All Saints, Stamford, Lincs.	IV.
c. 1475	Anon., w., Hempstead, Essex	I.
c. 1475	Anon., St. Mary-at-Tower, Ipswich. (A notary.) PLATE 43	I.
1476	John Everard, hf-eff. ins., Halesworth, Suff.	I.
1476	Wm. Pepyr, w., St. John Maddermarket, Norwich	IV.
1476	Rich. Do, ws. (2) Steventon, Berks.	I.
1477	John Croke, wid. ch. kng., All Hallows, Barking, London	IV.
1477	John Feld, and son John in armour, ins., Standon, Herts. PLATE 42	III.
1478	Thos. Rowley, w. ins., St. John, Bristol	I.
1478	Wm. Robertson, w. ins., St. Peter-in-the-East, Oxford	I.
1478	Rich. Mille, ins., Pulborough, Suss.	III.
1479	Nich. Deen, w. ch. ins., Barrowby, Lincs.	I.
1479	Thos. Selby, w. ins., East Malling, Kent	I.
1479	Wm. Shosmyth, w., Mereworth, Kent	II.
1479	Edm. Howton, w. ins., Wormley, Herts.	II.
1480	John Coblegh, ws. (2) ch. ins., Chittlehampton, Devon	II.
c 1480	? — Coket, w. ch. kng., Ampton, Suff.	I.
c. 1480	? Wm. Crane, w., Baldock, Herts.	IV.
c. 1480	Anon., w., Braughing, Herts.	I.
c. 1480	John Jay, w. ch. ins., St. Mary Redcliffe, Bristol	IV.
c. 1480	Anon., British Museum	I(5).
c. 1480	Anon., w. kng., St. Mary, Bury St. Edmunds, Suff.	I.
c. 1480	Anon., Carlton, Suff.	I.
c. 1480	Wm. Walrond, w. ins., Childrey, Berks.	IV.
c. 1480	Anon., w. kng., Chrishall, Essex	III.
c. 1480	Anon., w., Cirencester, Glos.	X.

Date.	Name, Description, Place and Emblems, etc.	M.S.
c. 1480	Anon., w., Euston, Suff.	I.
c. 1480	Hen. Jarmon, w., Geddington, Northants	I.
c. 1480	Anon., ch., Hempstead, Essex	II.
c. 1480	Edm. Grene, w. ins., Hunstanton, Norf.	I.
c. 1480	Anon., Littlebury, Essex	I.
c. 1480	Anon., w., Odiham, Hants	I.
c. 1480	Anon., Orford, Suff.	I.
c. 1480	Anon., w., Little Plumstead, Norf.	I.
c. 1480	Anon., ins., Turvey, Beds.	I.
c. 1480	— Songar, w. ch., Victoria and Albert Museum. (Deposited on loan by the vicar and churchwardens of Clavering, Essex.)	III.
c. 1480	— Humberstone, w., Walkern, Herts.	I.
1481	Thos. Abbot, w., Hitchin, Herts.	VIII.
1483	Wm. Crofton, w. ins., Trottescliffe, Kent	I.
1483	Geoff. Kidwelly, ins., Little Wittenham, Berks.	IV.
1484	Wm. Gybbys, ws. (3) ch. ins., Chipping Campden, Glos.	IV.
1484	John Pergetter, w. ch. ins., Chipping Norton, Oxon.	IV.
1484	Thos. Radley, w. ch. ins., Garsington, Oxon.	I.
1485	Rich. Westbroke, ins., Great Berkhampstead, Herts.	V.
1485	Wm. Goldwell, w., Great Chart, Kent	II.
1485	John Parker, w. ins., Faringdon, Berks.	III.
1485	Rich. Colmer, w. ins., St. Peter, Thanet	II.
1485	Geoff. Porter, w. ins., Little Walsingham, Norf.	II.
1485	Wm. Frankeleyn, w. ins., Watlington, Oxon.	I.
c. 1485	Anon., w. ch. ins., Northleach, Glos.	IV.
1486	Wm. Lee of Morton, w. ins., Dinton, Bucks.	II.
1486	Roger Perot, ins., Snodland, Kent	II.
1487	Robt. Warham, w. ch. ins., Church Oakley, Hants	I.
1487	John Lambard, w. ch. ins., Hinxworth, Herts.	II.
1487	Wm. Wheteaker, w. and son Thos., ins., Radwell, Herts.	I.
1487	Edw. Bischoptre, w. ins., Snodland, Kent	III.
1487	John Barton, w. ins., Nether Winchendon, Bucks.	III.
1488	Geo. Aynesworth, ws. (3) ch. ins., Harrow, Middx.	VI.
1488	John Hertcombe, w. kng. ins., Kingston-on-Thames, Surr.	II.
1488	Wm. Monde and John Sayer, ins., Newington-next-Sittingbourne, Kent	I.
1488	Symon Brooke, ws. (3) Ufford, Suff.	I.
1488	John Godwyn, ins., Wooburn, Bucks.	I.
1489	Rich. Carlyll, w. ins., Campton, Beds.	I.
1489	Nich. Byldysdon, w. ch. ins., St. John, Stamford, Lincs.	II.
1489	Harry Blaknall, w. ins., Wing, Bucks.	I.
1490	Philip Bosard, w. ch. ins., Ditchingham, Norf.	I.
c. 1490	Anon., Aldborough, Norf.	IV.
c. 1490	Anon., ws. (2) ch., Great Amwell, Herts.	II.

Date.	Name, Description, Place and Emblems, etc.	M.S.
c. 1490	Robt. Farman, ins., Aylsham, Norf.	II.
c. 1490	Anon., Barton-in-the-Clay, Beds.	III.
c. 1490	Wm. Faldo, w. and John Faldo, ins., Biddenham, Beds.	I.
c. 1490	Anon., Braughing, Herts.	II.
c. 1490	Wm. Smyth, ws. (2) ch. ins., Bray, Berks.	V.
c. 1490	Laur. Marton, Broughton, Hunts.	I.
c. 1490	Rich. Amondesham, or Awnsham, w. ch. kng. ins., Ealing, Middx.	I.
c. 1490	? Wm. Stiles, St. Nicholas, Ipswich	II.
c. 1490	Wm. Goldyngton, w. ch. ins., Lidlington, Beds. H.T. E.S.	I.
c. 1490	Anon., w. ch., North Mimms, Herts.	IV.
c. 1490	Anon., ws. (2) ch., Newnham, Herts.	I.
c. 1490	John Taylour, w. ch. ins., Northleach, Glos. E.S.	V.
c. 1490	Wm. Corbald, w. ins., Occold, Suff.	I.
c. 1490	Anon., w. ch., Polstead, Suff.	II.
c. 1490	Anon., ca., St. Clement, Sandwich, Kent	I.
c. 1490	Thos. Grene, ws. (2) ins., Turweston, Bucks.	II.
c. 1490	Anon., w., Wing, Bucks	II.
c. 1490	John Cok, w. ch., Wormley, Herts.	III.
1492	Christ. Elcok, ins., St. Mary Magdalen, Canterbury. Now lost.	
1492	Barth. Willesden, ws. (2) ch., Willesden, Middx.	I.
1492	Rich. Burgehill, originally in Hereford Cathedral. (At one time in the Nichols Collection, and in 1894 in the possession of the late E. Cleghorn of Plumpstead.)	
1493	Roger Harper, w. kng. ins., Axbridge, Som.	I.
1493	Thos. Broke, w. ch. ins., Barking, Essex	III.
1493	Robt. Doughty, w. ins., Metton, Norf.	II.
1493	John Bartellot, kng. ins., Stopham, Suss.	IV.
1493	John Caysyll, ins., Tormarton, Glos.	I.
1495	Wm. Foxe, w. ins., Great Barford, Oxon.	I.
1495	Thos. Hoore, w. ch. ins., Digswell, Herts.	V.
1495	John Brook, w. ch. ins., Farley, Surr.	I.
1495	Thos. Wylliams, w. ins., St. Helen, Bishopsgate, London	IV.
1495	John Horslee, w., St. Swithin, Norwich	III.
c. 1495	? Thos. Bothe, hf-eff. ch., Sparsholt, Berks.	II.
1496	John Beryf, ws. (3) ch., Brightlingsea, Essex	I.
1496	Rich. Burlton, w. ins., Dartford, Kent	V.
1496	Hen. Spelman, w. ins., Narborough, Norf.	I.
1497	John Benet, w. ins., Cirencester, Glos.	XII.
1497	John Clerk, w. ins., Basildon, Berks.	I.
1497	Mighell Skinner, ins., St. Giles, Camberwell, Surr.	I.
1497	Wm. Maynwaryng, ins., Ightfield, Salop. PLATE 43	II.
1497	Wm. Millys, ins., West Malling, Kent	I.
1498	John Rusche, ins., All Hallows, Barking, London	VI.
1498	Wm. Basset, wid. ins., Blore Ray, Staffs.	I.

Date.	Name, Description, Place and Emblems, etc.	M.S.
1498	Robt. Fulmer, w. ch. ins., Hedgerley, Bucks.	I.
1498	John Snellyng, w. ins., East Horsley, Surr.	III.
1498	John Bedell, ins., Winchester College	IX.
1498	Thos. Nysell, w. ch. ins., Wrotham, Kent	I.
1499	Thos. Bartlett, w. ins., Billinghurst, Suss.	I.
1499	Nich. Wottun, w. ch. ins., Boughton Malherbe, Kent	I.
1499	John Gyll, ch. ins., Buckland, Herts.	III.
1499	Rich. Skynner, ch. ins., Camberwell, Surr.	II.
1499	Wm. Sharp, w. ins., Great Chart, Kent	III.
1499	John Roberts, w. ch., Hawkhurst, Kent	I.
1499	Wm. Curteys, w. ins., Necton, Norf. (A notary.)	III.
1500	Thos. Goodriche, w. ins., Aspenden, Herts.	I.
1500	Robt. Grote, ins., Bawburgh, Norf.	III.
1500	Thos. Payne, w. ins., Bushley, Worc.	I.
1500	Thos. Twesden, w. ins., Great Chart, Kent	IV.
1500	Wm. Turnour, w. ch. ins., Hadley, Middx.	III.
1500	Hen. Myllet, ws. (2) ch. ins., Perivale, Middx.	I.
1500	Rich. Wenman, ws. (2) ch. ins., Witney, Oxon.	I.
c. 1500	Rich. Wakehurst, w. ca. ins., Ardingley, Suss.	I.
c. 1500	Anon., w., Aylsham, Norf.	IV.
c. 1500	Anon., Cirencester, Glos.	XIII.
c. 1500	? John Avenyng, w. ch. kng. ins., Cirencester, Glos.	XIV.
c. 1500	John a Gate, ins., Cowfold, Suss.	II.
c. 1500	? Sir Wm. Calthorpe, ca., North Creake, Norf.	I.
c. 1500	John Aspleyn and Godfrey Askew, w. ins., Edmonton, Middx.	I.
c. 1500	Anon., w., South Elmham, Suff.	I.
c. 1500	Anon., w., St. Mary, Guildford, Surr.	I.
c. 1500	Christ. Ford and Thos. Wheler, w. ins., Handborough, Oxon.	I.
c. 1500	Anon., ws. (2) St. Mary Tower, Ipswich	II.
c. 1500	Anon., w. ca. ins., Nayland, Suff. PLATE 43	IV.
c. 1500	Anon., Luton, Beds.	V.
c. 1500	Anon., w., Middleton, Suff.	I.
c. 1500	Anon., w., Minchinhampton, Glos.	I.
c. 1500	? Robt. Gardiner, w., St. Andrew, Norwich	IV.
c. 1500	Anon., hf-eff. Said to be from St. Laurence, Norwich.	
c. 1500	Anon., w., Orford, Suff.	III.
c. 1500	Anon., w., Rainham, Essex	II.
c. 1500	Anon., w., Royston, Herts.	III.
c. 1500	? Christ. Browne, w., All Saints, Stamford, Lincs.	VI.
c. 1500	Anon., w. ch. ins., Thame, Oxon.	IV.
c. 1500	Robt. Lytton, w. ins., Tideswell, Derb.	II.
c. 1500	Anon., w., East Tuddenham, Norf.	I.
c. 1500	John Bedbere, ins., Weare, Som.	I.
c. 1500	? Benedict Medley, w., Whitnash, Warw.	I.

Date.	Name, Description, Place and Emblems, etc.	M.S.
c. 1500	Anon., Wimpole, Cambs.	II.
c. 1500	Christ. Askowe, w. ins., Wooburn, Bucks.	II.
c. 1500	Anon., Worstead, Norf.	III.
c. 1500	John Burgoyne, ins., Wrotham, Kent	II.
c. 1500	Anon., w. Locality unknown.	

16TH CENTURY

1501	Wm. Andrew, w. ins., March, Cambs.	I.
1501	Robt. Serche, w. ch. ins., Northleach, Glos.	VII.
1502	Wm. Lane, w., Orlingbury, Northants	II.
1502	John Turnay, w. ins., Soulbury, Bucks.	II.
1502	Wm. Gregory, ins., St. Mary-in-the-Marsh, Kent	II.
1502	Geoff. Dormer, ws. (2) ch., Thame, Oxon. E.S.	V.
1503	Thos. Pallyng, w. ins., Clippesby, Norf.	II.
1503	Wm. Andrew and John Monkeden, w. ins., Cookham, Berks.	III.
1503	Nich. Esstone, w. ins., St. Peter, Thanet, Kent	II.
1503	Christ. Bridgman, w. ch. ins., Thame, Oxon.	VI.
1503	Hen. Elyot, w. ch. ins., Wonersh, Surr.	II.
1503	John Reed, w. ch. ins., Wrangle, Lincs.	I.
1504	Thos. Thorston, w. ins., Challock, Kent	I.
1504	John Smyth, w. ins., Cottingham, Yorks.	II.
1504	Wm. Thorpe, wid. ch. ins., Higham Ferrers, Northants. E.S.	VI.
1504	Wm. Knyght, w. ins., Norton, Northants	I.
1504	John Ardalle, w. ins., Stifford, Essex	III.
1504	John Adene, w. ins., Stoke Talmage, Oxon.	I.
1504	Simon Bolwar, ins., Wood Dalling, Norf.	VI.
1505	John Hawtt, *alias* Cryscyan, w. ch. ins., Caddington, Beds.	I.
1505	Roger Bozard, and son Wm., ins., Ditchingham, Norf.	II.
1505	Rich. at Hyll, ins., Guestwick, Norf.	II.
1505	John Peddar, w. ch. ins., Salford, Beds.	I.
1505	Rich. Blackwall, w. ch. ins., Taddington, Derb.	I.
1505	Wm. Pescod, ins., Themelthorpe, Norf.	IV.
1505	Rich. Barowe, w. ch. ins., Winthorpe, Lincs.	I.
1506	Rich. Maulaye, w. ins., Blunham, Beds.	I.
1506	John Gregory, ws. (2) ch. ins., Cuxham, Oxon.	I.
1506	Wm. Croke, w. ch. ins., Great Gaddesden, Herts.	I.
1506	Robt. Wymbyll and Thos. Baldry, w. ch. ins., St. Mary Tower, Ipswich. (A notary.)	III.
1506	Regenolde Tylney, ch. ins., Leckhampstead, Bucks.	II.
1506	Roger Legh, ch. kng. ins., Macclesfield, Ches. R. (A representation of the Mass of St. Gregory, with a pardon inscribed below.) PLATE 43	I.
1506	John Goodyere, w. ins., Teddington, Middx.	I.
1506	John Colman, w. ch. ins., Little Waldingfield, Suff. E.S.	I.

Date.	Name, Description, Place and Emblems, etc.	M.S.
1506	John Hyll, w. ins., Wilburton, Cambs. E.S.	II.
1507	Rich. Fyssher, ins., Goldington, Beds.	I.
1507	Wm. Boys, w. ch. ins., Goodnestone-next-Wingham, Kent. H.T.	I.
1507	John Crane, ins., Wood Dalling, Norf.	VIII.
c. 1507	? Robt. Foster, w., Mattishall, Norf.	V.
1508	Wm. Hyklott, ins., Althorne, Essex. B.V. H.T.	II.
1508	John Best, w. ins., Boughton-under-Blean, Kent	II.
1508	— Wiltshire, Dartford, Kent	VI.
1508	Thos. Baker, w. ch., St. Leonard, Deal, Kent	I.
1508	Robt. Cokyram, Lydd, Kent	IV.
1508	John Wylmot, w. ins., Stadhampton, Oxon.	II.
1508	Rich. Abery, ws. (3) ins., St. Mary Cray, Kent	II.
1508	Walter Pratt, w. ins., Thame, Oxon.	VII.
1509	Robt. Court, w. ins., Brightwell, Berks.	II.
1509	Wm. Morys, ch. ins., Great Coxwell, Berks.	I.
1509	Rich. Norton, ins., South Creake, Norf.	II.
1509	Wm. Eyre, ins., Great Cressingham, Norf.	II.
1509	Wm. Merden, w. ch. ins., Leeds, Kent	I.
1509	Robt. Heyward, ch. ins., Teynham, Kent	II.
1509	Hen. Clederowe, w. ins., Little Walsingham, Norf.	IX.
1510	John Seymoure, ins., Great Bedwyn, Wilts.	II.
1510	Rich. Iwardby, ins., Quainton, Bucks.	V.
1510	Thos. Lamberd, ins., New Romney, Kent	II.
c. 1510	? Thos. Underhill, w. kng., Little Bradley, Suff.	I.
c. 1510	Anon., Horley, Surr.	II.
c. 1510	Anon., Lechlade, Glos.	II.
c. 1510	Anon., w., Littlebury, Essex	III.
c. 1510	Geoff. Dene, ins., Mattishall, Norf.	IV.
c. 1510	Anon., Orford, Suff.	V.
c. 1510	Anon., New College, Oxford. (A notary.)	IX.
c. 1510	Anon., Staple, Kent	I.
c. 1510	? — Tredeneck, w. ch., St. Breock, Cornw.	I.
c. 1510	Anon., w. ch., Wheathampstead, Herts.	IV.
c. 1510	Anon., w. ch., Wirksworth, Derb.	I.
c. 1510	Anon., ws. (4) ch., Writtle, Essex	II.
c. 1510	Anon. In possession of the Society of Antiquaries	VI.
1511	John Mylner, w. ins., Erith, Kent	VI.
1511	Rich. Potter, ws. (2) ch. ins., Westerham, Kent	II.
1511	Nich. Wrenne, w. ins., Worlingham, Suff.	II.
1512	Rich. Hampden, w. ins., Brightwell, Berks.	III.
1512	John Muscote, w., Earls Barton, Northants	I.
1512	Habram Fare, ins., Harty, Kent	I.
1512	John Lamar, w. ch. ins., Luton, Beds.	VII.
1512	Rich. Pecok, ch. ins., Redbourn, Herts.	II.

Date.	Name, Description, Place and Emblems, etc.	M.S.
1512	Olever Sandes, ins., Shere, Surr.	III.
1513	Rich. Beweforest, w. ch. ins., Dorchester, Oxon.	VI.
1513	Wm. Rysley, w. ins., Lillingstone Lovell, Bucks.	III.
1513	Wm. Wyddowsoun, w. kng. ins., Mickleham, Surr. PLATE 45	I.
1513	Rich. Brasyer and son Rich., St. Stephen, Norwich	VII.
1513	John Hook, w. ins., Sherringham, Norf.	II.
1513	Thos. Heveningham, w. and son Thos., and his dau., Thomasin, w. of Thos. Berdefield, John Bedell and Walter Thomas, Writtle, Essex	III.
c. 1513	Robt. Brasyer, w. ins., St. Stephen, Norwich	VI.
1514	Robt. Southwell, w. ins., Barham, Suff.	I.
1514	John Dorant, w. ins., Barnham Broom, Norf.	II.
1514	Folke Poffe, w. ch., Chinnor, Oxon.	XIII.
1514	Thos. Fytche, w. ch. ins., Lindsell, Essex	I.
1514	Pawle Yden, w. ch. ins., Penshurst, Kent	II.
1514	John Wulvedon, w. ins., Probus, Cornw.	I.
1514	Edw. Saunders, w. ins., Rothwell, Northants	II.
1515	Edw. Dalyson, w. ins., Cransley, Northants	I.
1515	Thos. Brond, w. ch. ins., Newport, Essex. E.S.	I.
1515	Rich. Water, w. ins., Swaffham Prior, Cambs.	II.
1515	Robt. Palmer, ins., Winthorpe, Lincs.	II.
1516	Rich. Davy, w. ins., Nayland, Suff.	V.
1516	John Bele, ws. (2) ch. ins., Radwell, Herts.	II.
1516	John Redfford, w. ch. ins., Shere, Surr.	IV.
1516	Wm. Byrd, w. ch. ins., Wilburton, Cambs.	III.
1517	Thos. Crekett, ins., Bisham, Berks.	II.
1517	Thos. Robertes, ws. (3) ch. ins., Brenchley, Kent	I.
1517	John Newman, w. ch. ins., Brightwalton, Berks.	I.
1517	Wm. Petham, kng. ins., Farningham, Kent	III.
1517	Thos. Mountagu, w. ins., Hemington, Northants	I.
1517	Rich. Blackhed, w. ins., Ivinghoe, Bucks.	II.
1517	Thos. Heron, ins., Little Ilford, Essex	I.
1517	Thos. Goddard, w. ins., Ogbourne St. George, Wilts.	I.
1517	Roger Cheverell, hf-eff. ins., Piddletown, Dorset	I.
1517	Roger Opy, ins., St. Minver, Cornw.	I.
1517	Thos. Apsley, ins., Thakeham, Suss.	II.
1517	Thos. Freshwater, w. ch., Tollesbury, Essex	I.
1517	Wm. Lawerd, w. ch. ins., Yateley, Hants	II.
1518	Edw. Dormer, ws. (2) ch. ins., Caddington, Beds.	II.
1518	Thos. Goodyere, w., Hadley, Middx.	V.
1518	Wm. Mordaunt, ch. ins., Hempstead, Essex	VI.
1518	Arthur Sotheryn, Higham Ferrers, Northants	VIII.
1518	Christ. Rawson, ws. (2) ins., All Hallows, Barking, London	VIII.
1518	John Howard, ins., Poddington, Beds.	I.

Date.	Name, Description, Place and Emblems, etc.	M.S.
1518	John Barley, w. ch. ins., Preshute, Wilts.	I.
1518	Edm. Wayte, w. ins., Renhold, Beds.	I.
1518	John and Thos. Bulwer, ins., Wood Dalling, Norf.	X.
1519	John Rokys, w. ins., Calverton, Bucks.	I.
1519	Thos. Sibill, w. ins., Farningham, Kent	IV.
1519	Edw. Halyday, w. ins., Minchinhampton, Glos.	III.
1519	John Smalwode, *alias* Wynchcom, w. ch. ins., Newbury, Berks.	I.
1519	Jas. Tornay, ws. (2) ch. ins., Slapton, Bucks.	II.
1519	Rauff Rowlatt, ch. ins., St. Albans Abbey, Herts.	XV.
1519	Thos. Pygott, ws. (2) ch. ins., Whaddon, Bucks.	I.
1519	Giles Penne, w. ins., Yeovil, Som.	II.
1520	Rich. Pygott, w. ins., Compton Parva, Berks.	I.
1520	Wm. Crysford, kng., Ewhurst, Suss.	I.
1520	Wm. Palmer, ins., Ingoldmells, Lincs.	I.
1520	John Shepard, ws. (2) ch. ins., Kingsbury, Middx.	I.
1520	John Heyworth, w. ch. ins., Wheathampstead, Herts.	III.
1520	John Alblastyr, ins., Worstead, Norf.	VII.
c. 1520	Anon., w. ch., Aldenham, Herts.	III.
c. 1520	Anon., ch., Aldenham, Herts.	IV.
c. 1520	John Goldwell, w. ch. ins., Biddenden, Kent	I.
c. 1520	Thos. Horton, w. ins., Bradford-on-Avon, Wilts.	I.
c. 1520	Thos. Wolrond, w. ins., Childrey, Berks. H.T.	X.
c. 1520	? — Peacock, w., Coggeshall, Essex	II.
c. 1520	Anon., ch., Cranbrook, Kent	I.
c. 1520	John Wyther, w. ins., Dunster, Som.	I.
c. 1520	Anon., w., Euston, Suff.	II.
c. 1520	Anon., Godmanchester, Hunts.	I.
c. 1520	Anon., East Grinstead, Suss.	II.
c. 1520	Jas. at Hylle, ins., Guestwick, Norf.	IV.
c. 1520	Anon., w., Great Hadham, Herts.	III.
c. 1520	Thos. Goodenouth, w. ins., All Saints, Hastings, Suss.	I.
c. 1520	Anon., ws. (2) ch. br., St. Mary Tower, Ipswich	IV.
c. 1520	Anon., Littlebury, Essex	IV.
c. 1520	Robt. Su............, ws. (2) ins., Luton, Beds.	XII.
c. 1520	Anon., Lydd, Kent	V.
c. 1520	Anon., w., Orford, Suff. H.T.	VII.
c. 1520	Anon., Orford, Suff.	VIII.
c. 1520	John Sedley, w. ch. ins., Southfleet, Kent	VII.
c. 1520	Anon., w., Tisbury, Wilts.	I.
c. 1520	John Peyton, ins., Wicken, Cambs.	II.
c. 1520	Anon., w., Wokingham, Berks.	I.
1521	John de la Penne, w. ins., Amersham, Bucks.	V.
1521	John Beriff, ws. (2) ch., Brightlingsea, Essex	IV.
1521	Wm. Cheswryght, w. ins., Forsham, Cambs.	II.

E

Date.	Name, Description, Place and Emblems, etc.	M.S.
1521	Walter Hichman, w. ch. ins., Kempsford, Glos. E.S.	I.
1521	John Bowyer, w. ins., St. Giles, Reading	I.
1521	John Humpton, w. ch. ins., Sculthorpe, Norf.	IV.
1521	Laur. Slyffeld, w. ins., Send, Surr.	I.
1521	Robt. Fairfax, w. ins., St. Albans Abbey, Herts. (Renewed in 1921.)	
1521	Wm. Water, w. ch. ins., Swaffham Prior, Cambs.	III.
1522	Walter Mylys, ch. ins., Birling, Kent. E.S.	I.
1522	Thos. Laurence, w. ch. ins., Netteswell, Essex	I.
1522	Rich. Ryege, ws. (3) ins., Newington-next-Hythe, Kent	IV.
1522	Thos. Symeon, w. ins., Pyrton, Oxon.	I.
1522	Wm. Cobbe, w. and son Thos., ins., Sharnbrook, Beds.	I.
1522	Walter Tawbott, ws. (2) ch. ins., Wantage, Berks.	V.
c. 1522	Raff Brown, ins., St. Mary Northgate, Canterbury	I.
1523	Nich. Boone, w. ins., Edmonton, Middx.	II.
1523	Stevyn Audyan (Odyarne), ins., Wittersham, Kent	I.
1524	Wm. Chaucey, w. ins., Charlton, Wilts.	I.
1524	Robt. Colshill, w. ins., Luton, Beds. Now lost.	
1524	John Terry, w. ch. br. ins., St. John Maddermarket, Norwich	VII.
1525	Wm. Leus, w. ins., Ash-next-Sandwich, Kent	III.
1525	Wm. Beriff, w., Brightlingsea, Essex	V.
1525	John Haryson, ws. (2) ch. kng. ins., St. Mary, Hull	I.
1525	Thos. Pownder, w. ch. ins., St. Mary Quay, Ipswich. E.S. PLATE 44	I.
1525	John Marsham, w. br., St. John Maddermarket, Norwich. PLATE 43	VIII.
1525	John Awodde, w. ch. ins., Sanderstead, Surr.	I.
1525	Anon., Selling, Kent	II.
1525	Thos. Blakewall, w. ch. ins., Wirksworth, Derb.	II.
1526	Wm. Freme, ins., Berkeley, Glos. (Holding heart.)	I.
1526	John Gybbis, w. ch. ins., Capel-le-Ferne, Kent	I.
1526	Christ. Crowe, w. ch. ins., Mileham, Norf.	I.
1526	Thos. Busche, w. ca. ins., Northleach, Glos. E.S.	VIII.
1526	John Ips, w. ins., Old Romney, Kent	I.
1527	John Deynes, w. ins., Beeston Regis, Norf.	V.
1527	John Shadet, w. ins., Woking, Surr.	II.
1528	Hen. Redmayne, w. ch. kng. ins., New Brentford, Middx.	I.
1528	Wm. Petley, w. ins., Halstead, Kent	II.
1528	John Bacon, ins., Necton, Norf.	V.
1529	Rich. Carter, w. ins., Bramley, Hants	III.
1529	John Cook, wid., St. Mary-de-Crypt, Gloucester. J.B. PLATE 45	I.
1529	John Samwel, w. ch. ins., Offley, Herts.	I.
1529	Wm. Bloor, ins., Rainham, Kent	IV.
1529	Rich. Hayward, ins., Westerham, Kent	III.

Date.	Name, Description, Place and Emblems, etc.	M.S.
1530	John Saye, w. ch. kng. ins., St. Peter, Colchester . . .	I.
1530	Hen. Dacres, w. kng. ins., St. Dunstan-in-the-West, London .	I.
1530	Edw. Watson, w. ch., Lyddington, Rutland	II.
1530	John Upton, ins., Ringwould, Kent	II.
c. 1530	Rich. Bulkley, w. ch. kng. ins., Beaumaris, Anglesea. B.V. H.T.	I.
c. 1530	Anon., w., Binham, Norf.	I.
c. 1530	Anon., w., Digswell, Herts. (Appropriated by the addition of an inscr. to Robt. Batyll, 1557, his w. Margt. and son Wm., and of another inscr. stating that Wm. had by his w. Joan 4 sons and 6 daus., whose effigies are added.) . . .	VI.
c. 1530	Anon., ws. (2) ch. ins., Elmdon, Essex. E.S. . . .	I.
c. 1530	Anon., w. ch., Hempstead, Essex	VI.
c. 1530	Anon., w., Lakenheath, Suff.	I.
c. 1530	John Watson, w. ins., Leake, Yorks.	I.
c. 1530	Anon., ws. (2) ch. ins., Offley, Herts.	II.
c. 1530	— Fastolfe, w. ch., Pettaugh, Suff.	I.
c. 1530	Anon., w., Swaffham Prior, Cambs.	IV.
c. 1530	Anon., Upminster, Essex	II.
c. 1530	John Younge, ins., Welford, Berks.	II.
c. 1530	Anon., Wilby, Suff.	I.
c. 1530	Anon., w. ch. Locality unknown.	
c. 1530	Anon., w. Formerly at Cassiobury House, Herts., now in possession of W. H. Fenton, Heston, Middx.	
1531	Geo. Wyndbourne, w. ch. ins., St. Paul, Canterbury. Now lost.	
1531	Thos. Duncombe, ch., Ivinghoe, Bucks.	III.
1531	Thos. Potter, ins., Westerham, Kent	IV.
1532	Antony Maycot, w. ch. ins., Hoath, Kent . . .	II.
1532	Wm. Skott, ins., West Malling, Kent	II.
1532	Robt. Goodwyn, w. ch. ins., Necton, Norf. . . .	VI.
1532	Thos. Challoner, w. ch. ins., Rusper, Suss. . . .	II.
1532	Wm. Rygg, w. ch. ins., Yately, Hants	III.
1533	John Swanne, ins., Acle, Norf.	II.
1533	John Paycock, w., Coggeshall, Essex	III.
1533	Hen. Hatche, merchant-adventurer, w. ca. ins., Faversham, Kent. E.S.	XII.
1533	Rich. Colwell, ws. (2) ch. ins., Faversham, Kent . . .	XIII.
1533	Andrew Evyngar, w. ch. ca. ins., All Hallows, Barking, London. B.V. PLATE 46	IX.
1533	Rich. Bradbryge, w. ins., Slinfold, Suss. . . .	I.
1533	Wm. Wreke, ins., Teynham, Kent	III.
1533	John Stacy, Westerham, Kent	V.
1534	Morrys Osberne, w. ch. ins., Kelmarsh, Northants. Now lost.	
1534	John Cracherood, w. ch. ins., Toppesfield, Essex . .	I.
1535	Thos. Perys, w. ins., Little Barford, Beds. . . .	I.

Date.	Name, Description, Place and Emblems, etc.	M.S.
1535	Rich. Mewys, ch. ins., Kingston, Isle of Wight . . .	I.
1535	Edw. Love, w. ch. ins., Stoke Lyne, Oxon. R. . . .	I.
c. 1535	Anon., w., Hitchin, Herts.	XV.
c. 1535	Anon., w., St. John Sepulchre, Norwich	II.
c. 1535	Anon., ws. (2) ch. ins., Rettendon, Essex	I.
c. 1535	Civilian with staff, kng. at a desk. About 1860 in possession of the Rev. F. T. J. Bayly, of Brookthorpe, Glos. . .	
1536	Thos. Malyn, w. ch. ins., Great Linford, Bucks. . .	II.
1537	Wm. Bradschawe, w. ch. kng. ins., Wendover, Bucks. . .	II.
1538	Nich. Tufton, ins., Northiam, Suss.	II.
1538	Walter Barton, ins., St. Laurence, Reading, Berks. . .	III.
1539	Nich. Leveson, w. ch. kng. ins., St. Andrew Undershaft, London .	I.
c. 1540	Anon., w., Brenchley, Kent	II
c. 1540	? — Gardyner, w., Chalfont St. Giles, Bucks. . .	VI.
c. 1540	Anon., Higham Ferrers, Northants	X.
c. 1540	Anon., w., Lowestoft, Suff.	V.
c. 1540	Anon., Newark, Notts.	VI.
c. 1540	John Symonds, w. ch. ins., Shiplake, Oxon. . . .	I.
c. 1540	Anon., w., Stanstead Abbots, Herts.	III.
c. 1540	Anon., w., Little Walsingham, Norf. . . .	XVIII.
1541	Thos. Warde, w. ins., Bletchingley, Surr. H.T. . .	IV.
1541	John Stonnard, ws. (2) ins., Loughton, Essex . . .	I.
1542	Thos. Fromond, w. ch. kng. ins., Cheam, Surr. H.T. .	VII.
1542	Thos. Selwyn, w. ins., Friston, Suss.	I.
1542	Sir Thos. Nevell, kng. ins., Mereworth, Kent. L. PLATE 43 .	III.
1543	John Galer, ins., Thame, Oxon.	IX.
1543	Sir Geo. Monox, w. kng. ins., Walthamstow, Essex . .	II.
1544	John Leigh, w. ch. ins., Addington, Surr. . . .	II.
1544	Rich. Thorneton, ins., Great Greenford, Middx. . .	IV.
1544	John Wyncoll, ins., Little Waldingfield, Suff. . .	IV.
1545	John Newdegate, w. ch. ins., Harefield, Middx. . .	VI.
1545	Nich. Wayte, w. ins., Upminster, Essex . . .	III.
1546	Robt. Barfott, w. ch. ins., Lambourne, Essex . .	I.
1546	John Gille, w. ch. ins., Wyddial, Herts. . . .	II.
1549	Rich. Crook, ins. Formerly Brightwell Prior, Oxon. Now lost.	
1549	Wm. Hyll, ws. (2) ch. ins., Solihull, Warw. . .	I.
1553	Edw. Myrfin, kng. ins., Kirtling, Cambs. . .	I.
1554	Edw. Shelley, w. ch. kng. ins., Warminghurst, Suss. .	I.
1555	Peter Dormer, w. ch. ins., Newbottle, Northants . .	I.
1556	Francis Catesby, ins., Hardmead, Bucks. . . .	I.
1557	Thos. Harte, w. ins., Lydd, Kent . . .	VI.
1557	Wm. Phyllypott, ins., Newark, Notts. . . .	VII.
1557	Wm. Myddilton, ws. (2) ins., Westerham, Kent . .	VI.
1558	Humph. Cavell, kng. ins., Acton, Middx. . . .	I.

Date.	Name, Description, Place and Emblems, etc.	M.S.
1558	John Selyard, ins., Edenbridge, Kent	II.
1558	Vyncent Boys, w. ins., Goodnestone-next-Wingham, Kent	III.
1558	Robt. Rugge, w. ch. br. ins., St. John Maddermarket, Norwich. PLATE 45	X.
1558	Edw. Crane, w. ins., Stratford St. Mary, Suff.	I.
1559	Wm. Sumner, Harlow, Essex	IV.
1559	Thos. Bysshopp, ins., Henfield, Suss.	I.
1560	Edw. Goodman, ins., Ruthin, Denbigh	I.
1560	Rich. Coton, w. ins., Whittington, Glos.	I.
c. 1560	Allaine Dister, w. ch. kng. ins., Lavenham, Suff.	II.
c. 1560	Anon., w. kng., Southminster, Essex	II.
1561	Robt. Poynard, ws. (2) ch. ins., Barkway, Herts.	I.
1563	John Sayer, kng. ins., St. Peter, Colchester	III.
1563	Thos. Wekes, ins., St. Clement, Hastings	I.
1564	Arthur Chambre, w. ins., Myddle, Salop	I.
1564	Laur. Wasshington, ch. ins., Sulgrave, Northants	I.
1565	Hen. Toolye, w. ch. kng. ins., St. Mary Quay, Ipswich	II.
1565	Edw. Stacy, w. ch. kng. ins., Waltham Abbey, Essex	I.
1566	Peter Godfrye, w. ins., Lydd, Kent	VII.
1566	Wm. Stace, w. ch. ins., Westerham, Kent	VIII.
1567	Rich. Codington, w. ch. kng. ins., Ixworth, Suff.	I.
1567	Thos. Noke, ws. (2) ch. ins., Shottesbrooke, Berks. PLATE 45	V.
1568	Anth. Newdigate, ins., Hawnes, Beds.	I.
1568	Edm. Hunt, w. ch. kng. ins., Hindolvestone, Norf.	III.
1569	John Maynarde, ins., St. James, Colchester	I.
1570	John Bowyar, w. ch. kng. ins., Camberwell, Surr.	V.
1570	John Swifte, Roydon, Essex	III.
1570	John Webbe, w. ch. ins., St. Thomas, Salisbury	I.
1570	John Carre, w. ins., Stondon Massey, Essex	I.
c. 1570	Anon., Newington-next-Hythe, Kent	V.
·c. 1570	Erasmus Paston, ins., Paston, Norf.	I.
1571?	Thos. Glemham, kng. ins., Brundish, Suff.	V.
1571	Wm. Cressye, w. ins., Harpenden, Herts.	II.
1572	Wm. Brown, w. kng. ins., St. Peter, Colchester	IV.
1572	John Alleyn, w. ch. kng. ins., Hatfield Peverell, Essex	II.
1572	Simon Parret, w. ch. kng. ins., St. Peter-in-the-East, Oxford	III.
1573	Thos. Oken, w. ins., St. Mary, Warwick	II.
1574	Rich. Payton, w. ins., Isleham, Cambs.	XI.
1574	Rich. Atkinson, w. ch. ins., St. Peter-in-the-East, Oxford	IV.
1574	Edm. Chapman, w. ch. kng. ins., Sibton, Suff.	III.
1574	Valontyne Edvarod, ws. (2) ch. ins., St. Nicholas-at-Wade, Thanet	I.
1575	Rich. Middleton, w. ch. ins., Whitchurch, Denbigh	I.
1576	Wm. Hyldesley, ch. ins., Crowmarsh Gifford, Oxon.	I.

Date.	Name, Description, Place and Emblems, etc.	M.S.
1576	Wm. Duncumbe, ch. ins., Ivinghoe, Bucks.	IV.
1576	Edw. Bell, w. ch. ins., Writtle, Essex	VII.
1576	Thos. Colte, w. ch. kng. ins., Waltham Abbey, Essex	II.
1577	Mathye Draper, w. kng. ins., Camberwell, Surr.	VI.
1577	Raffe More, w. ins., Cookham, Berks.	VII.
1577	Edm. Horde and mother, w. ch. ins., Ewell, Surr.	VI.
1577	Edm. Hampdyn, w. ins., Stoke Poges, Bucks.	III.
1578	Wm. Beriff, ins., Brightlingsea, Essex	VII.
1578	Thos. Bate, ins., Lydd, Kent	VIII.
1578	Ralph Flexney, w. ins., St. Michael, Oxford	I.
1578	Thos. Fige, w. ch. ins., Winslow, Bucks.	I.
1579	Christ. Estoft, w. ins., Bishop Burton, Yorks.	III.
1579	Sir Edw. Fiton, w. ch. ins., St. Patrick's Cathedral, Dublin	III.
1579	Drew Saunders, w. ins., Hillingdon, Middx.	VI.
1579	Wm. Gresham, w. ch. kng. ins., Titsey, Surr.	I.
1580	Thos. Paycocke, ins., Coggeshall, Essex	IV.
1580	Roger Sawyer *or* Jas. Coo, ch. ins., Orford, Suff.	IX.
1580	Frances Bacon, ws. (2) ins., Petistree, Suff.	I.
1580	Cuthbert Blakeden, serjeant of the confectionery to Hen. VIII., and John Boothe, gentleman-usher to Hen. VIII. and Edw. VI., w. ch. ins., Thames Ditton, Surr.	II.
1580	Thos. Wyseman, w. ch. ins., Great Waltham, Essex	I.
c. 1580	Wm. at More *alias* Dommer, ch. ins., Dummer, Hants	III.
c. 1580	Anon., Faversham, Kent	XV.
c. 1580	John Norden, w. ch. ins., Rainham, Kent	VI.
c. 1580	? — Wyseman, Great Waltham, Essex	II.
c. 1580	Anon., Weston Turville, Bucks.	I.
1581	John Brinckhurst, ws. (2) ins., Bisham, Berks.	IV.
1581	Thos. Eyer, ws. (3) ch. ins., Burnham, Bucks.	VI.
1581	Jas. Good, w. ch. ins., West Drayton, Middx.	V.
1581	Fraunces Holbrok, ws. (2) ch. ins., Newington-next-Sittingbourne, Kent	IV.
1581	Wm. Saxaye, ins., Stanstead Abbots, Herts.	IV.
1582	John Rashleigh, ins., Fowey, Cornw.	III.
1582	Clement Newce, w. ch. ins., Great Hadham, Herts.	V.
1582	Edw. Bugge, w. ch. ins., Harlow, Essex	VI.
1582	John Chapman, w. ch. ins., Sibton, Suff.	IV.
1582	Wm. Holt, w. ch. kng. ins., Stoke Lyne, Oxon.	II.
1582	John Polsted, w. ch. kng. ins., Thames Ditton, Surr.	III.
1583	Wm. Strachleigh, w. ch. kng. ins., Ermington, Devon	I.
1583	John Tye, ws. (2) ch. ins., St. Clement, Ipswich	I.
1583	Edw. Goodman, w. ch. kng. ins., Ruthin, Denbigh	II.
1583	Griffin Clarke, Streatley, Berks.	III.
1583	Edw. Humbarstone, w. ch. ins., Walkern, Herts.	III.

Date.	Name, Description, Place and Emblems, etc.	M.S.
1584	Robt. Mariott, w. ch. ins., Ashton, Northants	I.
1584	Wm. Boddindam, ws. (2) ch. ins., Biddenden, Kent	IV.
1584	John Daye, w. ch. kng. ins., Little Bradley, Suff.	III.
1584	John Dryden, Canons Ashby, Northants	I.
1584	Rich. Makepeace, w. ch. ins., Chipping Warden, Northants	II.
1584	John Orgone, w. ins., St. Olave, Hart St., London	III.
1584	Thos. Morrey, ins., Christ Church Cathedral, Oxford	VII.
1584	John Rochester, ws. (2) ch. kng. ins., Terling, Essex	III.
c. 1584	Wm. Rochester, w. ch. kng. ins., Terling, Essex	II.
1585	Wm. Todde, kng. ins., Hever, Kent	V.
c. 1585	Anon., w., Harlow, Essex	VII.
c. 1585	Wm. Dunche, auditor of the mints to Hen. VIII. and Edw. VI., ins., Little Wittenham, Berks.	VI.
1586	Thos. Sharman, ch. ins., Hornton, Oxon.	I.
1586	Thos. Beri, ins., formerly St. Mary Magdalen, Old Fish St., London, now St. Martin, Ludgate Hill	I.
1586	Wm. Yelverton, ws. (2) ch., Rougham, Norf.	V.
1586	Thos. Inwood, ws. (3) ch. kng. ins., Weybridge, Surr. PLATE 46	II.
1587	Mich. Frauncis, w. ch. ins., St. Martin, Canterbury	II.
1587	Philip Marner, ins., Cirencester, Glos.	XVII.
1587	Geo. Clifton, w. ins., Clifton, Notts.	III.
1587	Robt. Smythe, w. ch. kng. ins., and Wm. Notte, w. ch. kng. ins., Thames Ditton, Surr.	IV.
1587	John Selwyn, w. ch. ins., Walton-on-Thames, Surr. (In hunting dress.)	I.
1587	Edw. Greneville, w. ins., Wotton Underwood, Bucks.	I.
1588	Thos. Leventhorpe, w. ch. ins., Albury, Herts.	III.
1588	Wm. Tooke, w. ch. kng. ins., Essendon, Herts.	II.
1588	John Carter, ws. (2) ch. ins., King's Langley, Herts.	III.
1588	John Bisshop, kng. ins., Christ Church Cathedral, Oxford	IX.
1588	— Hale, w. ins., Walthamstow, Essex	IV.
1588	Jerem Ewstes, ins., Watlington, Oxon.	III.
1589	Edm. Daniel, w. ch. ins., Acton, Suff.	IV.
1590	Wm. Death, ws. (2) ch. ins., Dartford, Kent	IX.
1590	Wm. Osborne, w. ch. ins., North Fambridge, Essex	I.
1590	Philip Williams, w. kng. ins., Matherne, Mon.	I.
1590	Thos. Hendley, w. ch. kng. ins., Otham, Kent	I.
1590	John Cheke, w. ch. ins., Thames Ditton, Surr.	V.
1590	Laur. Hyde, w. ch. kng. ins., Tisbury, Wilts.	II.
1590	Wm. Hodges, ins., Weston-sub-Edge, Glos.	I.
1590	Alex. Staples, ws. (2) ch. ins., Yate, Glos.	I.
c. 1590	? Geo. Myllet, Little Greenford (or Perivale), Middx.	II.
c. 1590	? Laur. Manley, ins., Isleworth, Middx.	V.
c. 1590	Anon., Lydd, Kent	IX.

Date.	Name, Description, Place and Emblems, etc.	M.S.
c. 1590	Anon., Yateley, Hants	V.
1591	Thos. Lovelace, ins., Bethersden, Kent. (Serjeant-at Law.)	II.
1591	Cyriac Petit, w. ins., Boughton-under-Blean, Kent	IV.
1591	Robt. Whalley, ins., Queen's Coll., Cambridge. PLATE 47	IV.
1591	Thos. Welbore, w. ch. kng. ins., Clavering, Essex	III.
1591	Thos. Drywood, w. ch. ins., Hornchurch, Essex	VIII.
1591	John Stace, ins., Leigh, Kent	V.
1591	Roger James, ins., All Hallows, Barking, London	XIV.
1591	Jas. Coe, w. ch. ins., Orford, Suff.	X.
1591	Robt. Cotton, "some time an officer of the remooving wardroppe of bedds " and groom of the privy chamber to Queen Mary, w. ch. kng. ins., Richmond, Surr.	I.
1591	Owen Ragesdale, kng. ins., Rothwell, Northants	III.
1592	Wm. Bradbridge, w. ch. kng. ins., Chichester Cathedral	III.
1592	Francis Rutland, w. ins., Chiselden, Wilts.	I.
1592	John Pigott, w. ins., Edlesborough, Bucks.	II.
1592	Wm. Smith, w. ins., Enfield, Middx.	III.
1592	Thos. Staples, ws. (4) ins., West Ham, Essex	I.
1592	John Ayshcombe, w. ch. ins., West Hanney, Berks	III.
1592	John Lyon, w. ins., Harrow, Middx.	X.
1592	Walter Bailey, physician to Queen Elizabeth, ins., New Coll., Oxford	XXII.
1592	Thos. Lyfelde, w. ch. kng. ins., Stoke d'Abernon, Surr.	VII.
1592	Philip Kinge, w. ch. kng. ins., Worminghall, Bucks.	I.
1593	Rich. Allarde, ws. (3) ch. ins., Biddenden, Kent	V.
1593	— Day, w., Victoria and Albert Museum. (Deposited on loan by the vicar and churchwardens of Clavering, Essex.)	IX.
1593	Arthur Pennyng, ws. (2) ins., Kettleburgh, Suff.	I.
1593	Simon Burton, w. ch. kng. ins., St. Andrew Undershaft, London	II.
1593	Thos. Beale, ws. (2) ch. ins., with five generations of ancestors (1399-1534), All Saints, Maidstone. PLATE 46	I.
1594	Nich. Grobham, w. ch. kng. ins., Bishops Lydiard, Som.	I.
1594	Geo. Duke, ins., Honington, Suff.	II.
1594	Ryce Hughes, w. ch. kng. ins., Ippolyts, Herts.	II.
1594	John Douncombe, ch. ins., Ivinghoe, Bucks.	V.
1594	Wm. Nodes, ch. ins., Loughton, Essex	III.
1595	John Fortescue, w. ins., East Allington, Devon	III.
1595	Edw. Gage, w. ch. kng. ins., Framfield, Suss.	I.
1595	John Browne, w. ins. Horton Kirby, Kent	III.
1595	Francis Yerburgh, w., Northorpe, Lincs.	I.
1595	Jas. Cotrel, hf-eff. ins., York Cathedral. PLATE 47	III.
1596	John Tedcastell, w. ch. ins., Barking, Essex. PLATE 47	V.
1596	Kenelme Cheseldyn, w. ins., Braunston, Rutland	I.
1596	Griffin Lloyd, w. ch. ins., Chevening, Kent	II.

Date	Name, Description, Place and Emblems, etc.	M.S.
1596	Rich. Makynges, ins., Morston, Norf.	I.
1597	Thos. Lovell, w. ch. kng. ins., Johnson Hospital, Spalding, Lincs.	I
1597	Edw. Talkarne, ins., Stoke-by-Clare, Suff.	III.
1597	Edw. Harris, kng. ins., Thame, Oxon.	XI.
1597	Thos. Cole, w. ch. kng. ins., St. Margaret, Westminster	I.
1597	Geo. Brigge, w. ins., Wiveton, Norf.	III.
1597	Robt. Askwith, hf-eff., St. Crux, York	IV.
1598	John Daniel, ins., Acton, Suff.	V.
1598	Edw. Duke, w. ch. ins., Benhall, Suff.	II.
1598	Hen. Slyfield, w. ch. ins., Great Bookham, Surr.	V.
1598	Wm. Norwoodd, w. ch. kng. ins., Leckhampton, Glos.	I.
1598	Wm. Manwayringe and Hen. Bradshawe, w. ch. kng. ins., Noke, Oxon.	I.
1598	Rich. Fogg, w. ch. kng. ins., Tilmanstone, Kent	I.
1598	John Woulde, w. ch. ins., Weybridge, Surr.	III.
1598	Walter Tooke, w. ch. ins., Wormley, Herts.	IV.
1599	Robt. Higham, w. ch. ins., Cowlinge, Suff.	I.
1599	— Stavertoon, w. ins., Cumnor, Berks.	III.
1599	Thos. Palmer, w. ch. kng. ins., Ewelme, Oxon.	XVI.
1599	Thos. Barwick, hf-eff. ins., Fornham All Saints, Suff.	I.
1599	John Jennens, w. ch. ins., Harwell, Berks.	I.
1599	John Atlee, ins., Hillingdon, Middx.	VIII.
1599	Rich. Ratcliff, w. kng. ins., St. Peter-in-the-East, Oxford	VI.
1599	Marmaduke Tirwhit, w. ch. kng. ins., Scotter, Lincs.	I.
1600	Rich. Thornhill, ws. (2) ch. ins., Bromley, Kent	III.
1600	John Whithead, ws. (2) ch. kng. ins., Holy Trinity, Coventry	I.
1600	Thos. Burrough, ins., Eastwood, Essex	I.
1600	Thos. Clarke, w. ch. ins., Streatley, Berks. Now under floor.	
c. 1600	John Martin, w. ins., Barton, Cambs.	I.
c. 1600	John Alleyn, ch. ins., Fingringhoe, Essex	IV.
c. 1600	Anon., w. ch., Goring, Oxon.	III.
c. 1600	Anon., w. ins., Harrow, Middx. PLATE 47	XI.
c. 1600	? — Wilson, w., Hereford Cathedral	XXIV.
c. 1600	Anon., w., St. Nicholas, Ipswich	III.
c. 1600	Emanuell Wollaye, w. ins., Latton, Essex	III.

17TH CENTURY

Date	Name, Description, Place and Emblems, etc.	M.S.
1601	John James, w. ch. ins., Aldeburgh, Suff.	IV.
1601	John Bailey, ch. ins., St. Clement, Hastings	II.
1601	Wm. Bartelot, w. ins., Stopham, Suss.	V.
1602	John Fosbroke, w. ins., Cranford St. Andrew, Northants	II.
1602	John Fettiplace, ins., Sparsholt, Berks.	IV.
1603	John Sankey, w. ins., Harrow, Middx.	XII.
1603	John Sutton, ch. ins., Horsell, Surr.	II.

Date.	Name, Description, Place and Emblems, etc.	M.S.
1603	Thos. Sutton, ins., Horsell, Surr.	IV.
1603	Thos. Buriton, w. ins., Streatley, Berks.	IV.
1603	Rich. Brooke, w. ch. ins., Whitchurch, Hants	I.
1604	Rice Davies, w. ch. ins., Backwell, Som.	I.
1604	Thos. Hone, w. ch. ins., Hornchurch, Essex	XI.
1604	John Sea, ws. (2) ins., Herne, Kent. PLATE 48	IX.
1604	John Knapp, w. ch. ins., St. Peter, Ipswich	I.
1604	Rich. Manning, w. ins., St. Mary Cray, Kent	III.
1605	John le Hunt, w. ins., Little Bradley, Suff.	IV.
1605	Thos. Bennet, w. ins., Westbury, Wilts.	I.
1606	Wm. Bence, w. ins., Aldeburgh, Suff.	V.
1606	Robt. Stocker, w. ch. ins., Basingstoke, Hants	II.
1606	John Bougins, w. ch., Helston, Cornw.	II.
1606	Rich. Curthoyse, w. ins., Stilton, Hunts.	I.
1606	Rich. Ayshcome, ins., Witney, Oxon.	II.
1606	Edw. Hunt, w. kng. ins., Writtle, Essex	IX.
1607	Thos. Cogdell, ws. (2) ins., Abbot's Langley, Herts.	II.
1607	Thos. Thompson, w. ch. ins., Berden, Essex	II.
1607	Jacob Verzelini, w. ch. ins., Downe, Kent. PLATE 48	IV.
1607	Wm. Cocke, ins., St. Clement, Ipswich	II.
1607	Anth. Mosley, w. ch. kng. ins., Manchester Cathedral	VI.
1607	John Bannister, w. ch. ins., Netteswell, Essex	II.
1607	Lewis and Griffin Owen, kng. ins., St. Aldate, Oxford	I.
1607	Rich. Humfrie, ch. ins., Rettendon, Essex	IV.
1607	Thos. Hamon, ins., Rye, Suss.	II.
1608	John Bowser, ins., Langley Marsh, Bucks.	VIII.
1608	Clement Stuppeny, ins., Lydd, Kent	XIV.
1608	Geoff. Nightingale, w. ins., Newport, Essex	II.
1608	Rich. Geale, w. ch. ins., Sandhurst, Berks.	I.
1609	Rich. Pyrke, w. ch. ins., Abbenhall, Glos.	I.
1609	Josiah Seyliard, ws. (2) ch. ins., Biddenden, Kent	VIII.
1609	Jas. Hobart, w. ins., Loddon, Norf.	IX.
1609	Edw. Bowland, w. ins., Writtle, Essex	X.
1610	Christ. Freeman, w. ch. kng. ins., Barnwell, Northants	II.
1610	Arthur Page, w. kng. ins., Bray, Berks.	X.
1610	Rich. Sayer, ws. (2) ins., St. Peter, Colchester	V.
1610	John Haywarde, ch. ins., Faversham, Kent	XVIII.
1610	Anth. Pettow, ins., Middleton, Suff.	II.
1610	Thos. Smyth, w. ch. ins., New Romney, Kent	III.
1610	John Cremer, w. ch. ins., Snettisham, Norf.	II.
1610	John Lyford, ins., Stanford Dingley, Berks.	II.
1610	Isake Wyncoll, w. ch. ins., Twinstead, Essex	I.
1610	John Fuller, ins., Uckfield, Suss.	I.
1610?	Clement ? Dawbnie, w. kng. ins., Wokingham, Berks.	II.

Date.	Name, Description, Place and Emblems, etc.	M.S.
c. 1610	Anon., w., Felmersham, Beds.	I.
1611	Leonard Farrington, w. ch. ins., Bredfield, Suff.	I.
1611	Oliver Ayshcombe, w. ch. ins., West Hanney, Berks.	VI.
1611	John Uvedall, w. ch. ins., Great Linford, Bucks.	III.
1612	Alexander Bence, ch. ins., Aldeburgh, Suff.	VI
1612	Wm. Mawnde, w. ins., Chesterton, Oxon.	I.
1612	Arthur Strode, kng. ins., St. Aldate, Oxford	II.
1612	Rich. Symonds, w. ch. kng., Great Yeldham, Essex	I.
1613	Oswald Fitch, ins., Bocking, Essex	II.
1613	Edm. Ansley, w. ch. ins., Chastleton, Oxon.	II.
1613	John Edwards, w. ch. kng. ins., Davington, Kent	I.
1613	John Style, ins., Little Missenden, Bucks.	I.
1613	Edw. Gee, w. ch. ins., Tedburn St. Mary, Devon	II.
1613	Hen. Dickson, Geo. Miller and Anth. Cooper, ins., Watford, Herts. PLATE 48	IV.
1613	Anth. Cooke, ins., Yoxford, Suff.	IX.
1614	John Osbaldeston, w. ch. kng. ins., Burford, Oxon.	IV.
1614	Wm. Gale, w. ch. ins., Hadley, Middx.	VIII.
1614	Christ. Harington, hf-eff. ins., St. Martin, Coney St., York	II
1615	John Gladwin, ins., Harlow, Essex	IX
1615	Roger Martyn, ws. (2) ch. ins., Long Melford, Suff.	IX.
1616	Rich. Hatton, w. ins., Long Ditton, Surr.	III.
1616	Edw. Nowell, w. ch. ins., Edmonton, Middx.	IV.
1616	Rich. Freston, ins., Mendham, Suff.	II.
1616	John Burrough, w. ch. ins., Tottenham, Middx.	II.
1617	Peter Preston, w. ins., Mickfield, Suff.	II.
1617	John Hooper, w. ins., Stockbury, Kent	II.
1617	Rich. Everard, w. ins., Great Waltham, Essex	IV.
1618	Math. Housley, ins., Norwood, Middx.	I.
1618	Thos. and John Curthoyse, ins., Stilton, Hunts.	II.
1619	Thos. Garrard, w. ins., Lambourne, Berks.	V.
1619	Edw. Boscawen, w. ins., St. Michael Penkevil, Cornw.	III.
1620	John Becke, w. ch. kng. ins., St. Peter-at-Arches, Lincoln	I.
c. 1620	Tobias Wood, w. ch., Low Leyton, Essex	IV.
c. 1620	Anon., w. ch. kng. Locality unknown.	
1621	John Rixman, w. kng. ins., Bray, Berks.	XI.
1621	John Worley, w. ins., Lynstead, Kent	II.
1621	Josias Bull, ch. ins., Sutton Coldfield, Warw.	II.
1622	Edw. Brampton, w. ch. ins., Brampton, Norf.	V.
1622	Wm. Lathum, w. ins., Stifford, Essex	IV.
1624	Rich. Gadburye, w. ins., Eyworth, Beds.	I.
1624	Edw. Keat, w. ins., East Lockinge, Berks.	I.
1624	Rich. Martin, ws. (3) ch. ins., Long Melford, Suff.	X.
1626	John Gunter, w. ins., Cirencester, Glos.	XVIII.

Date.	Name, Description, Place and Emblems, etc.	M.S.
1626	John Gunter, w. ins., Kintbury, Berks.	I.
1626	Sir John Wynn, ins., Llanrwst, Denbigh	I.
1626	Edm. Chapman *alias* Barker, w. ch. kng. ins., Sibton, Suff.	VII.
1626	Thos. Adams, w. ch. ins., Swanbourne, Bucks.	II.
1627	Robt. Hawse, ins., St. Mary, Bedford	I.
1627	John Whitacres, ins., Heybridge, Essex	I.
1627	Roger Pemberton, w. ch. ins., St. Peter, St. Albans, Herts.	I.
1628	Bernard Randolphe, w. ch. ins., Biddenden, Kent	IX.
1628	Thos. Hill, ins., Flitton, Beds.	V.
1628	Robt. Berney, ins., Langley, Norf.	I.
1628	Christ. Strickland, ins., Yelden, Beds.	III.
1629	Robt. Jackson, w., Croydon, Surr. Now lost.	
1629	Francis Awsiter, ins., Norwood, Middx.	II.
1630	John Kent, w. ins., Devizes, Wilts.	I.
1630	Thos. Holl, ins., Heigham, Norf.	III.
1630	Oswald Mosley, w. ch. kng. ins., Manchester Cathedral	VII.
1630	Cuthbert Sydnam, ins., Truro, Cornw.	III.
c. 1630	John Bartellot, 1493, kng. ins., Stopham, Suss. (Inscr. original, eff. a restoration of about 1630.)	IV.
1632	Rich. Chester, w. ch. ins., Leigh-on-Sea, Essex	V.
1632	Barth. Typping, ins., Stokenchurch, Bucks.	III.
1634	Rich. Freston, ins., Mendham, Suff.	III.
1634	John King, ins., Southminster, Essex	III.
1635	John Bence, ws. (2) ins., Aldeburgh, Suff.	VII.
1636	Thos. Allen, kng. ins., Eton Coll., Bucks.	XXI.
1636	Wm. Chapman, w. ch. ins., Walkern, Herts.	VI.
1637	Rich. Glanfield, w. hf-eff. ins., Hadleigh, Suff.	X.
1637	Abel Guilliams, w. ch., Loughton, Essex	IV.
1638	Wm. Jones, w. ins., St. Mary, Dover, Kent	I.
1638	Robt. Chambers, ins., Swaffham Prior, Cambs.	V.
1639	Robt. Alfounder, ins., East Bergholt, Suff.	I.
1639	Wm. Palmer, w. ins., Teynham, Kent	IV.
1640	Rich. Fynche and parents Thos. and Elizth. Fynche, ins., Dunstable, Beds.	VII.
1640	Jas. Plumley, w. ch. ins., Hoo St. Werburgh, Kent	VIII.
1640	Rich. Beeston, w. ch. kng. ins., All Saints, Maidstone	II.
1640	Geo. Coles, w. ch. ins., St. Sepulchre, Northampton. PLATE 48	I.
1640	John Coggeshall, w. ch. kng. ins., Orford, Suff.	XIII.
c. 1640	Anon., w., Leigh-near-Rochford, Essex	VI.
1641	Wm. Randolph, w. ch. ins., Biddenden, Kent	X.
1642	Walter Septvans *alias* Harflet of Checker-in-Ash, w. ch. ins., Ash-next-Sandwich, Kent	IX.
1642	Francis Reve, w. kng., Harlow, Essex	XII.
1642	Thos. Atkinson, ins., All Saints, North St., York	IV.

Date.	Name, Description, Place and Emblems, etc.	M.S.
1647	John Morewood, w. ch. ins., Bradfield, Yorks.	I.
1648	Latham Woodroofe, ins., Bakewell, Derb.	II.
1649	? Clere Talbot, LL.D., ws. (2) Dunston, Norf. (Wives in shrouds.)	I.
c. 1650	G. Box, w. kng. ins., St. Peter-le-Bailey, Oxford	IV.
1660	John Harris, w. ch. ins., Milton, Cambridge	II.
1668	Robt. Shiers, ins., Great Bookham, Surr.	VI.
1674	John Bosworth, ws. (2) ins., Long Itchington, Warw.	I.
1683	Edw. Turpin, w. ins., Bassingbourne, Cambs.	I.
1685	Hen. Balgay, ins., Hope, Derb.	I.

18TH CENTURY

1709	Wm. Massie, ch. ins., St. Peter, Leeds	XXIV.
1773	Benj. Greenwood, ins., St. Mary Cray, Kent	VI.

YEOMEN OF THE GUARD

1568	Wm. Payn, ws. (3) ins., East Wickham, Kent	II.
1630	Thos. Mountagu, hf-eff. ins., Winkfield, Berks.	I.

CHILDREN (MALE)

c. 1470	8 sons, ins., Fulbourn, Cambs. Now lost	III.
1478	John Davers, ins., Aldbury, Herts.	I.
c. 1490	2 sons, Ampton, Suff.	IV.
c. 1490	2 sons and 7 daus., Boston, Lincs.	VI.
c. 1490	4 sons and 4 daus., Hitchin, Herts.	XII.
1496	3 sons (Walden), Erith, Kent	V.
1500	7 sons (Pemberton), St. Helen, Bishopsgate, London	V.
1500	2 sons and 2 daus. (Bicknell), Northleach, Glos.	VI.
c. 1500	15 sons, Cobham, Surr. Now lost.	
c. 1500	1 son, Hawstead, Suff.	I.
c. 1500	5 sons, Hornchurch, Essex	III.
c. 1500	5 sons and 5 daus., Kenninghall, Norf.	I.
c. 1500	Geo. Townshend, ins., East Rainham, Norf.	I.
1504	8 sons and 5 daus. (Snellyng), ins., East Horsley, Surr.	IV.
1507	4 sons and 3 daus. (Darnowll), ins., Penshurst, Kent	I.
c. 1510	4 sons, Raunds, Northants. E.S.	II.
1512	6 sons (Onley), Withington, Salop. (Arms of the City of Coventry.)	I.
c. 1520	6 sons and 2 daus. (? Belhouse), Aveley, Essex	II.
c. 1520	6 sons and 2 groups of 6 and 5 daus., Bletchingley, Surr.	III.
c. 1520	4 sons and 7 daus., Worlingworth, Suff.	I.
c. 1520	7 sons (one a priest). In possession of Society of Antiquaries.	
1521	2 sons and 5 daus. (Stutfield), Brinckley, Cambs.	I.

Date.	Name, Description, Place and Emblems, etc.	M.S.
1533	8 sons and 7 daus. (Cryspe), ins., Birchington, Kent . . .	VII.
1535	3 sons and 11 daus. (Blacknolle), ins., Drayton Parslow, Bucks. .	I.
1559	4 sons and 8 daus. (Crawley), Elmdon, Essex	II.
c. 1560	6 sons and 3 daus., Hillingdon, Middx.	III.
1587	Peter and Rich. Best, ins., Merstham, Surr.	V.
1590	2 groups of sons and daus. (Mannok), Stoke-by-Nayland, Suff. .	V.
1597	Rise Griffyn, aet. 9 months, ins., Wixford, Warw. . . .	III.
1598	Edw. and Laur. Cox, ins., Isleworth, Middx. . . .	VI.
1599	Wm. Brome, aet. 10 years, ins., Holton, Oxon. . . .	II.
1601	John Shorlond, aet. 7 years, ins., Woodbridge, Suff. . . .	I.
1610	5 sons and 8 daus. (Gale), ins., Hadley, Middx. . . .	VII.
1611	Thos. (aet. 5 years) and Thos. (aet. 6 months) Hoskins, ins., Oxted, Surr.	III.
1612	Wm. Simond, kng., Walton, Suff.	II.
1621	John Hilliard, ins., Basingstoke, Hants	III.
1621	Wm. Michell, Totternhoe, Beds.	III.
1623	John Drake, kng. ins., Amersham, Bucks. . . .	VI.
1626	John and Anne Stanley, Upminster, Essex. Now lost . .	VII.
1631	Edw. Saintmaur, ins., Collingbourne Ducis, Wilts. . . .	I.
1633	Meneleb Rainsford, aet. 8 years, Henfield, Suss. . . .	II.
1633	Wm. King, aet. 10 wks., ins., St. George's Chapel, Windsor. (In cradle.)	X.
1633	Wm. Glynne, aet. 2 years, ins., Clynnog, Carn. . . .	I.
1636	John Byrd, aet. 6½ years, Headcorn, Kent	I.

CIVIL COSTUME

FEMALE

(Widows are given in a separate list)

14TH CENTURY

c. 1310	Margarete de Camoys, Trotton, Suss.	I.
c. 1320	Dame Jone de Kobeham, ca. ins., Cobham, Kent . . .	I.
c. 1325	Alyne Clopton *or* Chamberleyn, w. of Sir J. de Creke, Westley Waterless, Cambs.	I.
c. 1325	Maud, w. of J. de Bladigdone, hf-eff., East Wickham, Kent .	I.
c. 1335	? Joan de Badlesmere, w. of Sir J. de Northwood, Minster, Kent .	II.
1347	Ellen, w. of Sir J. de Wautone, Wimbish, Essex . . .	I.
1349	Margaret, w. of A. de Walksokne, St. Margaret, Lynn, Norf. .	I.
c. 1350	Anon., hf-eff., Upchurch, Kent	I.
1356	Margaret, w. of R. Torryngton, ins., Great Berkhampstead, Herts.	I.
c. 1360	Anon., br. hf-eff., Clifton Campville, Staffs.	I.
c. 1360	Dame Joan, mother of J. de Feversham, hf-eff. ins., Graveney, Kent	I.

Date.	Name, Description, Place and Emblems, etc.	M.S.
c. 1360	Joan Plessi, hf-eff. ins., Quainton, Bucks. (Spinster.)	I.
c. 1360	Margaret, sister of R. Brocas, ins., Sherborne St. John, Hants. (Spinster.)	I.
1364	Letice and Margaret, ws. of R. Braunche, ca. ins., St. Margaret, Lynn, Norf.	II.
c. 1370	? Margaret Briggs, Great Berkhampstead, Herts.	III.
c. 1370	Beatrice, w. of R. de Heylesdone, hf-eff. ins., Hellesdon, Norf.	I.
c. 1370	Agneys, w. of J. de Kyggesfolde, hf-eff. ins., Rusper, Suss.	I.
c. 1370	Isabel Beaufo, Waterperry, Oxon.	I.
1372	Ismayne de Wynston, Necton, Norf.	I.
1375	Elizth., dau. of Hen., Lord Ferrers of Groby, w. of David de Strabolgi, Earl of Athol, ca., Ashford, Kent	II.
1375	Dame Margt. de Cobham, w. of (1) Matthew Fitzherbert, (2) Sir Wm. Pympe, ca. ins., Cobham, Kent	V.
1375	Lady Elizabeth, dau. of Ralph, Earl of Stafford, w. of Sir Reginald Cobham, Lingfield, Surr.	I.
1378	Maud Brocas and Joan Martin, ws. of Sir J. de Foxle, Bray, Berks. Armf.	I.
1380	Dame Maude de Cobham, ca. ins., Cobham, Kent.	VI.
c. 1380	Anon., hf-eff. ins., Barton-on-Humber, Lincs.	I.
c. 1380	Joan de Cobham, w. of Sir J. de la Pole, ins., Chrishall, Essex	I.
c. 1380	Alice Thorpe, w. of S. de Felbrig, and Elizth., w. of R. de Felbrig, ins., Felbrigg, Norf.	I.
c. 1380	Anon., w. of Sir — Dallingridge, Fletching, Suss.	I.
c. 1380	Maud Weyland, w. of J. Pecok, ins., St. Michael, St. Albans, Herts.	I.
1384	Kath. Calthorpe, w. of Sir J. Harsick, ins., Southacre, Norf. Armf.	I.
1385	Anon., w. of Sir R. de Malyns, ins., Chinnor, Oxon.	III.
c. 1385	Isabel, w. of E. de Malyns, hf-eff. ins., Chinnor, Oxon.	IV.
1390	Margt., w. of R. Albyn, ins., Hemel Hempstead, Herts.	I.
c. 1390	Anon., w. of ? Sir — de Redford, Broughton, Lincs.	I.
c. 1390	? — Malyns, hf-eff., Chinnor, Oxon.	VI.
c. 1390	— Roos, Gedney, Lincs.	I.
1391	Cecily Brewes, w. of Sir W. de Kerdeston, Reepham, Norf.	I.
1391	Margery, dau. of Wm., Lord Zouch of Harringworth, w. of Robt. de Wylughby, Lord of Eresby, ins., Spilsby, Lincs. E.S.	I.
1391	Eleanor, granddau. of J. Corp, ins., Stoke Fleming, Devon	I.
1391	Mabel, w. of T. de Topclyff, ins., Topcliffe, Yorks. (N.R.)	I.
1392	Margt., dau. of Gerard Warren, Lord Lisle, w. of Thos., Lord Berkeley, Wotton-under-Edge, Glos.	I.
1393	Dame Kath., w. of Sir T. Walsch, ins., Wanlip, Leic.	I.
1393	Margt., w. of H. Englisshe, Wood Ditton, Cambs.	I.
1394	Dennis, w. of Sir R. Attelese, ins., Sheldwich, Kent	I.
1395	Dame Margt., dau. of Hugh Courtenay, Earl of Devon, w. of Sir J. de Cobham, ca. ins., Cobham, Kent	VII.

Date.	Name, Description, Place and Emblems, etc.	M.S.
1400	Eleanor de Midleton, w. of Sir J. Mauleverere, ins., Allerton Mauleverer, Yorks. (W.R.)	I.
1400	Alice Giffard, w. of Sir J. Cassy, ins., Deerhurst, Glos. . .	I.
1400	Joan, w. of John Mulsho, kng. ins., Newton-by-Geddington, Northants	I.
1400	Ele Ufford, w. of R. Bowet, ins., Wrentham, Suff. . . .	I.
c. 1400	? — Astley, Astley, Warw.	I.
c. 1400	Anon., br. ca., Boston, Lincs.	III.
c. 1400	Anon., Cirencester, Glos.	I.
c. 1400	? Julian, w. of T. Petle, Downe, Kent	I.
c. 1400	Anon., w. of J.Covesgrave, ins., Eaton Socon, Beds. . .	I.
c. 1400	Anon., w. of — Massyngberd, Gunby, Lincs. . . .	I.
c. 1400	Marion, w. of T. Somer, hf-eff. ins., Ickleford, Herts. . .	I.
c. 1400	Isabel, w. of W. Overbury, hf-eff. ins., Letchworth, Herts. .	I.
c. 1400	Anon., Northleach, Glos.	I.
c. 1400	Anon., Ore, Suss.	I.
c. 1400	Lucy, dau. of Roger, Lord Strange of Knokyn, w. of Wm., Baron Willoughby d'Eresby, Spilsby, Lincs.	II.
c. 1400	? Kath., w. of Sir Wm. Tendring, Stoke-by-Nayland, Suff. .	I.
c. 1400	Anon., Tilbrook, Beds.	I.
c. 1400	? Jean Lucas, Ware, Herts.	I.
c. 1400	Anon. Locality unknown.	

15TH CENTURY

Date.	Name, Description, Place and Emblems, etc.	M.S.
1401	Marion, w. of W. Grevel, ins., Chipping Campden, Glos. .	I.
1401	Isabel Kingston, w. of Sir M. Russell, ins., Dyrham, Glos. .	I.
1401	Elizabeth — , ca. ins., Goring, Oxon.	II.
1401	Margt. Pennebrygg, ins., Shottesbrooke, Berks. . . .	II.
1402	Anon., w. of R. Martyn, ins., Dartford, Kent. PLATE 40 .	I.
1404	Mary, w. of Sir W. Moyne, ins., Sawtrey, Hunts. . .	I.
1405	Margery Naunton, w. of Sir R. Drury, ins., Rougham, Suff. PLATE 12	I.
c. 1405	Anon., w. of H. Notingham, ins., Holme-by-the-Sea, Norf. .	I.
1406	Agnes, w. of J. de Estbury, hf-eff., Lambourne, Berks. E.S. .	I.
1406	Margt., dau. of Wm., Lord Ferrers of Groby, w. of Thos. de Beauchamp, Earl of Warwick, St. Mary, Warwick. Armf. PLATE 13	I.
1407	Margt. Whatton, w. of Sir W. Bagot, ins., Baginton, Warw. .	I.
1407	Margt. St. John, w. of Sir T. Brounflet, Wymington, Beds. .	II.
1408	Joan and Alice, ws. of J. Hauley, ins., St. Saviour, Dartmouth, Devon	I.
1408	Eleanor Busteler, w. of R. de Paris, kng., Hildersham, Cambs. PLATE 40	I.
1409	Alice Charlis, w. of W. Snayth, ins., Addington, Kent . .	I.
1409	Eleanor Vyzsdelou, w. of Sir W. de Burgate, ins., Burgate, Suff. .	I.

Date.	Name, Description, Place and Emblems, etc.	M.S.
1409	Ade, w. of R. de Haitfeld, ins., Owston, Yorks.	I.
c. 1410	Clarice, w. of R. de Frevile, Little Shelford, Cambs.	I.
c. 1410	Anon., Baldock, Herts.	I.
c. 1410	Margery Greenham, w. of Sir T. Burton, ins., Little Casterton, Rutland	I.
c. 1410	Kath. atte Heelde, ins., Chinnor, Oxon.	X.
c. 1410	Pernel, w. of N. Roland, ins., Cople, Beds.	I.
c. 1410	Anon., Hilmorton, Warw.	I.
c. 1410	Joan Aske, w. of R. Hansard, ins., South Kelsey, Lincs.	I.
c. 1410	Anon., South Ormsby, Lincs.	I.
1411	Agnes Wanton, w. of R. Thornton, ins., All Saints, Newcastle-on-Tyne.	I.
1411	Alice, w. of T. Fayreman, ins., St. Albans Abbey, Herts.	III.
1411	Julian, w. of T. de Cruwe, ins., Wixford, Warw.	I.
c. 1411	Isabel Barstaple, Trinity Almshouse Chapel, Bristol	II.
1412	Isabel, w. of W. Moneslee, ins., St. John Maddermarket, Norwich	I.
1413	Margt., dau. of Edw., Lord le Despencer, w. of Robt., Lord Ferrers of Chartley, Merevale, Warw.	I.
1414	Philipe Carreu, ch. ins., Beddington, Surr.	I.
1414	Dame Philippe Byschoppesdon, ins., Broughton, Oxon.	I.
1414	Cristine, w. of J. Cressy, ins., Dodford, Northants	I.
1414	Joan Reskemer, w. of J. Urban, br. ins., Southfleet, Kent	I.
1414	Margt. Gernon, w. of Sir J. Peyton, ins., Wicken, Cambs.	I.
1415	Joan Risain, w. of J. Peryent, chief lady-in-waiting to Joan of Navarre, Queen of England, ins., Digswell, Herts.	I.
1415	Maud Harcourt, w. of W. Cookesey and Sir J. Phelip, ins., Kidderminster, Worc.	I.
1415	Joan, w. of W. West, ins., Sudborough, Northants	I.
c. 1415	Joan, w. of J. Kent, hf-eff. ins., St. Laurence, Reading, Berks.	I.
1416	Ellen, w. of T. Stokes, ch. ins., Ashby St. Legers, Northants	I.
1416	Margt., dau. of Primislaus, Duke of Teschen, w. of Sir S. Felbrygge, ins., Felbrigg, Norf.	III.
1416	Margt. and Kath., ws. of Sir T. de Skelton, ins., Hinxton, Cambs.	I.
1416	Margt. de Holes, Watford, Herts.	II.
1417?	Augnes Bowf, ins., Pakefield, Suff.	I.
1418	Maud, w. of J. Fossebrok, ins., Cranford St. Andrew, Northants	I.
1418	Joan, w. of J. Fildyng, ins., Lutterworth, Leic.	I.
1418	Edith, w. of T. Polton, ins., Wanborough, Wilts.	I.
1419	Margt. Cheyne, ins., Hever, Kent. PLATE 50	II.
1419	Alice, w. of J. Lyndewode, ins., Linwood, Lincs.	I.
1419	Dame Millicent Meryng, ins., East Markham, Notts.	I.
1419	Elizth. Mortimer, w. of Baron Camoys, ch. ins., Trotton, Suss.	II.
1420	Margery Erchedeken, w. of T. Arundell, ca., East Anthony, Cornw.	I.
1420	Isabel, w. of J. Doreward, Bocking, Essex	I.

Date.	Name, Description, Place and Emblems, etc.	M.S.
1420	Cristine Bray, hf-eff. ins., Felsted, Essex	II.
1420	Dame Eleanor Cobham, ca. ins., Lingfield, Surr.	IV.
1420	Joan Reskemer, w. of J. Urban, ins., Southfleet, Kent. PLATE 42	II.
1420	Joan Waltham, ch. ins., Waltham, Lincs.	II.
1420	Kath. Manningham, w. of R. Norton, ins., Wath, Yorks. (N.R.)	I.
c. 1420	Elizth., w. of J. Clerk, ins., Ardeley, Herts.	I.
c. 1420	? Margt., w. of W. Vynter, Baldock, Herts.	II.
c. 1420	Anon., w. of ? Sir J. Holt, Brampton-by-Dingley, Northants	I.
c. 1420	Isabel Kelke, w. of R. Barnardston, ins., Great Coates, Lincs.	I.
c. 1420	Anon., Dunton, Bucks.	I.
c. 1420	Alys Brunham, w. of G. Thorndon, ins., Frettenham, Norf.	I.
c. 1420	Margt. Sutton and Iden Lovey, ws. of Barth., Lord Bourchier, Halstead, Essex	I.
c. 1420	? — Salman, ca., Horley, Surr.	I.
c. 1420	Kath. Stoket, hf-eff. ins., Lingfield, Surr.	V.
c. 1420	— Clopton, Long Melford, Suff. (Spinster.)	I.
c. 1420	Anon., St. Peter-le-Bailey, Oxford	II.
c. 1420	Kath. Breton, w. of T. Quatremayn, ins., Thame, Oxon.	I.
c. 1420	Anon., w. of W. Barton, ins., Thornborough, Bucks.	I.
c. 1420	Anon., w. of ? — de Boys, Tolleshunt Darcy, Essex	II.
c. 1420	Anon., w. of T. Walysch, ins., Whitchurch, Oxon.	I.
c. 1420	Anon., Nether Winchendon, Bucks.	II.
1421	Alice, w. of J. Pulter, ins., Hitchin, Herts.	II.
1422	Elizth. Hebden, w. of Sir T. Dymoke, Scrivelsby, Lincs. Now lost.	
1424	Margery Harley, w. of J. Compton, ins., Dinton, Bucks.	I.
1424	Elizth., w. of J. Poyle, Hampton Poyle, Oxon.	I.
1424	Alice Uvedale, w. of Sir R. Shelton, Great Snoring, Norf. Armf.	I.
1425	Beatrice Barret, w. of W. Chichele, ins., Higham Ferrers, Northants	III.
c. 1425	? Margt., w. of J. Framlingham, hf-eff., Debenham, Suff.	I.
1426	Sarra, w. of J. Cosyngton, ins., Aylesford, Kent	I.
1426	Isabel, w. of J. Cely, ins., Sheldwich, Kent	II.
1427	Alice Payn, ins., Haversham, Bucks.	I.
1427 ?	Margt. Poche, w. of H. Paris, Hildersham, Cambs. PLATE 19	II.
1427	Wenllan Walsche, w. of W. Moreton, ins., Llandough, Glamorgan	I.
1427	Isabel, w. of R. Leverer, Weston Colville, Cambs.	I.
1428	Maud, w. of J. Norwiche, Yoxford, Suff.	I.
1430	Eleanor Preston, w. of H. Brudenell, ins., Amersham, Bucks.	I.
1430	Agnes Salmon, ca. ins., Arundel, Suss.	IV.
1430	Joan Tamworth, w. of T. Godefray, ins., Lydd, Kent	III.
1430	Alice Ledewich, ins., Little Marlow, Bucks.	I.
1430	Amabel Straunge, ins., Warkworth, Northants	IV.
c. 1430	Isabel Carew, w. of B. Harsick and R. Buckton, ins., Beddington, Surr.	IV.

Date.	Name, Description, Place and Emblems, etc.	M.S.
c. 1430	Anon., w. of J. Staverton, Eyke, Suff.	I.
c. 1430	Anon., Harlow, Essex	I.
c. 1430	Elizth. Waleys, w. of P. Halle, ins., Herne, Kent	I.
c. 1430	Isabel Chakbon, ins., Hoath, Kent	I.
c. 1430	Anon., Melton, Suff.	I.
c. 1430	Joan Kelly, hf-eff., Tintagel, Cornw.	I.
c. 1430	Anon., Wroxall, Warw.	I.
c. 1430	Anon., ca. Locality unknown.	
1432	Isabel, w. of N. Carew, ins., Beddington, Surr.	III.
1433	Elizth. Seynt John, w. of T. Slyfeld, ins., Great Bookham, Surr.	I.
1433	Joan, Lady Cobham, ch. ins., Cobham, Kent	XIII.
1433	Kath., w. of W. Rickhill, Northfleet, Kent	III.
1435	Elizth. and Alice, ws. of Thos. Widville of Grafton, Bromham, Beds. (Appropriated to Elizth. Wilde and Isabel Hastings, mother and wife of Sir John Dyve, 1535.)	I.
1435	Margt., w. of J. Launcelyn, ins., Cople, Beds.	III.
1435	Margery, w. of J. Ailemer, ins., Erith, Kent	III.
1435	Alice, w. of J. Henege, ins., Hainton, Lincs.	I.
1435	Isabel, w. of R. Delamare, ins., Hereford Cathedral	IX.
1435	Marion, w. of R. Adane, ins., Kelshall, Herts.	I.
1436	Anne Botiler, w. of J. Martyn, ins., Graveney, Kent	IV.
1437	Alys, w. of J. Spycer, br. kng. ins., Burford, Oxon.	I.
1437	Joan, w. of R. Skern, ins., Kingston-on-Thames, Surr.	I.
1437	Joan, w. of J. Bacon, ins., All Hallows, Barking, London	I.
1437	Joan Fineux, w. of T. Brokhill, ins., Saltwood, Kent	II.
1437	Joan Hanap, w. of Sir T. Brook, ins., Thorncombe, Dorset. PLATE 41	I.
1439	Elizth., w. of T. Carbonell, ins., Amersham, Bucks.	II.
1439	Amice Bruley, w. of J. Cottusmore, ins., Brightwell Baldwin, Oxon.	II.
1439	Alice, w. of W. Markeby, w. ins., St. Bartholomew-the-Less, London	I.
1440	Margt., w. of R. Pagge, ch., Cirencester, Glos.	III.
1440	Joan — , ca. ins., Minehead, Som. F.S.	I.
1440	Alice, w. of G. Boleyn, ins., Sall, Norf.	II.
c. 1440	Anon., Ashen, Essex	I.
c. 1440	Anon., Bigbury, Devon	I.
c. 1440	Philippe, dau. of David de Strabolgi, Earl of Athol, w. of J. Halsham, ca. ins., West Grinstead, Suss.	I.
c. 1440	Anon., Hellingley, Suss.	I.
c. 1440	Alice Estbury, ins., Letcombe Regis, Berks.	I.
c. 1440	Elizth. Engeyne and Joan Dawbeney, ws. of Sir L. Pabenham, ins., Offard Darcy, Hunts.	I.
c. 1440	Anon., hf-eff., Great Ormesby, Norf.	I.

Date.	Name, Description, Place and Emblems, etc.	M.S.
c. 1440	Alice, w. of J. Andrew and T. Palmere, ch. ins., Wye, Kent	I.
1441	Joyce, w. of Sir H. Halsham, West Grinstead, Suss. PLATE 20	II.
1441	Joan, w. of J. Parker, ins., St. John, Margate	III.
1441	Elizth. Kymbell, w. of J. Boteler, ins., Mepshall, Beds.	II.
1441	Kath., w. of T. Roose, br. ins., Sall, Norf.	III.
1441	Joan Trevet, Stratfield Mortimer, Berks.	II.
1442	Margt., Julian, Margt., Joan, ws. of R. Spycer, ins., Cirencester, Glos.	IV.
1442	Mary Leek, w. of Sir G. Daubeney, ins., South Petherton, Som.	II.
1442	Cecily, w. of V. Baret, ins., Preston-by-Faversham, Kent	I.
1443	Margt., w. of T. Faryndon, ins., Faringdon, Berks.	II.
1444	Elizth. Chelry, w. of W. Fynderne, ins., Childrey, Berks. Armf.	II.
1444	Joan Arundel, w. of Sir W. Echyngham, ins., Etchingham, Suss.	II.
1444	Edith Bowett, w. of Wm. Neudegate, Harefield, Middx.	I.
1444	Margt. Dyneley, ins., Stanford Dingley, Berks.	I.
1445	Isabel, w. of R. Coppyn, Aston Rowant, Oxon.	I.
1446	Margery, w. of Wm. Whappelode, ins., Chalfont St. Peter, Bucks.	II.
1446	Joan and Dame Beatrix, ws. of D. Barantyn, ins., Chalgrove, Oxon.	III.
c. 1446	Elizth. Restwold, w. of Wm. Whappelode, ins., Chalfont St. Peter, Bucks.	I.
1447	Agnes, w. of Wm. Scors and T. Fortey, ch. ins., Northleach, Glos.	II.
1449	Alice, w. of W. Halsted, ins., Biggleswade, Beds.	I.
1449	Elen, w. of W. Pyke, ins., Cheshunt, Herts.	II.
1449	Elizth. Knightley, w. of J. Arderne, ins., Leigh, Surr.	I.
1450	Denis Finch, Brabourne, Kent. (Spinster.)	II.
1450	Alice, w. of W. Welley, ins., Chipping Campden, Glos.	II.
1450	Alice, w. of L. Pygot, ins., Dunstable, Beds.	I.
c. 1450	Alice, w. of J. Stokes, ins., Chipping Norton, Oxon.	I.
c. 1450	Anon., Chrishall, Essex	II.
c. 1450	Anon., Eaton Socon, Beds.	II.
c. 1450	Anon., w. of ? — Treffry, Fowey, Cornw.	I.
c. 1450	Anon., Kimpton, Herts.	I.
c. 1450	Anon., w. of ? J. Townsend, Lechlade, Glos.	I.
c. 1450	Susan Arderne, ins., Leigh, Surr.	II.
c. 1450	Anon., Lingfield, Surr. (Spinster.)	VIII.
c. 1450	? Thomasin, w. of J. Barrington, Rayleigh, Essex	I.
c. 1450	Anon., New Shoreham, Suss.	I.
c. 1450	Margt., w. of H. Bostok, ins., Wheathampstead, Herts.	I.
1451	Alice Boteler, ins., Buckland, Herts.	I.
1451	Isabel, w. of J. Yonge, ins., Chipping Norton, Oxon.	II.
1451	Margt., w. of R. Byll, hf-eff. ins., Holy Trinity, Hull	I.
1451	Ellen, w. of Sir J. Bernard, ins., Isleham, Cambs.	I.
1452	Anon., Hitchin, Herts.	III.
1452	Maud, w. of E. Mille, ins., Pulborough, Suss.	II.

Date.	Name, Description, Place and Emblems, etc.	M.S.
1453	Cristine and Alice, ws. of R. and J. Haddok, ins., Leigh-on-Sea, Essex	I.
1453	Alice and Joan Funteyn, ins., Sall, Norf.	IV.
1454	Cecilie, w. of R. Felthorp, ins., Blickling, Norf.	III.
1454	Margt., w. of J. Godfrey, ins., Haddenham, Cambs.	II.
1454	Cecily Cornwall, w. of J. Stathum, kng. ins., Morley, Derb.	V.
1454	Ellen Coke, w. of R. Warbulton, ins., Ware, Herts.	II.
1455	Jane Cletherowe, w. of J. Keriell, ins., Ash-next-Sandwich, Kent. PLATE 50	II.
1455	Isabel Hay, ins., Luton, Beds.	III.
1455	Isabel, sister of R. Manfeld, ins., Taplow, Bucks. (Spinster.) PLATE 42	II.
1455	Elizth. de la Felde, w. of R. Dencourt, Upminster, Essex	I.
1455	Joan Bardolf, Watton, Herts.	IV.
c. 1455	? Agnes Wightham, w. of W. Browning, Wytham, Berks.	I.
1456	Isabel, w. of W. Anabull, ins., Harpenden, Herts.	I.
1457	Marion, w. of J. Smyth, hf-eff. ins., Shorne, Kent	I.
1458	Cecilie Boleyn, ins., Blickling, Norf. (Spinster.)	IV.
1458	Agnes, w. of R. Staunton, ch. ins., Castle Donington, Leic.	I.
1458	Joan, w. of J. Compton, hf-eff. ins., Cheam, Surr.	III.
1458	Margt. de Vipont, w. of W. Stapilton, ins., Edenhall, Cumb.	I.
1458	Elizth. Knolles, ch. ins., North Mimms, Herts.	II.
1458	Jamon de Cherneys, maid of honour to Queen Margt. of Anjou, w. of T. Shernborne, Shernbourne, Norf.	I.
1459	Agnes, w. of W. Tabard, ins., Walton, Suff.	I.
1460	Maude, w. of J. Jenney, ins., Knodishall, Suff.	I.
1460	Margery, w. of J. Browne, ins., All Saints, Stamford, Lincs. PLATE 41	I.
1460	Douce Venables, w. of Sir R. del Bothe, ins., Wilmslow, Ches.	I.
c. 1460	Anon., Adderbury, Oxon. PLATE 21	I.
c. 1460	Anon., Boston, Lincs.	IV.
c. 1460	Anon., ins., Frettenham, Norf.	III.
c. 1460	Agnes, w. of T. Clarell, ins., Lillingstone Lovell, Bucks.	II.
c. 1460	Anon., hf-eff., Monk's Risborough, Bucks.	II.
c. 1460	Elizth. Culpepir, ins., West Peckham, Kent	I.
c. 1460	Joan de Stopham, w. of J. Bartelot, Stopham, Suss.	I.
c. 1460 ?	Joan Leukenore, w. of J. Bartelot, ch. ins., Stopham, Suss.	II.
c. 1460	Sibil Englefeld, w. of R. Quatremayne, Thame, Oxon.	II.
c. 1460	Anon., ch., South Weald, Essex	I.
c. 1460	Kath., w. of W. Lucas, ins., Wenden Lofts, Essex	I.
1462	Margt., w. of J. Frankeleyn, ch. ins., Chearsley, Bucks.	I.
1462	Agnes Martyn and Joan de Cobyndon, ws. of W. Prelatte, ins., Cirencester, Glos.	VI.
1462	Parnell Walton, w. of R. Bertlot, ch. ins., Stopham, Suss.	III.

Date.	Name, Description, Place and Emblems, etc.	M.S.
1462	Anon., w. of J. Tothyll, ins., Swaffham Prior, Cambs.	I.
1463	Anon., w. of J. Pedder, ins., Dunstable, Beds.	II.
1463	Joan Padley, w. of R. Eyr, ch. ins., Hathersage, Derb.	I.
1463	Margt., w. of J. Ballard, ins., Merstham, Surr.	I.
1464	Joan Rothele, Dartford, Kent	III.
c. 1465	Anon., St. Helen, Bishopsgate, London	II.
c. 1465	Joan, w. of W. Graffton, ins., Nutfield, Surr.	I.
c. 1465	Margt. Stokke, w. of W. Browne, ins., All Saints, Stamford, Lincs.	II.
1466	Margt. John, ins., Ingrave, Essex	I.
1466	Margery Letterford, ins., Swallowfield, Berks.	I.
1467	Joan, w. of J. Lethenard, ins., Chipping Campden., Glos.	III.
1467	Joyce Jokuosa, w. of S. Snelling, ins., Iwade, Kent	I.
1467	Kath. Bohun, w. of Sir P. Arderne, Latton, Essex	I.
1467	Lettice Catesby, Newnham, Northants	I.
1467	Kath. Hatton, w. of R. Bothe, ch. ins., Sawley, Derb.	I.
1467	Alice, w. of T. Elyot, ins., Wonersh, Surr.	I.
1468	Agnes, w. of J. Canon, ch. ins., Long Crendon, Bucks.	I.
1468	Florens, w. of B. Halley *or* Halsey, St. Albans Abbey, Herts.	VII.
1469	Isabel and Joan, ws. of J. Waliston, ins., Chenies, Bucks.	I.
1469	Isabel, w. of G. More, ch. ins., Tilehurst, Berks.	I.
1470	Alice Clerk, w. of R. Watton, ins., Addington, Kent	VI.
1470	Dame Cristine Phelip, ins., Herne, Kent	IV.
1470	Elizth. Langley and Thomasine Curzon, ws. of Sir T. Stathum, ins., Morley, Derb.	VI.
1470	Kath. and Joan, ws. of G. Joslyne, ins., Sawbridgeworth, Herts.	II.
1470	Anne, w. of R. St. Leger, ins., Ulcombe, Kent	III.
c. 1470	Anon., ch., Aston Rowant, Oxon.	II.
c. 1470	Anon., Bletchingley, Surr. (Spinster.)	I.
c. 1470	Cristine, w. of W. Notyngham, ins., Cirencester, Glos.	VII.
c. 1470	Anon., St. Saviour, Dartmouth, Devon	II.
c. 1470 ?	Joyce Charlton, w. of Sir J. Tiptoft, ca. ins., Enfield, Middx. Armf.	I.
c. 1470	Anon., Fakenham, Norf.	II.
c. 1470	Anon., ch., Flamstead, Herts.	II.
c. 1470	Emma Appleyard, w. of Sir H. Grey, ins., Ketteringham, Norf.	I.
c. 1470	Anon., w. of ? J. Renolds, Lutterworth, Leic.	II.
c. 1470	Anon., Shorne, Kent	III.
c. 1470	Anon., w. of J. Croston, ch. ins., Swinbrook, Oxon.	I.
c. 1470	Agnes and Alice, ws. of W. Pyrry, ch. ins., Ware, Herts.	III.
1471	Joan Drury, w. of Sir J. Cursun, ins., Bylaugh, Norf.	I.
1471	Emme Walden, w. of J. Wode, ins., Erith, Kent	IV.
1471	Joan Trusbut, w. of T. Colte, ins., Roydon, Essex	I.
1471	Margt. Elmes, ins., All Saints, Stamford, Lincs.	III.
1471	Anne Leek, w. of R. Wylloughby, ins., Wollaton, Notts.	I.

Date.	Name, Description, Place and Emblems, etc.	M.S.
1472	Alice, w. of W. Norwiche, ch. br. ins., St. George Colegate, Norwich. PLATE 42	I.
1472	Agnes, w. of R. Segrym, St. John Maddermarket, Norwich	III.
1472	Agnes Brewes, w. of Sir W. Yelverton, Rougham, Norf.	I.
1472	Margt. Dymoke, Clemens Cantilupe and Isabel Lester, ws. of R. Ingylton, ch. ins., Thornton, Bucks.	I.
1472	Cecily Kydwelly, ins., Little Wittenham, Berks.	III.
1473	Margt. and Mergery, ws. of W. Turnor, ins., Berden, Essex	I.
1473	Elizth. Cheyne, w. of Sir J. Say, ins., Broxbourne, Herts. Armf.	II.
1473	Joan, w. of R. Hunt, ins., Great Linford, Bucks.	I.
1473	Isabel Jamys and Anne Prophete, ws. of J. Elmebrygge, ch. ins., Merstham, Surr.	II.
1474	Elizth. Mundeford, w. of J. Berney, ins., Reedham, Norf.	I.
1474	Joan, w. of R. Parnell, ins., Spratton, Northants	I.
1475	Anon., w. of P. Mede, kng. ins., St. Mary Redcliffe, Bristol. Armf.	II.
1475	Isabel, w. of W. Style, ins., St. Nicholas, Ipswich	I.
c. 1475	Maud, w. of J. Weddeot, ch. ins., Aldington, Kent	I.
c. 1475	Anon., Hempstead, Essex	I.
c. 1475	Joan Mauleverer, w. of N. Kniveton, ch. ins., Mugginton, Derb. PLATE 22	I.
1476	Eleanor, w. of B. Bolne, ins., West Firle, Suss.	I.
1476	Joan, w. of W. Pepyr, St. John Maddermarket, Norwich	IV.
1476	Agnes and Joan, ws. of R. Do, Steventon, Berks.	I.
1478	Margt., w. of T. Rowley, ins., St. John, Bristol	I.
1478	Kath. Bedingfield, w. of J. Fastolff, ins. Formerly Oulton, Suff. Now lost.	
1478	Joan, w. of W. Robertson, ins., St. Peter-in-the-East, Oxford	I.
1479	Kath. Pedwardyn, w. of N. Deen, ch. ins., Barrowby, Lincs.	I.
1479	Anon., w. of Sir T. Urswyk, ch., Dagenham, Essex	I.
1479	Iseult Clarke, w. of T. Selby, ins., East Malling, Kent	I.
1479	Julian, w. of W. Shosmyth, Mereworth, Kent	II.
1479	Anne Denneis, w. of T. Playters, ins., Sotterley, Suff.	II.
1479	Kath. Gyfford, w. of Sir T. Billyng, ins., Wappenham, Northants	II.
1479	Annes, w. of E. Howton, ins., Wormley, Herts.	II.
1480	Isabel Cornew and Joan, ws. of J. Coblegh, ch. ins., Chittle-hampton, Devon	II.
1480	Elizth. Echyngham and Agnes Oxenbrigg, ch. ins., Etchingham, Suss. (Spinsters.)	III.
1480	Margt. Copuldyk, Harrington, Lincs.	I.
1480	Joan Haseldene, ins., Oxted, Surr.	II.
1480	Elizth., w. of J. Fitz-Geffrey, ch. ins., Sandon, Herts.	I.
c. 1480	? — Coket, ch. kng., Ampton, Suff.	I.
c. 1480	Anon., Ampton, Suff.	II.
c. 1480	Margt. or Joan, w. of ? W. Crane, Baldock, Herts.	IV.

Date.	Name, Description, Place and Emblems, etc.	M.S.
c. 1480	Anon., Braughing, Herts.	I.
c. 1480	Joan, w. of J. Jay, ch. ins., St. Mary Redcliffe, Bristol	IV.
c. 1480	Anon., kng., St. Mary, Bury St. Edmunds, Suff.	I.
c. 1480-90	Margt. Sidney, w. of N. Gaynesford, ins., Carshalton, Surr.	I.
c. 1480	Anon., ch., Chelsfield, Kent	V.
c. 1480	Elizth. Roches, w. of W. Walrond, ins., Childrey, Berks.	IV.
c. 1480	Anon., kng., Chrishall, Essex	III.
c. 1480	Anon., Cirencester, Glos.	X.
c. 1480	Anon., Cirencester, Glos.	XI.
c. 1480	Anon., Euston, Suff.	I
c. 1480	Anon., Felbrigg, Norf. (Spinster.)	IV.
c. 1480	Anon., ch., Fulbourne, Cambs.	V.
c. 1480	Anne, w. of H. Jarmon, Geddington, Northants	I.
c. 1480	Anon., Great Greenford, Middx.	II.
c. 1480	? Elizth. Tyrwhit, w. of J. Whichcote, Harpswell, Lincs.	I.
c. 1480	? — Cockayne, Hatley Cockayne, Beds.	III.
c. 1480	Anon., Helmsley, Yorks. (N.R.)	II.
c. 1480	Agnes, w. of E. Grene, ins., Hunstanton, Norf.	I.
c. 1480	? Margery Francis, w. of Sir W. Clopton, ca., Long Melford, Suff. Armf.	IV.
c. 1480	? Alice Clopton, w. of J. Harleston, ca., Long Melford, Suff. Armf.	V.
c. 1480	Anon., hf-eff., Newington-next-Hythe, Kent	I.
c. 1480	Anon., Odiham, Hants	I.
c. 1480	Anon., Little Plumstead, Norf.	I.
c. 1480	Anon., Saffron Walden, Essex	II.
c. 1480	Anon., w. of — Songar, Victoria and Albert Museum. (Deposited on loan by the vicar and churchwardens of Clavering, Essex.)	III.
c. 1480	Anon., w. of — Humberstone, Walkern, Herts.	I.
c. 1480	Anon., ch., Wheathampstead, Herts.	II.
c. 1480	? Elizth., w. of Wm. Hasylden, Little Chesterford, Essex. (In the possession of Mr. Philip Nelson, F.S.A., and on loan to the Victoria and Albert Museum.)	II.
1481	Joan, w. of T. Abbot, Hitchin, Herts.	VIII.
1481	Anne Bothe, Elizth. Seynclow, Margt. Stanhop, ws. of H. Stathum, ch. ins., Morley, Derb. PLATE 27	VII.
1482	Kath., w. of W. Robins, ch., St. Stephen, St. Albans, Herts.	I.
1483	Isabel Plantagenet, dau. of Rich., Earl of Cambridge, w. of H. Bourchier, Earl of Essex, Little Easton, Essex. Armf. PLATE 25	II.
1483	Margt. Mitford, w. of J. Weston, ins., Ockham, Surr.	III.
1483	Margt. Willughby, ins., Raveningham, Norf.	I.
1483	Margery, w. of W. Crofton, ins., Trottescliffe, Kent	I.

Date.	Name, Description, Place and Emblems, etc.	M.S.
1484	Agnes Laxham, w. of E. Molyneux, ins., Chenies, Bucks.	II.
1484	Alice, Margt. and Marion, ws. of W. Gybbys, ins., Chipping Campden, Glos.	IV.
1484	Agnes, w. of J. Pergetter, ins., Chipping Norton, Oxon.	IV.
1484	Elizth., w. of T. Radley, ch. ins., Garsington, Oxon.	I.
1484	Margt. Bernard and Margt. Francis, ws. of T. Peyton, ins., Isleham, Cambs.	III.
1485	Anne Herward, ins., Aldborough, Norf.	III.
1485	Margt. Lodyngton, ins., Ampthill, Beds.	II.
1485	Elizth., w. of J. Seyntmour, ins., Beckington, Som.	I.
1485	Isabel Boleyn, w. of W. Cheyne, ins., Blickling, Norf.	VIII.
1485	Alice, w. of W. Goldwell, Great Chart, Kent	II.
1485	Margt., w. of J. Parker, ins., Faringdon, Berks.	III.
1485	Margt., w. of R. Colmer, ins., St. Peter, Thanet, Kent	II.
1485	Beatrice, w. of G. Porter, ins., Little Walsingham, Norf.	II.
1485	Sibill, w. of W. Frankeleyn, ins., Watlington, Oxon.	I.
c. 1485	Anon., ch., Little Hadham, Herts.	II.
c. 1485	Anon., ch. ins., Northleach, Glos.	IV.
1486	Audrey Castell, ins., East Dereham, Norf.	II.
1486	Alice, w. of W. Lee of Morton, ins., Dinton, Bucks.	II.
1486	Helyn Hardy, ins., Liddington, Rutland	I.
1487	Elizth. Abbot, w. of Sir W. Mauntell, ins., Nether Heyford, Northants. PLATE 25	II.
1487	Amy, w. of J. Lambard, ch. ins., Hinxworth, Herts.	II.
1487	Elizth., w. of R. Warham, ch. ins., Church Oakley, Hants	I.
1487	Joan, w. of W. Wheteaker, ins., Radwell, Herts.	I.
1487	Margt., w. of E. Bischoptre, ins., Snodland, Kent	III.
1487	Isabel Kemp, w. of Sir R. Strelly, ins., Strelley, Notts.	I.
1487	Margt., w. of J. Barton, ins., Nether Winchendon, Bucks.	III.
1488	Agnes, Isabel and Joan, ws. of G. Aynesworth, ch. ins., Harrow, Middx.	VI.
1488	Kath., w. of J. Hertcombe, kng. ins., Kingston-on-Thames, Surr.	II.
1488	Mildred, w. of J. Eveas, ch. ins., Murston, Kent	I.
1488	Isabel, w. of M. Chyrche, ins., Otterden, Kent	II.
1488	Elizth. Charles, w. of E. Clere, ins., Stokesby, Norf.	II.
1488	Emot, Margt. and Alice, ws. of S. Brooke, Ufford, Suff.	I.
1489	Joan, w. of R. Carlyll, ins., Campton, Beds.	I.
1489	Elizth., w. of W. Brewes, ins., Fressingfield, Suff.	I.
1489	Kath., w. of N. Byldysdon, ch. ins., St. John, Stamford, Lincs.	II.
1489	Agnes, w. of H. Blaknall, ins., Wing, Bucks.	I.
1490	Emme Knightley, w. of T. Andrewe, ch. ins., Charwelton, Northants	I.
1490	Margery, w. of P. Bosard, ch. ins., Ditchingham, Norf.	I.
1490	Anne Gaynesford, w. of R. Bowett, ins., Checkendon, Oxon.	V.

Date.	Name, Description, Place and Emblems, etc.	M.S.
c. 1490	Anon., Ampton, Suff.	III.
c. 1490	Anon., ch., Great Amwell, Herts.	II.
c. 1490	Agnes, w. of W. Faldo, ins., Biddenham, Beds.	I.
c. 1490	Agnes and Maud, ws. of W. Smyth, ch. ins., Bray, Berks.	V.
c. 1490	Anon. Cheshunt, Herts. Now lost.	
c. 1490	Anon., Coggeshall, Essex	I.
c. 1490	? Jenit Sherrey, Dorchester, Oxon.	IV.
c. 1490	Kath., w. of R. Amondesham, ch. kng. ins., Ealing, Middx.	I.
c. 1490	Anon., Goring, Suss.	I.
c. 1490	Anon., Green's Norton, Northants	II.
c. 1490	Elizth. Wychyngham, w. of W. Berdewell, ins., West Harling, Norf.	II.
c. 1490	Anne Arderne, w. of W. Harper, ch., Latton, Essex	II.
c. 1490	Margt., w. of W. Goldyngton, ch. ins., Lidlington, Beds.	I.
c. 1490	Anon., ch., North Mimms, Herts.	IV.
c. 1490	Anon., ch., Newnham, Herts.	I.
c. 1490	Joan, w. of J. Taylour, ch. ins., Northleach, Glos. E.S.	V.
c. 1490	Joan, w. of W. Corbald, ins., Occold, Suff.	I.
c. 1490	Anon., ch., Orford, Suff.	II.
c. 1490	Anon., ch., Polstead, Suff.	II.
c. 1490	Joan and Agnes, ws. of T. Grene, ins., Turweston, Bucks.	II.
c. 1490	Anon., Wing, Bucks.	II.
c. 1490	A—, w. of J. Cok, ch., Wormley, Herts.	III.
1491	Margt., w. of P. Dayrell, ins., Lillingstone Dayrell, Bucks.	I.
1491	Emme and Anne, ws. of R. Salisbury, ins., Horton, Northants	I.
1492	Anne Longford and Anne Rogers, ws. of J. Brocas, Sherborne St. John, Hants	III.
1492	Joyce Assheby, w. of G. Sherard, ch. ins., Stapleford, Leic.	I.
1492	Margt. and Margt., ws. of B. Willesden, ch., Willesden, Middx.	I.
1493	Joan, w. of R. Harper, kng. ins., Axbridge, Som.	I.
1493	Alice, w. of T. Broke, ch. ins., Barking, Essex	III.
1493	Ann Oxenbrigg, ins., Brede, Suss.	I.
1493	Elizth. Oxspring, w. of R. Eyre, ins., Hathersage, Derb.	II.
1493	Isabel Gamage, w. of R. Conquest, ch. ins., Houghton Conquest, Beds.	I.
1493	Ursula Gasper, ins., Low Leyton, Essex. (Spinster.)	I.
1493	Maud, w. of R. Doughty, ins., Metton, Norf.	II.
1493	Joan Manston, w. of T. St. Nicholas, St. Laurence, Thanet	III.
1494	Margt. Elcok, ins. Formerly St. Mary Magdalen, Canterbury.	
1494	Joan Hammerton, w. of B. Roucliff, ins., Cowthorpe, Yorks. (W.R.)	I.
1494	Agnes and Margt., ws. of W. Duredent, ch. ins., Denham, Bucks.	I.
1495	Joan, w. of W. Foxe, ins., Great Barford, Oxon.	I.

Date.	Name, Description, Place and Emblems, etc.	M.S.
1495	Joan Collingbourne, w. of C. Darell, ins., Collingbourne Kingston, Wilts.	I.
1495	Alice, w. of T. Hoore, ch. ins., Digswell, Herts.	V.
1495	Ame, w. of J. Brook, ch. ins., Farley, Surr.	I.
1495	Margt., w. of T. Wylliams, ins., St. Helen, Bishopsgate, London	IV.
1495	Mary Bedingfield and Grace Teye, ws. of W. de Grey, Merton, Norf.	III.
1495	Agnes, w. of J. Horslee, St. Swithin, Norwich	III.
c. 1495	Dame Margery Calveley, dau. of W. Maynwaryng, ca., Ightfield, Salop. J.B.	I.
1496	Margt., Amy and Margt., ws. of J. Beryf, ch., Brightlingsea, Essex	I.
1496	Joan Bourne, ins., Bobbing, Kent. (Spinster.)	III.
1496	Kath., w. of R. Burlton, ins., Dartford, Kent	V.
1496	Elizth., w. of J. Payne, ch. ins., Hutton, Som.	I.
1496	Alice Willoughby, w. of R. Curzon, ch., Kedleston, Derb.	I.
1496	Ele Narburgh, w. of H. Spelman, ins., Narborough, Norf.	I.
1497	Lucy, w. of J. Clerk, ins., Basildon, Berks.	I.
1497	Agnes and Agnes, ws. of J. Benet, ins., Cirencester, Glos.	XII.
1497	Thomasine, w. of R. Rysle, ins., Great Cressingham, Norf.	I.
1498	Agnes, w. of T. Karesburght, ins., Floore, Northants	I.
1498	Margt. Tyrrell, w. of T. Huntingdon, Hempstead, Essex	III.
1498	Joan, w. of R. Fulmer, ch. ins., Hedgerley, Bucks.	I.
1498	Alys, w. of J. Snellyng, ins., East Horsley, Surr.	III.
1498	Alice, w. of T. Nysell, ch. ins., Wrotham, Kent	I.
1499	Elizth., w. of T. Bartlett, ins., Billinghurst, Suss.	I.
1499	Elizth., w. of N. Wottun, ch. ins., Boughton Malherbe, Kent	I.
1499	Anon., ws. of W. Sharp, ins., Great Chart, Kent	III.
1499	Alice, w. of J. Roberts, ch., Hawkhurst, Kent	I.
1499	Anne Yerde, w. of T. Hevenyngham, kng. ins., Ketteringham, Norf. Armf.	II.
1499	Alice, w. of W. Curteys, ins., Necton, Norf.	III.
1499	Maud Jamys, ins., St. Mary-in-the-Marsh, Kent	I.
1499	Margt. Wode, ins., Tidmarsh, Berks.	I.
1499	Constance Veer, w. of J. Butler, ins., Wappenham, Northants	III.
1500	Alice, w. of T. Goodriche, ins., Aspenden, Herts.	I.
1500	Ursula, w. of T. Payne, ins., Bushley, Worc.	I.
1500	Bennet, w. of T. Twesdon, ins., Great Chart, Kent	IV.
1500	Alice Twynihoe, w. of J. Tame, ins., Fairford, Glos.	I.
1500	Joan, w. of W. Turnour, ch. ins., Hadley, Middx.	III.
1500	Elizth., w. of R. Conquest, ins., Houghton Conquest, Beds.	II.
1500	Alice and Joan, ws. of H. Myllet, ch. ins., Perivale, Middx.	I.
1500	Anne Bushe and Cristian, ws. of R. Wenman, ch. ins., Witney, Oxon.	I.
c. 1500	Elizth. Echingham, w. of R. Wakehurst, ins., Ardingley, Suss.	I.

Date.	Name, Description, Place and Emblems, etc.	M.S.
c. 1500	Anon., Assington, Suff.	I.
c. 1500	Anon., Aylsham, Norf.	IV.
c. 1500	? Alice, w. of J. Avenyng, ch. kng. ins., Cirencester, Glos.	XIV.
c. 1500	— Trewarthen, w. of J. Samwell, ch. kng., Cottisford, Oxon.	I.
c. 1500	Elizth., w. of J. Aspleyn, and G. Askew, ins., Edmonton, Middx.	I.
c. 1500	? Anne Conyers, w. of R. Wyllughby, Great Ellingham, Norf.	I.
c. 1500	Anon., South Elmham, Suff.	I.
c. 1500	Anon., St. Mary, Guildford, Surr.	I.
c. 1500	Joan, w. of T. Wheler and C. Ford, ins., Handborough, Oxon.	I.
c. 1500	Elizth. Fitzwilliam, w. of R. Eyre, ch. kng. ins., Hathersage, Derb. Armf.	III.
c. 1500	Anon., St. Mary Tower, Ipswich	II.
c. 1500	Margery Hodge and Alice Walwyn, ws. of T. Baynham, Micheldean, Glos.	I.
c. 1500	Anon., Middleton, Suff.	I.
c. 1500	Anon., w. of J. Norwood, Milton-next-Sittingbourne, Kent	II.
c. 1500	Anon., Minchinhampton, Glos.	I.
c. 1500	Anon., ca. ins., Nayland, Suff. PLATE 43	IV.
c. 1500	Anon., w. of R. Gardiner, St. Andrew, Norwich	IV.
c. 1500	Anon., Orford, Suff.	III.
c. 1500	Anon., Rainham, Essex	II.
c. 1500	Anon., Royston, Herts.	III.
c. 1500	Anon., w. of ? C. Browne, All Saints, Stamford, Lincs.	VI.
c. 1500	Dame Mawde Cradock, w. of Sir H. Johnys, ch. ins., Swansea, Glam.	I.
c. 1500	Anon., ch. ins., Thame, Oxon.	IV.
c. 1500	Isabel, w. of R. Lytton, ins., Tideswell, Derb.	II.
c. 1500	Anon., East Tuddenham, Norf.	I.
c. 1500	? Anne Drayton, w. of T. Lovett, Wappenham, Northants	IV.
c. 1500	Elizth. Butler, w. of T. Lovett, ins., Wappenham, Northants	V.
c. 1500	Anon., w. of ? B. Medley, Whitnash, Warw.	I.
c. 1500	Margery, w. of C. Askowe, ins., Wooburn, Bucks.	II.
c. 1500	Anon., ch., Writtle, Essex.	I.
c. 1500	Anon., w. of — Compton, kng. ins. (In possession of the Surrey Archæological Society, Guildford.)	
c. 1500	Anon., ch. Locality unknown.	
c. 1500	Anon. Locality unknown.	

16TH CENTURY

1501	Elizth. Ludlow, w. of R. Baynard, ch. ins., Lacock, Wilts. Armf.	I.
1501	Joan, w. of W. Andrew, ins., March, Cambs.	I.
1501	Thomasin, w. of T. Chylton (in shroud), ins., Newington-next-Hythe, Kent	II.
1501	Anne, w. of R. Serche, ch. ins., Northleach, Glos.	VII.

Date.	Name, Description, Place and Emblems, etc.	M.S.
1502	Constance, w. of J. Parre, Cheshunt, Herts.	V.
1502	Elizth. Shaa, w. of W. Poyntz, ch. ins., North Ockendon, Essex	I.
1502	Elizth. Strickland, w. of W. Lane, Orlingbury, Northants	II.
1502	Agnes, w. of J. Turnay, ins., Soulbury, Bucks.	II.
1502	Elizth. Baynham, w. of R. Russell, ins., Strensham, Worc.	III.
1502	Margery and Alice Collingridge, ws. of G. Dormer, Thame, Oxon. E.S.	V.
1503	Elizth. Catesby, w. of R. Wake, ch. ins., Blisworth, Northants	I.
1503	Agnes Tanner, Chipping Norton, Oxon.	V.
1503	Emme, w. of T. Pallyng, ins., Clippesby, Norf.	II.
1503	Margt., w. of J. Monkeden and W. Andrew, ins., Cookham, Berks.	III.
1503	Alys Alegh, w. of W. Waleys, ch. ins., Cudham, Kent	I.
1503	Cesily Hobard, ins., Kingsclere, Hants	I.
1503	Alys, w. of R. Borrow, ins., Stanford Rivers, Essex	II.
1503	Alice, w. of N. Esstone, ins., St. Peter, Thanet, Kent	III.
1503	Dame Elizth. Bygod, w. of O. St. John, ch. ins., Stoke Rocheford, Lincs.	II.
1503	Mawde, w. of C. Bridgman, ch. ins., Thame, Oxon.	VI.
1503	Edith and Agnes, ws. of J. Wybarne, ins., Ticehurst, Suss. (The female effigies and the inscription were added in 1503 to the male effigy which was engraved c. 1370.)	I.
1503	Joan, w. of H. Elyot, ch. ins., Wonersh, Surr.	II.
1503	Margt., w. of J. Reed, ch. ins., Wrangle, Lincs.	I.
1504	Margt. Wakehurst, w. of R. Culpepyr, ins., Ardingly, Suss.	II.
1504	Gwen More, w. of J. Shelford, ins., Bramley, Hants. PLATE 51	II.
1504	Joan, w. of J. Smyth, ins., Cottingham, Yorks.	II.
1504	Joan Goodyere, ins., Hadley, Middx.	IV.
1504	Kath., w. of W. Knyght, ins., Norton, Northants	I.
1504	Elizth. Haydok, ch. ins., Odiham, Hants	III.
1504	Anne, w. of J. Ardalle, ins., Stifford, Essex	III.
1504	Joan, w. of J. Adene, ins., Stoke Talmage, Oxon.	I.
1504	Anon., ws. of J. Rudd, ins., Winterton, Lincs.	I.
1505	Mary Beryf, ch., Brightlingsea, Essex	II.
1505	Elizth., w. of J. Hawtt *alias* Cryscyan, ch. ins., Caddington, Beds.	I.
1505	Elizth. Anstye, w. of W. Taylard, ca., Diddington, Hunts. Armf. L. B.V. SS.	I.
1505	Margt., w. of J. Burgoyn, ch. ins., Impington, Cambs. Armf.	I.
1505	Alys *or* Amis, w. of W. Abere, ch. ins., Ringwould, Kent	I.
1505	Alice, w. of J. Peddar, ch. ins., Salford, Beds.	I.
1505	Dame Agnes, w. of R. Blackwall, ch. ins., Taddington, Derb.	I.
1505	Margt. Roberts, ins., Willesden, Middx.	II.
1505	Baterich, w. of R. Barowe, ch. ins., Winthorpe, Lincs.	I.
1505	Dame Anne Grey, w. of J. Harewell, ch. ins., Wootton Wawen, Warw.	I.

Date.	Name, Description, Place and Emblems, etc.	M.S.
1506	Alice, w. of R. Maulaye, ins., Blunham, Beds.	I.
1506	Joan Rudhale, Brampton Abbots, Hereford	I.
1506	Margt. Nevill, w. of Sir J. Broke, ch. ca. ins., Cobham, Kent	XVIII.
1506	Alice Digby, w. of R. Clifton, ins., Coleshill, Warw.	II.
1506	Parnel and Agnes, ws. of J. Gregory, ch. ins., Cuxham, Oxon.	I.
1506	Alice Faryngton, w. of W. Croke, ch. ins., Great Gaddesden, Herts.	I.
1506	Alys, w. of R. Wymbyll and T. Baldry, ch. ins., St. Mary Tower, Ipswich	III.
1506	Joan *or* Helen, w. of T. Caus, St. John Maddermarket, Norwich	VI.
1506	Thomasyn, w. of J. Goodyere, ins., Teddington, Middx.	I.
1506	Kath., w. of J. Colman, ch. ins., Little Waldingfield, Suff. E.S.	I.
1506	Joan Beauchamp, w. of R. Decons, ins., White Waltham, Berks.	II.
1506	Margt., w. of J. Hyll, ins., Wilburton, Cambs.	II.
1507	Anne Babyngton, w. of J. Rolleston, ch. ins., Ashover, Derb.	II.
1507	Kath. Berecroft, ins., Beddington, Surr.	VI.
1507	Margt. Ashefyld, ch. ins., Chipping Norton, Oxon.	VI.
1507	Agnes *or* Joan, w. of Christ. Gay, Elmsted, Kent	I.
1507	Isabel, w. of W. Boys, ch. ins., Goodnestone-next-Wingham, Kent. H.T.	I.
1507	Kath. Southwell, w. of A. Hansart, kng. ins., March, Cambs. Armf.	II.
c. 1507	Anon., w. of ? R. Foster, Mattishall, Norf.	V.
1508	Jane Smyth, ins., Adderbury, Oxon.	II.
1508	Elizth. Barley, w. of Sir R. Clyfford, kng. ins., Aspenden, Herts.	II.
1508	Eleanor Eggerley, Aston Rowant, Oxon.	III.
1508	Edith and Elizth. Wylde, ins., Barnes, Surr. (Spinsters.)	I.
1508	Margt. Armine, w. of J. Deen, ch. ins., Barrowby, Lincs. Armf.	II.
1508	Joan, w. of J. Best, ins., Boughton-under-Blean, Kent	II.
1508	Joyce Peryent and Margt. Pyrton, ws. of W. Roberts, ch. ins., Little Braxted, Essex	I.
1508	Elizth. Follett, ins., Collyweston, Northants	I.
1508	Feyth Brooke, ins., Cowling, Kent	I.
1508	Deonys, w. of T. Baker, ch., St. Leonard, Deal, Kent	I.
1508	Margt., w. of W. Berdewell, ins., West Harling, Norf.	III.
1508	Elizth. Forde, w. of R. Blount, ch. ins., Iver, Bucks.	I.
1508	Joan, Agnes, Elynor, ws. of R. Abery, ins., St. Mary Cray, Kent	II.
1508	Alys, w. of J. Wylmot, ins., Stadhampton, Oxon.	II.
1508	Isabel, w. of W. Pratt, ins., Thame, Oxon.	VII.
1508	Mary Tyringham, w. of A. Catesby, ins., Tyringham, Bucks.	III.
1509	Jane, w. of R. Court, ins., Brightwell, Berks.	II.
1509	Jacquette Widville, w. of John le Strange, Lord Strange of Knockyn, ch. ca., Hillingdon, Middx. PLATE 26	I.
1509	Alice, w. of W. Merden, ch. ins., Leeds, Kent	I.

Date.	Name, Description, Place and Emblems, etc.	M.S.
1509	Margery Iwarby, w. of Sir R. Verney, ch. ins., Quainton, Bucks .	IV.
1509	Margery Hylyarde, w. of Sir W. Ayscugh, ins., Stallingborough, Lincs. Armf.	I.
1509	Joan, w. of H. Clederowe, ins., Little Walsingham, Norf. .	IX.
1510	Elizth. Wakehurst, w. of N. Culpepyr, ch. ins., Ardingly, Suss. .	III.
1510	Alice Bonaventur, w. of T. Bray, ins., Chelsfield, Kent . .	VI.
1510	Annes, w. of R. Pecke, ins., Cookham, Berks. H.T. . .	IV.
1510	Philippe, w. of H. Michell, ins., Floore, Northants . . .	II.
1510	Margt., w. of T. Ramsey, ch. ins., Hitcham, Bucks. . .	I.
c. 1510	? — Caldebeck, w. of T. Underhill, kng., Little Bradley, Suff. .	I.
c. 1510	Anon., Chalfont St. Giles, Bucks.	IV.
c. 1510	Joan, w. of W. Morys, ins., Great Coxwell, Berks. . . .	II.
c. 1510	— Collys, w. of Rich. —, ch. ins. Dunton, Bucks. . . .	II.
c. 1510	Audrie Narborow, ins., Fakenham, Norf.	V.
c. 1510	Anon., Littlebury, Essex	III.
c. 1510	? Isabel Talbot, w. of Sir R. Ashton, ch., Middleton, Lancs. .	I.
c. 1510	Anon., Great Missenden, Bucks.	II.
c. 1510	Anon., ch., Orford, Suff.	VI.
c. 1510	Anon., Raunds, Northants	II.
c. 1510	Kath., w. of W. Yelverton, ch. ins., Rougham, Norf. . .	III.
c. 1510	Anon., Sparsholt, Berks.	III.
c. 1510	Anon., ch., Gray's Thurrock, Essex	I.
c. 1510	Anon., ch., Wheathampstead, Herts.	IV.
c. 1510	Anon., ch., Wirksworth, Derb.	I.
c. 1510	Anon., Writtle, Essex	II.
c. 1510	Anon., ins. Locality unknown.	
1511	Bennet, w. of J. Mylner, ins., Erith, Kent	VI.
1511	Anon., ws. (2) of R. Potter, ch. ins., Westerham, Kent . .	II.
1511	Mary, w. of N. Wrenne, ins., Worlingham, Suff. . . .	II.
1512	Anne a Wode, w. of T. Asteley, ch. ins., Blickling, Norf. . .	XIX.
1512	Jane, w. of R. Hampden, ins., Brightwell, Berks. . . .	III.
1512	Alice, w. of J. Muscote, Earl's Barton, Northants . . .	I.
1512	Dorothy Horne, w. of T. Pekham, ch. ins., Wrotham, Kent .	IV.
1513	Margt. Walworth and Anne Engeham, ws. of J. Toke, ins., Great Chart, Kent	V.
1513	Anon., w. of W. Greville, ch. ins., St. Mary, Cheltenham, Glos. .	I.
1513	Margt., w. of R. Beweforest, ch. ins., Dorchester, Oxon. . .	VI.
1513	Elizth. Foys, Horsham, Suss.	II.
1513	Agnes, w. of W. Rysley, ins., Lillingstone Lovell, Bucks. . .	III.
1513	Elizth. and Joan, ws. of J. Sylam, ins., Luton, Beds. . .	VIII.
1513	Alys and Amys, ws. of J. Acworth, ins., Luton, Beds. . .	IX.
1513	Jone, w. of W. Wyddowsoun, kng. ins., Mickleham, Surr. PLATE 45	I.
1513	Magdalen, w. of J. Hook, ins., Sherringham, Norf. . . .	II.

Date.	Name, Description, Place and Emblems, etc.	M.S.
1513	Thomasin Heveningham, w. of Thos. Berdefield, John Bedell and Walter Thomas, and her grandmother Thomasin, w. of Thos. Heveningham, Writtle, Essex	III.
1513	Kath., w. of R. Dellvys, ins., Wybunbury, Ches.	I.
c. 1513	Cristian, w. of R. Brasyer, ins., St. Stephen, Norwich	VI.
1514	Cecily Sheryngton, w. of R. Southwell, ins., Barham, Suff.	I.
1514	Ellen, w. of J. Dorant, ins., Barnham Broom, Norf.	II.
1514	Margt. Beriff, Brightlingsea, Essex	III.
1514	Susan Fetyplace, w. of J. Kyngeston, ins., Childrey, Berks. H.T.	VII.
1514	Anon., w. of F. Poffe, ch., Chinnor, Oxon.	XIII.
1514	Anne Stradling, w. of Sir J. Danvers, ins., Dauntsey, Wilts.	I.
1514	Alys Taillor, ins., Farningham, Kent	II.
1514	Anne, dau. of Lord Awdeley, and Elizth. Mores, ws. of Sir R. Delabere, ch. ins., Hereford Cathedral	XVIII.
1514	Kath. Lambe, ins., Leeds, Kent. (Spinster.)	II.
1514	Agnes, w. of T. Fytche, ch. ins., Lindsell, Essex	I.
1514	Margt. Pettwode, ins., St. Clement, Norwich	I.
1514	Agnes, w. of P. Yden, ch. ins., Penshurst, Kent	II.
1514	Cecily, w. of J. Wulvedon, ins., Probus, Cornw.	I.
1514	Mary Dilcok, Rochford, Essex	I.
1514	Joan, w. of E. Saunders, ins., Rothwell, Northants	II.
1515	Kath. Sewell, ch. ins., Bisley, Glos.	I.
1515	Elizth., w. of E. Dalyson, ins., Cransley, Northants	I.
1515	Elizth. Lock, w. of E. Cockayne, ch. ins., Hatley Cockayne, Beds.	V.
1515	Agnes Barbar, ins., Luton, Beds.	X.
1515	Margery, w. of T. Brond, ch. ins., Newport, Essex. E.S.	I.
1515	Alice, w. of R. Water, ins., Swaffham Prior, Cambs.	II.
1515	Beatrix Apsley, ins., Thakeham, Suss.	I.
1515	Elizth., w. of R. Caterall, ch. kng. ins., Whalley, Lancs.	I.
c. 1515	Anon., w. of ? — Latton, ch., Blewbury, Berks.	IV.
1516	Elizth. Cheyne, ins., Chesham Bois, Bucks.	I.
1516	Agnes Lovingcott, w. of O. Hyde, ins., Denchworth, Berks.	II.
1516	— Byfield and Kath. Morland, ws. of Sir R. Haddon, ch. kng., St. Olave, Hart Street, London	I.
1516	Joan, w. of R. Davy, ins., Nayland, Suff.	V.
1516	Anne and Agnes, ws. of J. Bele, ch. ins., Radwell, Herts.	II.
1516	Anon., w. of J. Redfford, ch. ins., Shere, Surr.	IV.
1516	Kath. Courtenay, w. of Sir W. Huddesfeld, ch. kng. ins., Shillingford, Devon. Armf.	I.
1516	Agnes, w. of J. Mallet, ch. ins., Soulbury, Bucks.	III.
1516	Elen Camby, ch. ins., Stanton Harcourt, Oxon.	II.
1516	Margt., w. of W. Byrd, ch. ins., Wilburton, Cambs.	III.
1517	Elizth., Joan and Agnes, ws. of T. Robertes, ch. ins., Brenchley, Kent	I.

Date.	Name, Description, Place and Emblems, etc.	M.S.
1517	Ellen, w. of J. Newman, ch. ins., Brightwalton, Berks.	I.
1517	Agnes Dudley, w. of T. Mountagu, ins., Hemington, Northants	I.
1517	Maude, w. of R. Blackhed, ins., Ivinghoe, Bucks.	II.
1517	Joan, w. of T. Goddard, ins., Ogbourne St. George, Wilts.	I.
1517	Margt., w. of T. Freshwater, ch., Tollesbury, Essex	I.
1517	Mary, Ellen, Margt., ws. of E. Bulstrode, ch., Upton, Bucks.	II.
1517	Agnes, w. of W. Lawerd, ch. ins., Yateley, Hants	II.
1518	Alys Cryspe, ch. ins., Birchington, Kent	III.
1518	Elizth., w. of E. Dormer, ch. ins., Caddington, Beds.	II.
1518	Margt. Counforth, ins., Cromer, Norf.	III.
1518	Elizth. *or* Agnes, w. of Robt. Alee, from Dunstable, Beds., now in the Victoria and Albert Museum	V.
1518	Elizth. Knevet, ins., Eastington, Glos. Armf.	I.
1518	Anne Bulstrode, w. of T. Broke, ins., Ewelme, Oxon.	XII.
1518	Mary Alington, w. of R. Newport, ch. kng., Furneux Pelham, Herts.	II.
1518	Joan Hawte, w. of T. Goodyere, Hadley, Middx.	V.
1518	Margt. and Agnes, ws. of C. Rawson, ins., All Hallows, Barking, London	VIII.
1518	Maryon, w. of J. Barley, ch. ins., Preshute, Wilts.	I.
1518	Agnes, w. of E. Wayte, ins., Renhold, Beds.	I.
1518	Elizth. Guldeford, w. of T. Isley, ch., Sundridge, Kent	III.
1519	Joan, w. of J. Rokys, ins., Calverton, Bucks.	I.
1519	Jane Agmondesham, w. of Sir J. Iwarby, kng. ins., Ewell, Surr. Armf.	III.
1519	Agnes, w. of T. Sibill, ins., Farningham, Kent	IV.
1519	Alys and Agnes, ws. of W. Henshaw, ins., St. Michael, Gloucester	I.
1519	Margery, w. of E. Halyday, ins., Minchinhampton, Glos.	III.
1519	Alice, w. of J. Smalwode *alias* Wynchcom, ch. ins., Newbury, Berks.	I.
1519	Amye and Elizth., ws. of J. Tornay, ch. ins., Slapton, Bucks.	II.
1519	Agnes Foster and Elizth. Iwardeby, ws. of T. Pygott, ch. ins., Whaddon, Bucks.	I.
1519	Isabel, w. of G. Penne, ins., Yeovil, Som.	II.
1520	Margt. Conyers, w. of H. Pudsey, kng. ins., Bolton-by-Bowland, Yorks. (W.R.). Armf.	I.
1520	Alice, w. of R. Pygott, ins., Compton Parva, Berks.	I.
1520	Margt. Mundford, ins., Feltwell, Norf.	II.
1520	Anne and Mawde, ws. of J. Shepard, ch. ins., Kingsbury, Middx.	I.
1520	Mary Belknap, w. of G. Danet, ch. ins., Tilty, Essex	II.
1520	Elizth., w. of J. Heyworth, ch. ins., Wheathampstead, Herts.	III.
c. 1520	Anon., Aldeburgh, Suff.	II.
c. 1520	Anon., ch., Aldenham, Herts.	III.
c. 1520	Margt., w. of J. Goldwell, ch. ins., Biddenden, Kent	I.

G

Date.	Name, Description, Place and Emblems, etc.	M.S.
c. 1520	Elizth. Tyrwhit, w. of W. Skypwith, ins., Bigby, Lincs.	I.
c. 1520	Anon., Bishop's Sutton, Hants	I.
c. 1520	Edith, w. of T. Fowler, ins., Christ's Coll., Cambridge	I.
c. 1520	Anon., Cheshunt, Herts. Now lost.	
c. 1520	Alice Englefield, w. of T. Wolrond, ins., Childrey, Berks.	X.
c. 1520	Anon., Crawley, Suss.	II.
c. 1520	Anon., Deerhurst, Glos.	II.
c. 1520	Agnes, w. of J. Wyther, ins., Dunster, Som.	I.
c. 1520	Anon., Ellough, Suff.	III.
c. 1520	Anon., Euston, Suff.	II.
c. 1520	Anon., Euston, Suff.	III.
c. 1520	Anon., Great Hadham, Herts.	III.
c. 1520	Margt., w. of T. Goodenouth, ins., All Saints, Hastings	I.
c. 1520	? Kath. Haseldon, w. of J. Dockra, East Hatley, Cambs.	I.
c. 1520	Anon., ch. br., St. Mary Tower, Ipswich	IV.
c. 1520	Annys, w. of R. Su......, ins., Luton, Beds.	XII.
c. 1520	Anon., Orford, Suff. H.T.	VII.
c. 1520	Anon., Sharrington, Norf.	V.
c. 1520	Elizth., w. of J. Sedley, ch. ins., Southfleet, Kent	VII.
c. 1520	Kath. Pound, w. of J. White, ch. ins., Southwick, Hants	I.
c. 1520	Anon., ch. kng., Theydon Gernon, Essex. PLATE 28	II.
c. 1520	Anon., Little Thurlow, Suff.	I.
c. 1520	Anon., Tisbury, Wilts.	I.
c. 1520	Anon., Wokingham, Berks.	I.
1521	Elizth. Hally, w. of J. De la Penne, ins., Amersham, Bucks.	V.
1521	Joan Holme, w. of R. Rokeby, ins., Bishop Burton, Yorks.	II.
1521	Margery Treghstin, ins., Ewell, Surr.	IV.
1521	Maud, w. of W. Cheswryght, ins., Fordham, Cambs.	II.
1521	Jane Blenerhayset, ins., Frenze, Norf.	V.
1521	Cristyan, w. of W. Hichman, ch. ins., Kempsford, Glos. E.S.	I.
1521	Jone, w. of J. Bowyer, ins., St. Giles, Reading	I.
1521	Elizth. Eldrington and Mary Anle, ws. of J. Colt, ch. ins., Roydon, Essex. Armf. E.S.	II.
1521	Elizth., w. of J. Humpton, ch. ins., Sculthorpe, Norf.	IV.
1521	Alys, w. of L. Slyffeld, ins., Send, Surr.	I.
1521	Anne, w. of Geo. Carr, ch. ins., Sleaford, Lincs.	II.
1521	Agnes, w. of R. Fairfax, ins., St. Albans Abbey, Herts. (Renewed in 1921.)	
1521	Alice, w. of W. Water, ch. ins., Swaffham Prior, Cambs.	III.
1521	Elizth. or Alice, w. of Nich. Purvey, from Dunstable, Beds., now in the Victoria and Albert Museum	VII.
1522	Joan Amerike, w. of J. Brook, ins., St. Mary Redcliffe, Bristol	V.
1522	Alys and Anne, ws. of R. Thornburgh, ch. kng. ins., Kimpton, Hants	I.

Date.	Name, Description, Place and Emblems, etc.	M.S.
1522	Elizth. Fitz-William, ins., Mablethorpe, Lincs. (Spinster.)	III.
1522	Alice, w. of T. Laurence, ch. ins., Netteswell, Essex	I.
1522	Alice, Joan and Kath., ws. of R. Ryege, ins., Newington-next-Hythe, Kent	IV.
1522	Agnes Chapman, ch., Odiham, Hants	IV.
1522	Margt., w. of T. Symeon, ins., Pyrton, Oxon.	I.
1522	Alice, w. of W. Cobbe, ins., Sharnbrook, Beds.	I.
1522	Agnes and Alice, ws. of W. Tawbott, ch. ins., Wantage, Berks.	V.
1523	Alice Latton, w. of Sir J. Daunce, ch. ins., Blewbury, Berks.	V.
1523	— Hunteley, ch. ins., Burnham Westgate, Norf.	I.
1523	Isabel Gifford, ins., Middle Claydon, Bucks.	I.
1523	Anne Verney, w. of E. Odyngsale, ins., Compton Verney, Warw. E.S.	I.
1523	Elizth., w. of N. Boone, ins., Edmonton, Middx.	II.
1523	— Goodnestone, ins., Goodnestone-next-Wingham, Kent	II.
1523	Alice Estington, w. of W. Brugge, ins., Longdon, Worc.	I.
1523	Joan Purdan, ch. ins., Woking, Surr.	I.
1524	Joan Ellynbrege, w. of H. Burton, ins., Carshalton, Surr.	V.
1524	Marion, w. of W. Chaucey, ins., Charlton, Wilts.	I.
1524	Elizth. Broughton, ins., Chenies, Bucks. (Spinster.) PLATE 51	VII.
1524	Margt. Broughton, w. of H. Everard, Denstone, Suff. Armf.	I.
1524	Anne Warren, w. of R. Colshill, ins., Luton, Beds. Now lost.	
1524	Lettys, w. of J. Terry, ch. br. ins., St. John Maddermarket, Norwich	VII.
1524	Dorothy Danvers, w. of J. Fetyplace, ch. kng. ins., Little Shefford, Berks.	I.
1524	Constans Berners, ins., Writtle, Essex. (Spinster.)	IV.
1525	Maude, w. of T. Blakewall, ch. ins., Wirksworth, Derb.	II.
1525	Anys, w. of W. Leus, ins., Ash-next-Sandwich, Kent	III.
1525	Joyce Colepeper, w. of R. Pekham, ins., Wrotham, Kent. Armf.	V.
1525	Elizth., w. of J. Marsham, br., St. John Maddermarket, Norwich. PLATE 43	VIII.
1525	Elizth. Bruges, w. of W. Rowdon, Deerhurst, Glos.	III.
1525	Joan Stathum, w. of J. Sacheverell, ch. kng. ins., Morley, Derb. H.T.	VIII.
1525	Isabel, w. of T. Englysche, ins., Ipsden, Oxon.	I.
1525	Emme, w. of T. Pownder, ch. ins., St. Mary Quay, Ipswich. E.S. PLATE 44	I.
1525	Joan, w. of W. Beriff, Brightlingsea, Essex	V.
1525	Dyones, w. of J. Awodde, ch. ins., Sanderstead, Surr.	I.
1525	Alys and Agnes, ws. of J. Haryson, ch. kng. ins., St. Mary, Hull	I.
c. 1525	Elizth. Sidney, w. of J. Hampden, ch. ins., Great Hampden, Bucks.	I.
c. 1525	Anon., Great Barford, Beds.	I.
c. 1525	Anon., Great Gaddesden, Herts.	II.

Date.	Name, Description, Place and Emblems, etc.	M.S.
c. 1525	Anon., ch., Hutton, Essex	I.
1526	Joan, w. of T. Busche, ca. ins., Northleach, Glos. E.S.	VIII.
1526	Margt., w. of J. Gybbis, ch. ins., Capel-le-Ferne, Kent	I.
1526	Julyen Deryng, ins., Pluckley, Kent	V.
1526	Cristian, w. of C. Crowe, ch. ins., Mitcham, Norf.	I.
1526	Margt., w. of J. Ips, ins., Old Romney, Kent	I.
1526	Mary Mountney, w. of R. Appleton, Little Waldingfield, Suff.	II.
1526	Anne Danvers, w. of R. Verney, ch. ins., Compton Verney, Warw.	II.
1526	Elizth. Michilgrove, w. of J. Shelley, ins., Clapham, Suss. Armf. H.T. PLATE 31	IV.
1527	Alice Sutton, w. of Sir J. Ratclif, ins., Crosthwaite, Cumb.	I.
1527	Joan Dallison, w. of T. Leventhorpe, Sawbridgeworth, Herts. Armf.	VI.
1527	Ellen Savage, w. of Sir P. Legh, ins., Winwick, Lancs. Armf. E.S. PLATE 30	II.
1527	Kath., w. of J. Deynes, ins., Beeston Regis, Norf.	V.
1527	Anon., w. of R. Babham, kng. ins., Cookham, Berks.	V.
1527	Isabell, w. of J. Shadet, ins., Woking, Surr.	II.
1528	Alice Harleston, anon., Elizth. Shelton, and Joan Hornby, ws. of Sir R. Fitzlewes, Ingrave, Essex. Armf.	II.
1528	Anon., w. of J. Fisher, ins., Clifton, Beds.	I.
1528	Margt. Rotherham, w. of J. Cryspe, ins., Birchington, Kent	V.
1528	Dame Elizth. Pownynges, ins., Brabourne, Kent	IV.
1528	Alys, w. of W. Petley, ins., Halstead, Kent	II.
1528	Margt. Molyneux, w. of W. Bulcley, ca. ins., Sefton, Lancs.	I.
1528	Elizth. Froxmere, w. of E. Whyte, ins., Shotesham-St. Mary, Norf.	I.
1528	Elizth., w. of T. Payne, ch. kng. ins., Hutton, Som.	II.
1528	— Lee, w. of R. Rowthall, Moulsoe, Bucks.	I.
1528	Agnes *or* Jacomyne, w. of H. Smyth, Eton Coll., Bucks.	X.
1528	Anon., ws. (2) of Sir E. Grey, ch. ins., Kinver, Staffs.	I.
1528	Alice Carter, ins., King's Langley, Herts.	I.
1528	Joan, w. of H. Redmayne, ch. kng. ins., New Brentford, Middx.	I.
1528	Agnes Button, ins., Alton Priors, Wilts.	I.
1529	Kath. Leake, w. of Sir G. Foljambe, ch. ins., Chesterfield, Derb. Armf.	III.
1529	Margt. Alefe, ch. kng. ins., Milton-next-Sittingbourne, Kent	III.
1529	Alys, w. of R. Carter, ins., Bramley, Hants	III.
1529	Elizth. and Joan, ws. of J. Samwel, ch. ins., Offley, Herts.	I.
1529	Dorothy Rede, w. of Sir E. Wotton, ins., Boughton Malherbe, Kent	II.
1529	Margt. Kendall, ins., Bapchild, Kent. Now lost.	
1529	Dorothy Haydon, w. of Sir T. Brooke, ch. ins., Cobham, Kent. PLATE 30	XIX.
1530	Elizth., w. of John Saye, ch. kng. ins., St. Peter, Colchester	I.
1530	Jane Clefforht, w. of — Eveas, ins., Chartham, Kent	V.

Date.	Name, Description, Place and Emblems, etc.	M.S.
1530	Elizth. Tante, Chipping Norton, Oxon.	VII.
1530	Emme Smith, w. of E. Watson, ch. Lyddington, Rutland . .	II.
1530	Elizth, w. of H. Dacres, kng. ins., St. Dunstan-in-the-West, London	I.
c. 1530	Elizth., w. of R. Bulkley, ch. kng. ins., Beaumaris, Anglesea. B.V. H.T.	I.
c. 1530	Anon., Binham, Norf.	I.
c. 1530	? Agnes Holden, Great Chesterford, Essex	I.
c. 1530	Anon., Cirencester, Glos.	XVI.
c. 1530	— Drury, Denstone, Suff.	II.
c. 1530	Anon., Digswell, Herts. (Appropriated by the addition of an inscr. to Robt. Batyll, 1557, his w. Margt. and son Wm., and of another inscr. stating that Wm. had by his w. Joan 4 sons and 6 daus., whose effigies are added.)	VI.
c. 1530	Anon., ch. ins., Elmdon, Essex. E.S.	I.
c. 1530	Anon., w. of — Rokewood, Euston, Suff.	IV.
c. 1530	Ursula Drury, w. of G. Alington, Hawstead, Suff. . . .	V.
c. 1530	Anon., ch., Hempstead, Essex	VI.
c. 1530	Constance, w. of J. Wodehows, ins., Kimberley, Norf. . .	I.
c. 1530	Anon., Lakenheath, Suff.	I.
c. 1530	Alice, w. of J. Watson, ins., Leake, Yorks. (W.R.) . . .	I.
c. 1530	Anon., ch. ins., Offley, Herts.	II.
c. 1530	Anon., w. of — Fastolfe, ch., Pettaugh, Suff. . . .	I.
c. 1530	Anon., ch., Rainham, Kent	V.
c. 1530	Anon., Stoke-by-Clare, Suff.	I.
c. 1530	Anon., Swaffham Prior, Cambs.	IV.
c. 1530	Anne Drury, w. of T. Underhill, ch., Great Thurlow, Suff. .	III.
c. 1530	Anon., Little Waldingfield, Suff.	III.
c. 1530	Anon. Formerly at Cassiobury House, Herts., now in possession of W. H. Fenton, Heston, Middx.	
c. 1530	Anon. Locality unknown.	
c. 1530	Anon. Locality unknown.	
c. 1530	Anon. Formerly in possession of — Edlin, Cambridge. Sold at Puttick and Simpson, Nov. 1903.	
1531	Kath., w. of G. Wyndbourne, ch. ins., St. Paul, Canterbury. Now lost.	
1531	— Heigham, ins., Goldhanger, Essex	I.
1531	Alice Ashton, w. of J. Laurence, R. Radclyffe and T. Bothe, ins., Middleton, Lancs.	III.
1531	Elizth. Turges, w. of J. Horsey, ins., Yetminster, Dorset. PLATE 32	I.
1532	Elizth. Skinner, w. of J. Scott, ch. kng. ins., Camberwell, Surr. .	III.
1532	Agnes, w. of A. Maycot, ch. ins., Hoath, Kent . . .	II.
1532	Sabine, w. of R. Goodwyn, ch. ins., Necton, Norf. . .	VI.
1532	Thomasyn Ardall, w. of R. Badby, ins., North Ockendon, Essex .	II.
1532	Margt., w. of T. Challoner, ch. ins., Rusper, Suss. . . .	II.

Date.	Name, Description, Place and Emblems, etc.	M.S.
1532	Tomysyn, w. of W. Rygg, ch. ins., Yately, Hants	III.
1533	Margt. Cryppys, ch. ins., Birchington, Kent	VI.
1533	Joan, w. of J. Paycock, Coggeshall, Essex	III.
1533	Anne Charlton, w. of F. Younge, ch. ins., Edgmond, Salop. (Husband in shroud.)	I.
1533	Joan, w. of H. Hatche, ins., Faversham, Kent. E.S.	XII.
1533	Agnes and Agnes, ws. of R. Colwell, ch. ins., Faversham, Kent	XIII.
1533	Ellyn, w. of A. Evyngar, ch. ca. ins., All Hallows, Barking, London. B.V. PLATE 46	IX.
1533	Alice Baldwyn, ins., Lullingstone, Kent	III.
1533	Denys, w. of R. Bradbryge, ins., Slinfold, Suss.	I.
1533	Elizth. Tymperley, w. of F. Rokewoode, ch. ins., Weston, Norf.	II.
1534	Agnes Greville and Elizth. Tyringham, ws. of Sir E. Tame, ch. ins., Fairford, Glos. Armf.	II.
1534	Grace and Alice, ws. of M. Osberne, ch. ins., Kelmarsh, Northants. Now lost.	
1534	Anne Hawes, w. of Sir W. Fitzwilliams, kng. ins., Marholm, Northants. Armf.	I.
1534	Agnes, w. of J. Cracherood, ch. ins., Toppesfield, Essex	I.
1535	Agnes, w. of T. Perys, ins., Little Barford, Beds.	I.
1535	Tomasseyng Jenny and Anne Brome, ws. of J. Brampton, ch. ins., Brampton, Norf.	IV.
1535	Kath. Vause, w. of Sir G. Throkmorton, ch. ins., Coughton, Warw.	I.
1535	Anon., St. Helen, Bishopsgate, London. Armf. PLATE 50	IX.
1535	Kath. Broughton, w. of Lord Wm. Howard, St. Mary, Lambeth, London. Armf. PLATE 50	I.
1535	Alys Arden, w. of E. Love, ch. ins., Stoke Lyne, Oxon. R.	I.
c. 1535	Anon., Aldenham, Herts.	VII.
c. 1535	Anon., Hitchin, Herts.	XV.
c. 1535	Anon., St. John Sepulchre, Norwich	II.
c. 1535	Anon., ch. ins., Rettendon, Essex	I.
c. 1535	Lady Kath. Molyns, w. of John Howard, Duke of Norfolk, Stoke-by-Nayland, Suff. Armf.	IV.
c. 1535	? Kath. Darcy, Tolleshunt Darcy, Essex	III.
c. 1535	Anon., ch., Wimpole, Cambs.	III.
1536	Dame Alice Beriffe and dau. Margt., br., Brightlingsea, Essex. (Widow and spinster.)	VI.
1536	Elizth., w. of T. Malyn, ch. ins., Great Linford, Bucks.	II.
1537	Elizth., w. of E. Hawte, ins., Erith, Kent	VII.
1537	Jane, w. of W. Assheby, ch. ins., Harefield, Middx.	V.
1537	Alice, w. of W. Bradschawe, ch. kng. ins., Wendover, Bucks.	II.
1537	Lady Elizth. Scroope, wid. of Viscount Beaumont, w. of John de Vere, Earl of Oxford, ca. ins., Wivenhoe, Essex. Armf. PLATE 50	III.

Date.	Name, Description, Place and Emblems, etc.	M.S
?1538	Joan Warner, ch. ins., Aldenham, Herts.	VIII.
1538	Dorothy Marrowe, w. of F. Cockayne, ca. ins., Ashbourne, Derb.	II.
1538	Maud Cotton, w. of Sir A. Fitzherbert, ch. ins., Norbury, Derb.	II.
1539	Honor Grenville and Anne Dennys, ws. of Sir J. Basset, ch., Atherington, Devon	I.
1539	Denys Bodley, w. of N. Leveson, ch. kng. ins., St. Andrew Undershalf, London	I.
1540	Margt. Bulstrode, ch. ins., Hedgerley, Bucks. R.	II.
1540	Alice, w. of R. Fowler, St. Mary, Islington, London	I.
1540	Margt., dau. of John, Lord Mordaunt, w. of E. Fetyplace, ch. kng. ins., Marcham, Berks.	I.
1540	Agnes Trewonwall and Kath., ws. of T. Manfeld, ins., Taplow, Bucks.	VI.
1540	Elizth. Pennington and — Winter, ws. of Sir W. Gascoigne, Cardington, Beds. Armf. PLATE 33	I.
c. 1540	Anon., w. of ? — Gardyner, Chalfont St. Giles, Bucks.	VI.
c. 1540	Anon., w. of — Hutton, Dry Drayton, Cambs.	I.
c. 1540	Anon., Lowestoft, Suff.	V.
c. 1540	Anon., Messing, Essex	I.
c. 1540	Joan, w. of J. Symonds., ch. ins., Shiplake, Oxon.	I.
c. 1540	Anon., Stanstead Abbots, Herts.	III.
c. 1540	Anon., Little Walsingham, Norf.	XVIII.
c. 1540	Isabel Saunders, w. of W. Curson, ins., Waterperry, Oxon. (Effigies of c. 1440, altered and adapted to the later date.)	II.
1541	Joan, w. of T. Warde, ins., Bletchingley, Surr. H.T.	IV.
1541	Agnes Newport, w. of T. Andrewes, ins., Charwelton, Northants	III.
1541	Joan and Kath., ws. of J. Stonnard, ins., Loughton, Essex	I.
1542	Elizth. Yerde, w. of T. Fromond, ch. kng. ins., Cheam, Surr. H.T.	VII.
1542	Mary Nansegles, w. of R. Gyffard, ch. ins., Middle Claydon, Bucks.	III.
1542	Margery, w. of T. Selwyn, ins., Friston, Suss.	I.
1543	Elizth. Babington, w. of G. Perepoynt, ins., West Malling, Kent. PLATE 51	III.
1543	Dame Ann, w. of Sir G. Monox, kng. ins., Walthamstow, Essex	II.
1544	Isabel Harvye, w. of J. Leigh, ch. ins., Addington, Surr.	II.
1544	Anne Launceleyn, w. of Sir W. Luke, kng. ins., Cople, Beds. Armf.	V.
1544	Elizth. Bond, w. of T. Heron, ch., Croydon, Surr.	IV.
1544	Elizth. Waren, ins., Flitton, Beds.	II.
1544	Elizth., w. of G. Cobham, ins., Lullingstone, Kent	IV.
1545	Margt. Willington, w. of T. Holte, ch. ins., Aston, Warw. E.S.	I.
1545	Anne, w. of J. Newdegate, ch. ins., Harefield, Middx.	VI. —
1545	Anne Bellyngham, w. of G. Lovell, ins., Harlington, Middx.	II.
1545	Alice Brokesby, w. of L. Saunders, ch. kng. ins., Harrington, Northants	I.

Date.	Name, Description, Place and Emblems, etc.	M.S.
1545	Margt. Pickenham, w. of J. Lymsey, ch. ins., Hackney, London .	II.
1545	Elizth. Frowick, w. of Sir J. Spelman, kng. ins., Narborough, Norf. Armf. R. PLATE 61 .	IV.
1545	Ellyn Dencourt, w. of N. Wayte, ins., Upminster, Essex . .	III.
1545	Elizth. Drury, w. of Sir P. Butler, ins., Watton-at-Stone, Herts. .	VII.
c. 1545	Anon., w. of ? J. Knighton, Bayford, Herts.	I.
1546	Kath., w. of R. Barfott, ch. ins., Lambourne, Essex . . .	I.
1546	Anne Bonde, w. of W. Thynne, ins., All Hallows, Barking, London	X.
1546	Margt. Fowler, w. of H. Savill, ins., St. Mary, Islington, London .	II.
1546	Margt. Canon, w. of J. Gille, ch. ins., Wyddial, Herts. . .	II.
1547	Elizth., dau. of Edm., Lord Bray, w. of Sir R. Verney, ch., Aldbury, Herts.	II.
1547	Elizth. Faggar, Elizth. Nevyle, Jane Ascheburnham, ws. of R. Covert, kng. ins., Slaugham, Suss. R.	II.
1548	Margt. Tame, w. of Sir H. Stafford, ch. ins., Blatherwyck, Northants	II.
1548	Anne, w. of J. Latton, ch. ins., Blewbury, Berks. . . .	VI.
1549	Dame Brygete, w. of T. Fyndorne and John, Lord Marnay, ins., Little Horkesley, Essex. PLATE 33	IV.
1549	Isabel and Agnes, ws. of W. Hyll, ch. ins., Solihull, Warw. . .	I.
1550	Mary Fitzwilliams, w. of J. Shelley, ch. kng. ins., Clapham, Suss. .	V.
c. 1550	Anon., ch., Margaretting, Essex	I.
1551	Elizth., w. of T. Grenewey, ins., Dinton, Bucks. . . .	IV.
1551	Joan Tylney, w. of R. Grenewey, ins., Dinton, Bucks. . .	V.
1551	Anne Blenerhaysett, w. of G. Duke, ins., Frenze, Norf. . .	VII.
1552	Anne Browne, w. of R. Fermer, ins., Easton Neston, Northants .	I.
1552	Elizth. Norrysse, w. of W. Fermoure, ins., Somerton, Oxon. .	I.
1553	Elizth. Savage and Philippa Wilford, ws. of Sir J. Hampden, ch. ins., Great Hampden, Bucks.	II.
1553	Alice, w. of W. Coke, ch. ins., Milton, Cambs. . . .	I.
1554	Jane Downe, w. of W. Foxe, ch. ins., Ludford, Hereford PLATE 34	I.
1554	Kath. Cheyne, w. of C. Lytkott, ch. ins., Swallowfield, Berks. .	II.
1554	Joan Iden, w. of E. Shelley, ch. kng. ins., Warminghurst, Suss. .	I.
1555	Lady Jane Guyldeford, w. of John Dudley, Duke of Northumberland, ins., Chelsea, Middx.	I.
1555	Anon., w. of P. Dormer, ch. ins., Newbottle, Northants . .	I.
1556	Joan Gascoyne, w. of R. Bulkeley, ch. kng. ins., Cople, Beds. .	VII.
1557	Elizth. Giffard and Dorothy Fitzherbert, ws. of Sir J. Porte, ch. kng. ins., Etwall, Derb. Armf.	II.
1557	Jane Seymour and Elizth. Sothill, ws. of Sir W. Drury, ins., Hawstead, Suff.	VI.
1557	Malyn, w. of T. Harte, ins., Lydd, Kent	VI.
1557	Jane Ingleton, w. of A. Seynct Johns, ins., Thornton, Bucks. .	II.

Date.	Name, Description, Place and Emblems, etc.	M.S.
1557	Elizth. and Dorothy, ws. of W. Myddilton, ins., Westerham, Kent .	VI.
1558	Elizth. Covert, w. of Sir W. Goringe, kng. ins., Burton, Suss. (In tabard.)	II.
1558	Anne Newdegate, w. of W. Gardyner, ch. ins., Chalfont St Giles, Bucks.	VII.
1558	Elizth. Lovett, w. of A. Cave, ins., Chichley, Bucks. . . .	I.
1558	Mary Honewood, w. of V. Boys, ins., Goodnestone-next-Wingham, Kent	III.
1558	Elizth., w. of T. Engeham, ch. ins., Goodnestone-next-Wingham, Kent	IV.
1558	Joan Fenner, w. of E. Shurley, ins., Isfield, Suss. . . .	II.
1558	Isabel Montgomery, w. of Sir H. Sacheverell, ins., Morley, Derb.	IX.
1558	Elizth., w. of R. Rugge, ch. br. ins., St. John Maddermarket, Norwich. PLATE 45	X.
1558	Elizth., w. of E. Crane, ins., Stratford St. Mary, Suff. . .	I.
1558	Elizth. Watno and Margt., ws. of T. Harlakynden, ch. kng. ins., Woodchurch, Kent	III.
1559	Julyan Salford, w. of E. Forde, ch. kng. ins., Thames Ditton, Surr.	I.
1559	Philipe Bedingfield, w. of T. Darcy, ins., Tolleshunt Darcy, Essex	V.
1560	Alice, w. of J. Colby, ch. ins., Brundish, Suff. . . .	III.
1560	Elizth. Stokys, ins., Eton Coll., Bucks.	XIII.
1560	Susan, w. of J. Gyfforde, ch. ins., Northolt, Middx. . .	II.
1560	Anne, w. of Sir R. Rede, ch. kng., Redbourn, Herts. . .	III.
1560	Margt., w. of R. Coton, ins., Whittington, Glos. . . .	I.
c. 1560	Elizth. Jenney, w. of R. Lytleburye, ch. ins., Ashby Puerorum, Lincs.	I.
c. 1560	Margt. Plompton, w. of Sir A. Eyre, kng. ins., Hathersage, Derb. Armf.	IV.
c. 1560	Agnes Woodthorpe, w. of A. Dister, ch. kng. ins., Lavenham, Suff.	II.
c. 1560	Martha Olyff, w. of R. Butler, ins., North Mimms, Herts. .	V.
c. 1560	Anon., Snettisham, Norf.	I.
c. 1560	Anon., kng., Southminster, Essex	II.
1561	Anne Drury, w. of C. Heydon, kng. ins., Baconsthorpe, Norf. Armf.	III.
1561	Joan and Bridget, ws. of R. Poynard, ch. ins., Barkway, Herts. .	I.
1561	Barbara Hanchett, ins., Braughing, Herts.	III.
1561	Margt. Blenerhaiset, w. of J. Eyer, kng. ins., Narborough, Norf.	VI.
1562	Margery Cater, w. of W. Hyde, ch. ins., Denchworth, Berks. .	III.
1562	Marie, Eme, Margt., Jane, ws. of A. Dericote, kng. ins., Hackney, London	III.
1562	Edeth Unton, w. of Sir J. Russell, kng. ins., Strensham, Worc. Armf.	IV.
1562	Mary Danet, w. of G. Medeley, ch. ins., Tilty, Essex . .	III.
1563	Dame Margt. Berney, w. of Sir W. Damsell, ins., Beckenham, Kent	II.

Date.	Name, Description, Place and Emblems, etc.	M.S.
1563	Cecyle Waulton, w. of N. Luke, ch. kng. ins., Cople, Beds.	VIII.
1563	Mary Gedge, w. of L. Berners, Fryerning, Essex	I.
1564	Joan Lee, ins., Eastwick, Herts.	I.
1564	Margt. Charlton, w. of A. Chambre, ins., Myddle, Salop	I.
1565	Cisley Kempe, w. of J. Toke, ch. ins., Great Chart, Kent	VI.
1565	Alice, w. of H. Toolye, ch. kng. ins., St. Mary Quay, Ipswich	II.
1565	Kath., w. of E. Stacy, ch. kng. ins., Waltham Abbey, Essex	I.
1566	Margt. Jonson, w. of J. Mayne, ch. kng. ins., Biddenden, Kent	II.
1566	Joan Eppes, w. of P. Godfrye, ins., Lydd, Kent	VII.
1566	Jone and Alice, ws. of W. Stace, ch. ins., Westerham, Kent	VIII.
1567	Alice Essex, w. of W. Hyde, ins., Denchworth, Berks.	IV.
1567	Elizth. Jenour, w. of R. Codington, ch. kng. ins., Ixworth, Suff.	I.
1567	Elizth. Parke, w. of J. Roper, ch. ins., Lynsted, Kent	I.
1567	Anon., w. of T. Noke, ch. ins., Shottesbrooke, Berks. PLATE 45	V.
1568	Mabel Staverton, w. of N. Williams, ins., Burghfield, Berks.	I.
1568	Margt., w. of E. Hunt, ch. kng. ins., Hindolvestone, Norf.	III.
1568	Eleanor Radcliffe and Eleanor Maghull, ws. of Sir R. Molyneux, ch. ins., Sefton, Lancs.	III.
1570	Anne Honings and Anne Waldegrave, ws. of Sir C. Heigham, ch. kng. ins., Barrow, Suff.	II.
1570	Elizth. Draper, w. of J. Bowyar, ch. kng. ins., Camberwell, Surr.	V.
1570	Barbara Francis and Brigett Springe, ws. of T. Fletewoode, ch. kng. ins., Chalfont St. Giles, Bucks.	VIII.
1570	Cecily Ashfield, w. of Sir J. Fortescue, ins., Mursley, Bucks.	I.
1570	Anne Wylford, w. of J. Webbe, ch. ins., St. Thomas, Salisbury	I.
1570	Anon., w. of J. Carre, ins., Stondon Massey, Essex	I.
1570	Margt. Buryngton, ins., Streatley, Berks.	II.
c. 1570	Emme Fox, ch. ins., Aldeburgh, Suff.	III.
c. 1570	Jane Rugge and Elizth. Clifton, ws. of Sir W. Molineux, ins., Sefton, Lancs.	II.
c. 1570	Anon. (fragment), Little Wittenham, Berks. Now lost.	
1571	Grace Johnson, w. of W. Cressye, ins., Harpenden, Herts.	II.
1571	Avice Bodie, w. of T. Tyndall, ins., Thornbury, Glos.	I.
1571	Elizth., dau. of Lord Hussey, w. of Sir R. Throkmarton, ch. ins., Weston Underwood, Bucks.	II.
1572	Jane Brouncker, w. of R. Jenyns, ins., Churchill, Som.	I.
1572	Anne Williams, w. of A. Forster, kng. ins., Cumnor, Berks.	I.
1572	Anon., w. of J. Alleyn, ch. kng. ins., Hatfield Peverell, Essex	II.
1572	Elizth. Love, w. of S. Parret, ch. kng. ins., St. Peter-in-the-East, Oxford	III.
1572	Anne Danvers, kng. ins. Locality unknown.	
1573	Margt. Leeder, w. of Sir W. Harper, ins., St. Paul, Bedford.	I.
1573	Alse, w. of T. Byng and J. Canceller, ch. ins., Boreham, Essex	I.
1573	Kath. Nevell, w. of C. Throkmorton, ch. ins., Haseley, Warw.	I.

Date.	Name, Description, Place and Emblems, etc.	M.S.
1573	Anon., w. of R. Holingworth, ins., Stondon Massey, Essex	II.
1573	Jone, w. of T. Oken, ins., St. Mary, Warwick	II.
1574	Mary Hyde, w. of R. Payton, ins., Isleham, Cambs.	XI.
1574	— and Annes, ws. of R. Atkinson, ch. ins., St. Peter-in-the-East, Oxford	IV.
1574	Margt. Revett, w. of E. Chapman, ch. kng. ins., Sibton, Suff.	III.
1574	Agnes and Joan, ws. of V. Edvarod, ch. ins., St. Nicholas-at-Wade, Thanet	I.
1575	Dorothy Lock, w. of J. Cosowarth, ch. ins., Colan, Cornw.	II.
1575	Jane Dryhurst, w. of R. Middleton, ch. ins., Whitchurch, Denbigh	I.
1575	Dame Margt. Nevyll, w. of W. Plumbe, hf-eff. ins., Wyddial, Herts.	IV.
1576	Elizth., w. of T. Higate, ch. ins., Hayes, Middx.	IV.
1576	Amphelice Chamberlin, w. of R. Faldo, ch. ins., Maulden, Beds.	I.
1576	Susan Cooke, w. of E. Tyrell, kng. ins., Rawreth, Essex. (Upper half of w. restored in 1882.)	II.
1576	Magdalen, w. of T. Colte, ch. kng. ins., Waltham Abbey, Essex	II.
1576	Margt. Barley, w. of E. Bell, ch. ins., Writtle, Essex	VII.
1577	Sence Blackwell, w. of M. Draper, kng. ins., Camberwell, Surr.	VI.
1577	Mary Babham, w. of R. More, ins., Cookham, Berks.	VII.
1577	Kath. Wyllyams, w. of Hen. Staverton, ch. ins., Cumnor, Berks.	II.
1577	Dorothy Roberds, w. (1) of Allen Horde, (2) of Sir L. Taylare, ch. ins., Ewell, Surr.	VI.
1577	Anne Blenerhayset, w. of P. Rede, ins., St. Margaret, Norwich	I.
1577	Isabel Curson, w. of E. Hampdyn, Stoke Poges, Bucks.	III.
1578	Anne Byll, w. of W. Bramfeld, ins., Clothall, Herts.	IV.
1578	Jane Poulton, w. of H. Bradbuirye, ins., Littlebury, Essex	VI.
1578	Margt. Skipwith, w. of H. Cheyne, King's Langley, Herts.	II.
1578	Margt. Joiner, w. of W. Disney ; Nele Hussey and Jane Ayscough, ws. of R. Disney, hf-effs. ins., Norton Disney, Lincs.	I.
1578	Thomazin Tyrrell, w. of W. Playters, ch. ins., Sotterley, Suff.	VII.
1578	Jane, w. of T. Fige, ch. ins., Winslow, Bucks.	I.
1578	Elizth. Morflett, w. of A. Smith, ins., Yateley, Hants	IV.
1579	Isabell Smethelaye, w. of C. Estoft, ins., Bishop Burton, Yorks.	III.
1579	Anne Warburton, w. of Sir E. Fiton, ch. ins., St. Patrick's Cathedral, Dublin	III.
1579	Awdrey, w. of W. Wightman, ins., Harrow, Middx.	IX.
1579	Anon., w. of D. Saunders, ins., Hillingdon, Middx.	VI.
1579	Anne Pelham, w. of T. Shurley, ins., Isfield, Suss.	III.
1579	Mary Mayne, w. of H. Clarke, ch. ins., Kingsnorth, Kent.	II.
1579	Beatrys Gybbone, w. of W. Gresham, ch. kng. ins., Titsey, Surr.	I.
1580	Alice Cobbe, w. of J. Cobham *alias* Brook, ch. ins., Newington-next-Sittingbourne, Kent	III.

Date.	Name, Description, Place and Emblems, etc.	M.S.
1580	Elizth. Cotton and Mary Blenerhaysett, ws. of F. Bacon, ins., Petistree, Suff.	I.
1580	Julyan Polsted, w. of C. Blakeden and J. Boothe, ch. ins., Thames Ditton, Surr.	II.
1580	Anon., w. of T. Wyseman, ch. ins., Great Waltham, Essex	I.
c. 1580	Anon., w. of J. Norden, ch. ins., Rainham, Kent	VI.
1581	Elizth. Blundell and Jane Wodfoorde, ws. of J. Brinckhurst, ins., Bisham, Berks.	IV.
1581	Anon., w. of T. Eyer, ch. ins., Burnham, Bucks.	VI.
1581	Joan Glinton, w. of J. Good, ch. ins., West Drayton, Middx.	V.
1581	John Browne, ch. hf-eff. ins., Halesworth, Suff.	III.
1581	Mary Barrentyne, w. of A. Huddleston, ch. ins., Great Haseley, Oxon.	V.
1581	Anon., ws. (2) of F. Holbrok, ch. ins., Newington-next-Sittingbourne, Kent	IV.
1582	Mary, w. of C. Newce, ch. ins., Great Hadham, Herts.	V.
1582	Jane, w. of E. Bugge, ch. ins., Harlow, Essex	VI.
1582	Margt. Tate and Anne Carlton, ws. of R. Lytton, ins., Knebworth, Herts.	III.
1582	Julyan, w. of J. Chapman, ch. ins., Sibton, Suff.	IV.
1582	Elizth. Lyne, w. of W. Holt, ch. kng. ins., Stoke Lyne, Oxon.	II.
1582	Anne Wheeler, w. of J. Polsted, ch. kng. ins., Thames Ditton, Surr.	III.
1583	Elizth. Parry, w. of H. Raynsford, ch. ins., Clifford Chambers, Glos.	I.
1583	Anne Gould, w. of W. Strachleigh, ch. kng. ins., Ermington, Devon	I.
1583	Ales and Julyan, ws. of J. Tye, ch. ins., St. Clement, Ipswich	I.
1583	— Merell, St. Mary Quay, Ipswich	III.
1583	Ciselye, w. of E. Goodman, ch. kng. ins., Ruthin, Denbigh.	II.
1583	Elynor Hearnden, w. of J. Allen, ins., Shorne, Kent	VII.
1583	Annes Welche, w. of E. Humbarstone, ch. ins., Walkern, Herts.	III.
1584	Anon., w. of R. Mariott, ch. ins., Ashton, Northants	I.
1584	Alis Walker, ch. kng. ins., Barford St. Martin, Wilts.	I.
1584	Julian and Anne, ws. of W. Boddindam, ch. ins., Biddenden, Kent	IV.
1584	Als Lehunte, w. of J. Daye, ch. kng. ins., Little Bradley, Suff.	III.
1584	Dorothy, w. of R. Makepeace, ch. ins., Chipping Warden, Northants	II.
1584	Ales Maynarde, ins., St. James, Colchester	II.
1584	Agnes Bussey and Aubrey Fernley, ws. of Sir E. Brudenell, ch. hf-eff. ins., Dene, Northants	I.
1584	Ellen Say, w. of E. Shoreditch, ch. ins., Ickenham, Middx.	III.
1584	Ellyne, w. of J. Orgone, ins., St. Olave, Hart Street, London	III.
1584	Malin Boys, ch. kng. ins., St. Mary the Virgin, Oxford	IV.

Date.	Name, Description, Place and Emblems, etc.	M.S.
1584	Anne Shelton, w. of W. Napper, ch. kng. ins., Stanford Rivers, Essex	V.
1584	Anne Hawkins, w. of E. Wiseman, ch. ins., Steventon, Berks. .	II.
1584	Elizth. Glascock, w. of J. Wyseman, ch. kng. ins., Stisted, Essex .	I. —
1584	Philippe Wheatley and Joan Starkey, ws. of J. Rochester, ch. kng. ins., Terling, Essex	III.
c. 1584	Joan Newton, w. of W. Rochester, ch. kng. ins., Terling, Essex .	II.
1585	Frances Tey and Mary Payne, ws. of E. Bockinge, ch. ins., Ash Bocking, Suff.	I.
1585	Anne Etton, w. of J. Copledike, kng. ins., Harrington, Lincs. .	III.
1585	Elizth. Tuthill, w. of R. Dalyson, ins., Trowse, Norf. . .	II.
1585	Frauncys Welles and Fayth Patenson, ws. of E. Roberts, ch. ins., Willesden, Middx.	IV.
c. 1585	Anon., Harlow, Essex	VII.
c. 1585	? Eleanor Agar, Putney, Surr.	III.
1586	Elizth. Fitzwilliam, w. of Sir T. Brudenell, ins., Dene, Northants	II. —
1586	Anne Fermour and Jane Cocket, ws. of W. Yelverton, ch., Rougham, Norf.	V. —
1586	Anon., w. of T. Inwood, ch. kng. ins., Weybridge, Surr. PLATE 46	II.
1587	Winifred Thorold, w. of G. Clifton, ins., Clifton, Notts. . .	III. —
1587	Margt. Forster, w. of E. Sulyard, kng. ins., Runwell, Essex .	I.
1587	Jane Quilter, w. of M. Frauncis, ch. ins., St. Martin, Canterbury	II.
1587	Kath. Blounte, w. of R. Smythe, ch. kng. ins., and Elizth. Smythe, w. of W. Notte, ch. kng. ins., Thames Ditton, Surr. .	IV.
1587	Margery, w. of R. Woddomes, ch. ins., Ufton, Warw. . .	I.
1587	Susan, w. of J. Selwyn, ch. ins., Walton-on-Thames, Surr. .	I.
1587	Alice Haselwood, w. of E. Greneville, ins., Wotton Underwood, Bucks.	I.
1588	Dorothy Barlee, w. of T. Leventhorpe, ch. ins., Albury, Herts. .	III.
1588	Elizth. Spring, w. of E. Fludd, Great Cressingham, Norf. . .	IV. —
1588	Alice Barlee, w. of W. Tooke, ch. kng. ins., Essendon, Herts. .	II.
1588	Anon., w. of J. Carter, ch. ins., King's Langley, Herts. . .	III.
1588	— Porter, w. of — Hale, ins., Walthamstow, Essex . . .	IV.
1589	Margt., w. of E. Daniel, ch. ins., Acton, Suff. . . .	IV.
1589	Elizth. King, w. of S. Fynche, ins., Croydon, Surr. Now lost.	
1589	Mary Huddye, w. of T. Carewe, ins., Haccombe, Devon . .	III.
1589	Jane Burington, w. of J. Eyston, ch. ins., East Hendred, Berks. .	III.
1589	Elizth. Dinn, w. of J. Stanley, ch. ins., Roydon, Essex . .	IV.
1589	Elizth. Snapp, w. of J. Pettie, ins., Stoke Talmage, Oxon. . .	II.
1590	Elizth. Comfort, w. of T. Alfraye, ins., Battle, Suss. . .	V.
1590	Elizth. Yorke, w. of W. Butler, ins., Coates-by-Stow, Lincs. .	II.
1590	Elizth. and Anne, ws. of W. Death, ch. ins., Dartford, Kent .	IX.
1590	Anne Tebolde, w. of T. Nevynson, ins., Eastry, Kent . .	I.
1590	Annes Walker, w. of W. Osborne, ch. ins., North Fambridge, Essex	I.

Date.	Name, Description, Place and Emblems, etc.	M.S.
1590	Alice, w. of P. Williams, kng. ins., Matherne, Mon.	I.
1590	Anon., ws. (3) of T. Hendley, ch. kng. ins., Otham, Kent	I.
1590	Isabel Seilearde, w. of J. Cheke, ch. ins., Thames Ditton, Surr.	V.
1590	Margt. Tuke, ch. kng. ins., Tilty, Essex	IV.
1590	Anne Sibell, w. of L. Hyde, ch. kng. ins., Tisbury, Wilts.	II.
1590	Avis and Elizth., ws. of A. Staples, ch. ins., Yate, Glos.	I.
c. 1590	Anon., hf-eff., Dartford, Kent	VIII.
c. 1590	Elenor Ashefield, w. of J. Walsingham, ins., Exhall, Warw.	I.
c. 1590	Anon., Lydd, Kent	X.
c. 1590	Anon., ins., Tunstall, Kent	IV.
1591	Florence Chernocke, w. of C. Petit, ins., Boughton-under-Blean, Kent	IV.
1591	Ursula Danvers, w. of T. Welbore, ch. kng. ins., Clavering, Essex	III.
1591	Anne, w. of T. Drywood, ch. ins., Hornchurch, Essex	VIII.
1591	Elizth., w. of J. Coe, ch. ins., Orford, Suff.	X.
1591	Grace Cawsen, w. of R. Cotton, ch. kng. ins., Richmond, Surr.	I.
1592	Anon., w. of J. Scrogs, ch. ins., Albury, Herts.	IV.
1592	Kath. Willington, w. of A. Throckmorton, ch. ins., Chastleton, Oxon.	I.
1592	Marie, w. of J. Revers, ch. ins., Chattisham, Suff.	I.
1592	Joan Brodnax, ins., Cheriton, Kent	III.
1592	Alice, w. of W. Bradbridge, ch. kng. ins., Chichester Cathedral	III.
1592	Mary Stephens, w. of F. Rutland, ins., Chiselden, Wilts.	I.
1592	Elinor Lovell, w. of J. Shellie, ch. kng. ins., Clapham, Suss.	VI.
1592	Wenefrid Sankye, w. of J. Pigott, ins., Edlesborough, Bucks.	II.
1592	Joan, w. of W. Smith, ins., Enfield, Middx.	III.
1592	Margery Welsborne, w. of J. Ayshcombe, ch. ins., West Hanney, Berks.	III.
1592	Anon., w. of J. Lyon, ins., Harrow, Middx.	X.
1592	Fraunces Bray, w. of T. Lyfelde, ch. kng. ins., Stoke d'Abernon, Surr.	VII.
1592	Elizth. Conquest, w. of P. Kinge, ch. kng. ins., Worminghall, Bucks.	I.
1592	Rose Redding, w. of W. Pinchon, ch., Writtle, Essex	VIII.
1593	Helen, Joan and Thomasin, ws. of R. Allarde, ch. ins., Biddenden, Kent	V.
1593	Jane Thornell, w. of P. Bell, ins., Hartlepool, Durham	I.
1593	Anon., ws. (2) of A. Pennyng, ins., Kettleburgh, Suff.	I.
1593	Elizth. and Ann, ws. of S. Burton, ch. kng. ins., St Andrew Undershaft, London	II.
1593	Elizth. Bardolfe and Anne Gower, ws. of G. Rotherham, ch. ins., Luton, Beds.	XIV.
1593	Joan and Alice, ws. of T. Beale, ch. ins., All Saints, Maidstone. PLATE 46	I.

Date.	Name, Description, Place and Emblems, etc.	M.S.
1593	Lettice Barnarde, ch. kng. ins., Newnham Murren, Oxon.	I.
1593	Elizth. Chester, Quainton, Bucks.	VI.
1593	Phillipa Robertes, w. of C. Dawbeney, ch. kng. ins., Sharrington, Norf.	VII.
1593	Joan, w. of — Day, Victoria and Albert Museum. (Deposited on loan by the vicar and churchwardens of Clavering, Essex.)	IX.
1594	Eleanor, w. of N. Grobham, ch. kng. ins., Bishop's Lydiard, Som.	I.
1594	Julian Ellis, w. of J. Clippesby, ch. ins., Clippesby, Norf.	III.
1594	Mary Hinton, ch. kng. ins., St. Michael, Coventry	I.
1594	Alice Bybsworth, w. of R. Hughes, ch. kng. ins., Ippolyts, Herts.	II.
1594	Anne Faldo, kng. ins., Maulden, Beds.	II.
1595	Owner, w. of J. Fortescue, ins., East Allington, Devon	III.
1595	Elizth. Littleton and Margt. Copley, ws. of J. Gage, ins., West Firle, Suss.	VI.
1595	Margt. Shellie, w. of E. Gage, ch. kng. ins., Framfield, Suss.	I.
1595	Elizth. Batherst, w. of J. Browne, ins., Horton Kirby, Kent	III.
1595	Anon., w. of F. Yerburgh, Northorpe, Lincs.	I.
c. 1595	Elizth. Parker, w. of Sir E. Gage, ins., West Firle, Suss.	III.
c. 1595	Elizth. Guldeford, w. of T. Gage, ch. ins., West Firle, Suss.	IV.
c. 1595	Anne Clere, w. of N. Garneys, ch. kng. ins., Ringsfield, Suff. Armf. (A copy of the brass at Kenton, Suff., to John Garneys, 1524.)	I.
1596	Elizth. Mey, w. of J. Tedcastell, ch. ins., Barking, Essex	V.
1596	Winefrid Say, w. of K. Cheseldyn, ins., Braunston, Rutland	I.
1596	Anne, w. of G. Lloyd, ch. ins., Chevening, Kent	II.
1596	Mary Goodwyn, w. of R. Rust, Necton, Norf. PLATE 51	VII.
1597	Elizth. Lambert, w. of E. Slyfeld, ins., Great Bookham, Surr.	IV.
1597	Anon., ws. (2) of J. Whithead, ch. kng. ins., Holy Trinity, Coventry	I.
1597 ?	Winifrid, sister of J. Browne, ins., St. John Sepulchre, Norwich	III.
1597	Ursula, w. of J. Pen, ch. ins., Penn, Bucks.	II.
1597	Margt. Pyckeringe, w. of T. Lovell, ch. kng. ins., Johnson Hospital, Spalding, Lincs.	I.
1597	Margt., w. of T. Cole, ch. kng. ins., St. Margaret, Westminster	I.
1597	Anne, w. of G. Brigge, ins., Wiveton, Norf.	III.
1598	Eden Truelove, w. of J. Baker, ins., Angmering, Suss.	I.
1598	Dorothy Jermine, w. of E. Duke, ch. ins., Benhall, Suff.	II.
1598	Elizth. Buckfold, w. of H. Slyfield, ch. ins., Great Bookham, Surr.	V.
1598	Elizth. Lygon, w. of W. Norwoodd, ch. kng. ins., Leckhampton, Glos.	I.
1598	Joan Hurste, w. of W. Manwayringe and H. Bradshawe, ch. kng. ins., Noke, Oxon.	I.
1598	Anne Sackville, w. of R. Fogg, ch. kng. ins., Tilmanstone, Kent	I.
1598	Jane Gibbs, w. of N. Browne, hf-eff. ins., Tysoe, Warw.	II.

Date.	Name, Description, Place and Emblems, etc.	M.S.
1598	Adrye Streete and Elizth. Notte, ws. of J. Woulde, ch. ins., Weybridge, Surr.	III.
1598	Angelett Woodliffe, w. of W. Tooke, ch. ins., Wormley, Herts.	IV.
1599	Alice Boggis, w. of W. Wade, ch. ins., Bildeston, Suff.	I.
1599	Margt., w. of R. Higham, ch. ins., Cowlinge, Suff.	I.
1599	Yedythe Wyllyams, w. of — Stavertoon, ins., Cumnor, Berks.	III.
1599	Kath., w. of T. Palmer, ch. kng. ins., Ewelme, Oxon.	XVI.
1599	Margt., w. of J. Jennens, ch. ins., Harwell, Berks.	I.
1599	Ellen Reresby, w. of M. Tirwhit, ch. kng. ins., Scotter, Lincs.	I.
1599	Cecil Croke, w. of E. Bulstrode, ch. ins., Upton, Bucks. PLATE 36	III. —
1600	Margt. Mills and Elizth. Watson, ws. of R. Thornhill, ch. ins., Bromley, Kent	III.
1600	Lady Brooke, ch. kng. ins., Kirkby Moorside, Yorks.	I.
1600	Elizth. Barton, w. of T. Clarke, ch. ins., Streatley, Berks. Now under floor.	
c. 1600	Margt., w. of J. Martin, ins., Barton, Cambs.	I.
c. 1600	Anon., ch., Goring, Oxon.	III.
c. 1600	Anon., Harrow, Middx. PLATE 47	XI.
c. 1600	Anon., St. Nicholas, Ipswich	III.
c. 1600	Margt. Germin, w. of E. Wollaye, ins., Latton, Essex	III.
c. 1600	Anne, w. of M. Englishe, and Anne Englishe, w. of J. Gyfford, ch. ins., Ludgershall, Bucks.	I.
c. 1600	Mary Hudsoun, w. of W. Bussie, ins., St. Peter Mancroft, Norwich. Now lost.	
c. 1600	Elizth. Barley, w. of E. Leventhorpe, ins., Sawbridgeworth, Herts.	VIII.
c. 1600	Mary Parker, w. of E. Leventhorpe, ins., Sawbridgeworth, Herts.	IX.
c. 1600	Anon., Slinfold, Suss.	II.

17TH CENTURY

1601	Mary Tirrell, w. of P. Heyman, ins., Acrise, Kent	I. —
1601	Joan, w. of J. James, ch. ins., Aldeburgh, Suff.	IV.
1601	Anne Yewe, w. of G. Longe, ch. ins., Bradford-on-Avon, Wilts.	II.
1601	Elizth. Raynsford, w. of E. Marrowe, ch. ins., Clifford Chambers, Glos.	II.
1601	Elizth. Vaux, w. of H. Bowyer, ch. kng. ins., Cuckfield, Suss.	IV. —
1601	Radcliff Gerrarde, w. of T. Wingfield, ins., Easton, Suff.	III.
1601	Anne Covert, w. of W. Bartelot, ins., Stopham, Suss.	V. —
1602	Mercy Hendley, w. of C. Septvans, ins., Ash-next-Sandwich, Kent	VI.
1602	Douglas Tirrwhit, w. of C. Butler, ch. kng. ins., Coates-by-Stow, Lincs.	III. —
1602	Anon., ws. (2) of J. Fosbroke, ins., Cranford St. Andrew, Northants	II.
1602	Alice and Eleanor Stafford, ws. of F. Wellesborne, ch. ins., West Hanney, Berks.	V.
1602	Kath. Butler, w. of J. Browne, ch. ins., Higham Gobion, Beds.	I.

Date.	Name, Description, Place and Emblems, etc.	M.S.
1602	— Drywoode, ins. Hornchurch, Essex	X.
1602	Margt. Barker, ins., South Ockendon, Essex	IV.
1602	Elizth. Cage, w. of J. Parker, ins., Radwell, Herts. . . .	III.
1602	Alice Lanyon, w. of J. Rashleigh, ins., Fowey, Cornw. . .	IV.
1603	Margt. Hyde, w. of R. Mohun, ch. kng. ins., Fleet, Dorset .	I.
1603	Susan Partheriche, ch. kng. ins., Harrietsham, Kent . . .	I.
1603	Alice, w. of J. Sankey, ins., Harrow, Middx. . . .	XII.
1603	Jane Butler, w. of E. Cason, ch. ins., Higham Gobion, Beds. .	II.
1603	Jane Godolphin, w. of J. Bassett, ch. ins., Illogan, Cornw. . .	I.
1603	Joan Wier, w. of T. Buriton, ins., Streatley, Berks. . . .	IV.
1603	Elizth. Twyne, w. of R. Brooke, ch. ins., Whitchurch, Hants. .	I.
1604	Anon., w. of T. Hone, ch. ins., Hornchurch, Essex . . .	XI.
1604	Dorothy Rodney, w. of R. Davies, ch. ins., Backwell, Som. .	I.
1604	Martha Hammond and Sara Boys, ws. of J. Sea, ins., Herne, Kent.	
	PLATE 48	IX.
1604	Martha, w. of J. Knapp, ch. ins., St. Peter, Ipswich . . .	I.
1604	Frances Roberts, w. of R. Frankelin, ch. ins., Latton, Essex .	IV.
1604	Margt. Tanfield, w. of M. Tresham, ins., Newton-by-Geddington,	
	Northants	II.
1604	Rachel White, w. of R. Manning, ins., St. Mary Cray, Kent .	III.
1604	Frideswide Gilbert, ins., Youlgreave, Derb.	I.
1605	Jane Colte, w. of J. Le Hunt, ins., Little Bradley, Suff. . .	IV.
1605	Aphra Norton, w. of H. Hawkins, ins., Fordwich, Kent . .	II.
1605	Bridgett Smith, w. of R. Coverdall and R. Bence, ch. ins., Orford,	
	Suff.	XI.
1605	Margt. Buriton, w. of T. Bennet, ins., Westbury, Wilts. . .	I.
1606	Mary Blome, w. of W. Bence, ins., Aldeburgh, Suff. . .	V.
1606	Ursula, w. of R. Stocker, ch. ins., Basingstoke, Hants. . .	II.
1606	Anon., w. of J. Brudenell, ins., Dene, Northants . . .	III.
1606	Alice Penhellick, w. of J. Bougins, ch., Helston, Cornw. . .	II.
1606	Mary Clare, w. of E. West, ch. ins., Marsworth, Bucks. . .	IV.
1606	Anne, w. of R. Curthoyse, ins., Stilton, Hunts. . . .	II.
1606	Barbara Simonds, w. of R. Eliot, ch. ins., Sutton Coldfield, Warw. .	I.
1606	Elizth. Coke and dau. Elizth. Wilde, ins., Great Totham, Essex .	I.
1606	Alice Chubnoll, w. of R. Bernard, ins., Turvey, Beds. . .	IV.
1606	Anon., w. of E. Hunt, kng. ins., Writtle, Essex . . .	IX.
1607	Jane and Alice, ws. of T. Cogdell, ins., Abbot's Langley, Herts. .	II.
1607	Anne Aldersey, w. of T. Thompson, ch. ins., Berden, Essex .	II.
1607	Elizth. Vanburen, w. of J. Verzelini, ch. ins., Downe, Kent.	
	PLATE 48	IV.
1607	Margt. Playters, w. of A. Chewt, ins., Ellough, Suff. . .	IV.
1607	Alice, w. of A. Mosley, ch. kng. ins., Manchester Cathedral .	VI.
1607	Elizth. North, w. of J. Bannister, ch. ins., Netteswell, Essex .	II.
1607	Joan Gowlshull, w. of J. Dowman, ch. ins., Newnham, Herts. .	II.

H

Date.	Name, Description, Place and Emblems, etc.	M.S.
1608	— Heydock, ch. ins., Broad Blunsden Wilts.	I.
1608	Agnes Bigge, dau. of T. Rogerson, ins., Ingoldisthorpe, Norf. .	I.
1608	Kath., w. of G. Nightingale, ins., Newport, Essex . . .	II.
1608	Margt. Carr, w. of J. Lambert, kng. ins., Pinchbeck, Lincs. . .	I.
1608	Elizth., w. of R. Geale, ch. ins., Sandhurst, Berks. . . .	I.
1609	Joan Ayleway, w. of R. Pyrke, ch. ins., Abbenhall, Glos. . .	I.
1609	Judith Boddendam and Anne Austen, ws. of J. Seyliard, ch. ins., Biddenden, Kent	VIII.
1609	Elizth. Garnett, w. of E. Collen, kng. ins., Cheshunt, Herts. .	VI.
1609	Anne Sewell, kng. ins., St. Michael, Coventry . . .	II.
1609	Francis Drury, w. of J. Hobart, ins., Lodden, Norf. . .	IX.
1609	Mary Hungerford, w. of N. Poulett, ch. kng., Minety, Wilts. .	I.
1609	Jane Barne, ch. ins., Willesden, Middx.	V.
1610	Sessely Brownesopp, w. of A. Page, kng. ins., Bray, Berks. .	X.
1610	Dorcas Bigg, w. of T. Musgrave, ch. ins., Cressing, Essex . .	I.
1610	Hester Neve, ins., East Ham, Essex	II.
1610	Mary, w. of T. Smyth, ch. ins., New Romney, Kent . . .	III.
1610	Anne, w. of J. Cremer, ch. ins., Snettisham, Norf. . . .	II.
1610	Kath. Hennage, w. of W. Ayscugh, ch. ins., Stallingborough, Lincs.	II.
1610	Mary Gaudy, w. of I. Wyncoll, ch. ins., Twinstead, Essex . .	I.
1610 ?	Anon., w. of C. Dawbnie, kng. ins., Wokingham, Berks. . .	II.
c. 1610	Anon., Felmersham, Beds.	I.
1611	Elizth. Coltrop, w. of A. Duke, ins., Benhall, Suff. . . .	III.
1611	Elizth. May, w. of L. Farrington, ch. ins., Bredfield, Suff. . .	I.
1611	Elizth. Hobart and Mary Brudenell, ws. of M. Hare, ins., Bruisyard, Suff.	I.
1611	Elizth. Hill, w. of J. Carewe, ins., Haccombe, Devon . .	IV.
1611	Martha Yeate, w. of O. Ayshcombe, ch. ins., West Hanney, Berks.	VI.
1611	Anne, w. of J. Uvedall, ch. ins., Great Linford, Bucks. . .	III.
1611	Ann Carthright, w. of W. Clerke, ch. ins., Wrotham, Kent .	VII.
1612	Elizth. Alington, w. of T. Soame, ch. kng. ins., Little Bradley, Suff.	V.
1612	Anne, w. of W. Mawnde, ins., Chesterton, Oxon. . . .	I.
1612	Frances Rogers, w. of A. Bostocke, ins., Dartford, Kent . .	X.
1612	Anne Churchill, w. of M. Mohun, ch. kng. ins., Fleet, Dorset .	II.
1612	Bennet Maycott, w. of T. Finch, ins., Preston-by-Faversham, Kent	III.
1612	Ann Cornwalys, w. of T. Dade, ins., Tannington, Suff. . .	I.
1612	Margt. Myssenden, ch. (skeleton), ins., Whaddon, Bucks. . .	II.
1612	Elizth. Plume, w. of R. Symonds, ch. kng., Great Yeldham, Essex	I.
1613	Anon., w. of E. Ansley, ch. ins., Chastleton, Oxon. . . .	II.
1613	Anne, w. of J. Edwards, ch. kng. ins., Davington, Kent . .	I.
1613	Jane, w. of E. Gee, ch. ins., Tedburn St. Mary, Devon . .	II.
1613	Dorothy Jocelyn, w. of T. Brewster, ins., Willingale Doe, Essex .	III.

Date.	Name, Description, Place and Emblems, etc.	M.S.
1614	Jane Lewkenor, w. of J. Paschall, ins., Great Baddow, Essex .	I.
1614	Grace Ashfield, w. of J. Osbaldeston, ch. kng. ins., Burford, Oxon.	IV.
1614	Anne Bragge, w. of W. Gale, ch. ins., Hadley, Middx. . .	VIII.
1614	Anne Heigham, w. of T. Clere, ch. ins., Stokesby, Norf. . .	V.
1615	Anne Tuer, w. of T. Fielde, ins., Elsenham, Essex . . .	I.
1615	Dorothy Plumley, ins., Hoo St. Werburgh, Kent . . .	VII.
1615	Ursula Jermyn and Margt. Bowles, ws. of R. Martyn, ch. ins., Long Melford, Suff.	IX.
1615	Cecily Felton, w. of R. Freston, ins., Mendham, Suff. . .	I.
1615	Elizth. Norton, w. of H. Crispe, ch. ins., Wrotham, Kent . .	VIII.
1616	Jane Floyde, ch. kng. ins., Barton Segrave, Northants . .	I.
1616	Kath. Lasheford, kng. ins., Davington, Kent	II.
1616	Mary Evelyn, w. of R. Hatton, ins., Long Ditton, Surr. .	III
1616	Mary Isham, w. of E. Nowell, ch. ins., Edmonton, Middx. .	IV.
1616	Agnes Ogle, ins., Potterspury, Northants	I.
1616	Elizth., w. of J. Burrough, ch. ins., Tottenham, Middx. . .	II.
1616	Joan, w. of E. Bowland, ins., Writtle, Essex	X.
1617	Thomasin, w. of P. Preston, ins., Mickfield, Suff. . . .	II.
1617	Francis Roberts, w. of J. Hooper, ins., Stockbury, Kent . .	II.
1617	Clemence Wyseman, w. of R. Everard, ins., Great Waltham, Essex	IV.
1618	Anne, w. of W. Palke, ins., High Halstow, Kent . . .	II.
1618	Theodosia Tyrrell, w. of E. West, kng. ins., Marsworth, Bucks. D.	V.
1618	Christian Foxe, ch. ins., Yoxford, Suff.	X,
1618	Joan Weld, w. of Sir R. Brooke, ins., Yoxford, Suff. . .	XI.
1619	Anne Grene, w. of C. Croke, kng. ins., Beckley, Oxon. . .	I.
1619	Alice Claydon, w. of Dr. Tuer, kng. ins., Elsenham, Essex .	II.
1619	Anne Tutt, w. of T. Garrard, ins., Lambourne, Berks. . .	V.
1619	Elizth. Bampfield and Gertrude Percevall, ws. of B. Leigh, ch. ins., Shorwell, Isle of Wight	II.
1619	Jane White, w. of E. Boscawen, ins., St. Michael Penkevil, Cornw.	III.
1619	Cecily Hyde, w. of W. Willmott, ins., Wantage, Berks. . .	VI.
1620	? Alice Lacy, w. of Sir H. Cholmeley, Burton Coggles, Lincs. .	II.
1620	Sarah Allanson, w. of J. Webb, ch. ins., Harpsden, Oxon. .	IV.
1620	Mary, w. of J. Becke, ch. kng. ins., St. Peter-at-Arches, Lincoln .	I.
c. 1620	Elizth., w. of T. Wood, ch., Low Leyton, Essex . . .	IV.
1621	Mary White, w. of J. Rixman, kng. ins., Bray, Berks. . .	XI.
1621	Mary Creswell, w. of H. Gunter, ch. kng. ins., Fawley, Berks. .	I.
1621	Alice, w. of J. Worley, ins., Lynsted, Kent	II.
1621	Sara Kemish, ch. kng. ins., Portbury, Som.	I.
1622	Jone Daubene, w. of E. Brampton, ch. ins., Brampton, Norf. .	V.
1622	Elizth. Harvey, w. of R. Heigham, ins., East Ham, Essex . .	III.
1622	Mary, w. of Sir C. Edmonds, ins., Preston Deanery, Northants .	I.
1622	Susan Sampson, w. of W. Lathum, ins., Stifford, Essex . .	IV.
1624	Margt. Anderson, w. of R. Gadburye, ins., Eyworth, Beds. .	I.

Date.	Name, Description, Place and Emblems, etc.	M.S.
1624	Joan Doe, w. of E. Keat, ins., East Lockinge, Berks.	I.
1624	Anne Perkin, w. of T. Byrd, ins., Littlebury, Essex .	VII.
1624	Eleanor Mannock, w. of R. Martin, ch. ins., Long Melford, Suff. .	X.
1625	Elizth. Clinton, w. of Sir A. Gorges, ch. kng., Chelsea, London .	II.
1625	Agnes Hopper, ch. kng. ins., St. Cross, Holywell, Oxford .	II.
1626	Alice, w. of J. Gunter, ins., Cirencester, Glos.	XVIII.
1626	Jane Dirkin, w. of J. Cradock, ins., Ightham, Kent .	VIII.
1626	Alice, w. of J. Gunter, ins., Kintbury, Berks.	I.
1626	Elizth., w. of T. Adams, ch. ins., Swanbourne, Bucks.	II.
1626	Grace Lathum, ins., Upminster, Essex. (Spinster.) .	VI.
1627	Mary and Anne Rowley, ins., Brent Pelham, Herts. .	I.
1627	Elizth., w. of R. Pemberton, ch. ins., St Peter, St. Albans .	I.
1627	Ann Lathum, ins., Stifford, Essex. (Spinster.) .	V.
1628	Jane Boddendam, w. of B. Randolphe, ch. ins., Biddenden, Kent .	IX.
1628	Colubery Lovelace, w. of S. Mayne, ch. ins., Dinton, Bucks.	VII.
1628	Mary Nedham, East Lockinge, Berks. (Spinster.) .	II.
1629	Elizth., w. of R. Jackson, Croydon, Surr. Now lost.	
1629	Elizth. Argall, w. of Sir E. Filmer, ch. ins., East Sutton, Kent. PLATE 37 .	I.
1630	Mary Wyatt, w. of J. Kent, ins., Devizes, Wilts.	I.
1630	Anne Goodman, w. of E. Sawyer, kng. ins., Kettering, Northants .	I.
1630	Anne, w. of O. Mosley, ch. kng. ins., Manchester Cathedral .	VII.
1630	Helen Sawkins, w. of H. Brockman, ch. ins., Newington-next-Hythe, Kent .	XI.
1630	Elizth., w. of T. Lathum, ins., Stifford, Essex .	VI.
c. 1630	Jane Jenney, w. of W. Playters, kng. ins., Sotterley, Suff. .	IV.
c. 1630	Mary Covert and Rose Hatton, ws. of R. Bartelot, ch. ins., Stopham, Suss. .	VII.
1631	Mary Tredwaye, w. of T. Horsman, ins., Burton Pedwardine, Lincs. .	I.
1632	Elizth., w. of R. Chester, ch. ins., Leigh-on-Sea, Essex .	V.
1632	Lady Sydney, w. of Sir J. Wynn, ins., Llanrwst, Denbighshire .	II.
1632	Dorothy Sanders, w. of Sir F. Mannock, ins., Stoke-by-Nayland, Suff. PLATE 51 .	VII.
1632	Martha Doyley, w. of B. Typping, ins., Stokenchurch, Bucks. .	IV.
1633	Elizth. Farnefold, w. of Sir E. Culpeper, ins., Ardingly, Suss. .	IV.
1633	Frances Gardner, w. of Sir T. Hord, ins., Bampton, Oxon. .	III.
1633	Ann Kenwellmersh, ch. ins., Henfield, Suss. .	II.
1635	Mary and Elizth., ws. of J. Bence, ins., Aldeburgh, Suff. .	VII.
1635	Elizth. Taylor, w. of J. Blighe, ch. ins., Finchampstead, Berks. .	III.
1636	Vahan Streinsham and Elizth. Bowles, ws. of R. Bugges, ins., Harlow, Essex .	XI.
1636	Anne, w. of W. Chapman, ch. ins., Walkern, Herts. .	VI.
1637	Margt. Herbert. w. of J. Robertes, ch. ins., Abergavenny, Mon. .	VII.

Date.	Name, Description, Place and Emblems, etc.	M.S.
1637	Elizth., w. of R. Glanfield, hf-eff. ins., Hadleigh, Suff.	X.
1637	Anon., w. of A. Guilliams, ch., Loughton, Essex	IV.
1638	Dorothy Gascoigne, w. of Sir J. Harvey, ch. ins., Cardington, Beds. PLATE 38	II.
1638	Kath., w. of W. Jones, ins., St. Mary, Dover, Kent	I.
1638	Elizth. Rotton, ins., Meriden, Warw.	I.
1638	Martha, w. of W. Pen, ch. ins., Penn, Bucks	III.
1639	Helen Nodes, w. of W. Boteler, hf-eff. ins., Biddenham, Beds.	IV.
1639	Elizth., w. of W. Palmer, ins., Teynham, Kent	IV.
1640	Elizth. (1607), mother of R. Fynche, ins., Dunstable, Beds.	VII.
1640	Anne, w. of J. Plumley, ch. ins., Hoo St. Werburgh, Kent	VIII.
1640	Elizth. Pawle, w. of R. Beeston, ch. kng. ins., All Saints, Maidstone	II.
1640	Sarah and Eleanor, ws. of G. Coles, ch. ins., St. Sepulchre, Northampton. PLATE 48	I.
1640	Elizth., w. of J. Coggeshall, ch. kng. ins., Orford, Suff.	XIII.
1640	Susan Stewkley, w. of Sir H. Drury, ins., Penn, Bucks.	IV.
1640	Margt. Barkham, w. of Sir A. Irby, ch. kng. ins., Tottenham, Middx.	III.
c. 1640	Anon., Leigh-near-Rochford, Essex	VI.
1641	Elizth. Curtis, w. of W. Randolph, ch. ins., Biddenden, Kent	X.
1641	Anne Bedingfield, ins., Darsham, Suff.	III.
1641	Sarah Drury, w. of J. Pen, ch. ins., Penn, Bucks.	V.
1642	Jane Challoner, w. of W. Septvans *alias* Harflet, ch. ins., Ash-next-Sandwich, Kent	IX.
1642	Joan Jocelin, w. of F. Reve, kng., Harlow, Essex	XII.
1647	Grace, w. of J. Morewood, ch. kng. ins., Bradfield, Yorks.	I.
1648	Dorothy Burrell, w. of T. Hooper, ch. ins., Stockbury, Kent	III.
1649	Elizth. Carter, ch. kng. ins., Warminster, Wilts.	II.
1650	Elizth. Kaye, w. of R. Assheton, ch. ins., Middleton, Lancs.	V.
c. 1650	Anon., w. of G. Box, kng. ins., St. Peter-le-Bailey, Oxford	IV.
1656	Anne Clifford, w. of T. Carew, ch. kng. ins., Haccombe, Devon. PLATE 38	V.
1658	Mary Wynne, w. of Sir R. Mostyn, ins., Llanrwst, Denbighshire	III.
1660	Martha Tempest, w. of J. Harris, ch. ins., Milton, Cambs.	II.
1663	Mary Horspoole, w. of G. Thorne, ch. ins., St. Mary, Bedford	IV.
1674	Ellinor and Isabel, ws. of J. Bosworth, ins., Long Itchington, Warw.	I.
1683	Elizth., w. of E. Turpin, ins., Bassingbourne, Cambs.	I.

18TH CENTURY

c. 1773	Philadelphia Merttins, w. of B. Greenwood, ins., St. Mary Cray, Kent	V.

WIDOWS

14TH CENTURY

Date.	Name, Description, Place and Emblems, etc.	M.S.
1383	Phelippe, dau. of Hen., Lord Ferrers, wid. of Guy de Beauchampe, Necton, Norf.	II.
c. 1390	Anon., Stebbing, Essex	I.
1391	Aubrey, wid. of J. Curteys, ca. ins., Wymington, Beds. E.S. PLATE 40	I.
1399	Alianora de Bohun, dau. of Humphrey de Bohun, Earl of Hereford, wid. of Thos. of Woodstock, Duke of Gloucester, ca. ins., Westminster Abbey. PLATE 49	VI.

15TH CENTURY

1410	Margt., wid. of T. de Frevile, Little Shelford, Cambs.	II.
c. 1420	Dame Joan, wid. of Sir A. Savage, ins., Bobbing, Kent	I.
c. 1420	Anon., Furneux Pelham, Herts.	I.
1422	Cecily, wid. of W. Wylde, ins., Dodford, Northants	II.
1425	Dame Margery, wid. of Sir W. Molyns, ins., Stoke Poges, Bucks.	I.
1427	Margery Parlys, wid. of Sir W. Argentine, ins., Elstow, Beds.	I.
1430	Alice Lambton, Chester-le-Street, Durham	I.
1432	Cristine, wid. of R. Baxter, ins., St. Giles, Norwich	I.
1433	Margery St. John, wid. of W. Harwedon, br. ins., Great Harrowden, Northants. E.S.	I.
1434	Dame Eleanor Conquest, ins., Flitton, Beds.	I.
1435	Alice de Bures, w. of Sir G. Bryan, ca., Acton, Suff. PLATE 50	II.
c. 1435	Dame Edith Chaunceler, Higham Ferrers, Northants	IV.
1436	Maud Burghersh, wid. of T. Chaucer, Ewelme, Oxon.	I.
1436	Margt., wid. of R. Purdaunce, ins., St. Giles, Norwich	II.
1441	Elizth., wid. of R. Walsshe, ins., Langridge, Som.	II.
1445	Eleanor Spiney, wid. of J. Throckmorton, Fladbury, Worc.	I.
1446	Agnes, wid. of J. Olyver, Naseby, Northants	I.
1448	Elizth. Frowyk, ch. ins., South Mimms, Middx.	II.
1450	Agnes, wid. of W. Hicchecok, Ampthill, Beds.	I.
1451	Alice Frowick, wid. of T. Reynes, ch. ins., Marston Mortaine, Beds.	II.
1454	Agnes Appleton, wid. of R. Molyngton, ins., Dartford, Kent	II.
1455	Maud Oldcastle, wid. of R. Clitherow, ca., Ash-next-Sandwich, Kent	I.
c. 1455	? Joan, wid. of J. Digges, Barham, Kent	II.
1459	Eupheme, wid. of Sir J. Langton, ins., St. Peter, Leeds, Yorks.	I.
c. 1460	? — Forster, ins., Harpsden, Oxon.	I.
1462	Isabel Langham, Little Chesterford, Essex	I.

Date.	Name, Description, Place and Emblems, etc.	M.S.
1462	Maud Throckmarton, wid. of Sir T. Grene, ch. ins., Green's Norton, Northants	I.
1464	Dame Anne Croyser, wid. of Sir H. Norbury, ch. ins., Stoke d'Abernon, Surr. PLATE 51	III.
1465	Maud, wid. of T. Cobham, ins., Hoo St. Werburgh, Kent . .	V
1466	Margt. Oughtred, wid. of R. Ask, ins., Aughton, Yorks. (E.R.) .	I.
1467	Margt. Roos, wid. of H. Grene, ins., Lowick, Northants. E.S. .	I.
1467	Margt. Swynfen, wid. of Sir W. Vernon, ch. ins., Tong, Salop .	I.
c. 1470	Joan Stanhope, Lady Cromwell, wid. of Sir Humph. Bourchier, ca. ins., Tattershall, Lincs. SS.	IV.
c. 1470	Lady Maud Stanhope, wid. of Robt., Lord Willoughby, ca. ins., Tattershall, Lincs. SS.	V.
1474	Elizth. Chaworth, wid. of W. Fitzwilliam, ins., Sprotborough, Yorks. (W.R.)	I.
1475	Agnes, wid. of J. Browne, ins., All Saints, Stamford, Lincs. .	IV.
c. 1475	Dame Isabel Scobahull, wid. of Sir T. Chedder, Cheddar, Som. .	II.
1476	Dame Anne Marney, wid. of Sir T. Tyrell, East Horndon, Essex .	I.
1476	Dame Margt. Frevill, wid. of Sir R. Byngham, ins., Middleton, Warw.	I.
1477	Margt., wid. of J. Croke, ch. kng., All Hallows, Barking, London	IV.
1478	Margt. Stanley, wid. of R. Bothe, ch. ins., Sawley, Derb. . .	II.
c. 1480	Anon., Grendon, Northants	II.
1488	Joan Leyke, wid. of T. Welby, ins., Holbeach, Lincs. . .	II.
c. 1490	? — Rotherham, ca., Luton, Beds.	IV.
1493	Elizth. Plumpton, wid. of J. Southill, Stockerston, Leic. . .	II.
1497	Dame Joan, wid. of J. Swan, Stretham, Cambs. . . .	I.
1498	Joan Byron, wid. of W. Basset, ins., Blore Ray, Staffs. . .	I.

16TH CENTURY

1504	Marion, wid. of W. Thorpe, ch. ins., Higham Ferrers, Northants	VI.
1507	Elizth. Barton, ins., Beddington, Surr.	VI.
1510	Dame Anne Semark, wid. of Sir D. Phelip, ca. ins., Chenies, Bucks.	IV.
1511	Agnes Johnston, ins., Chenies, Bucks.	V.
1512	Elizth. Porte, ch. ins., Etwall, Derb. L. B.V. . . .	I.
1513	Alice Forster, wid. of W. Taylard, ch., Diddington, Hunts. B.V.	II.
1529	Dame Joan, wid. of J. Cook, St. Mary-de-Crypt, Gloucester. J.B.	I.
c. 1530	Anon., ch. kng., Wickham Skeith, Suff.	I.
1536	Dame Alice Beriffe, ch. br., Brightlingsea, Essex . . .	VI.
1539	Elizth. Paston, wid. of Sir J. Fyneux, ins., Herne, Kent . .	VII.
1570	Ann Gygges, wid. of Sir T. Clere, ins., Stokesby, Norf. . .	IV.
1570	Dame Joan Wiseman, wid. of — Strangman, ins., Wimbish, Essex. Now lost.	
1582	Anne Torrell, wid. of J. Sackville, ins., Willingale Doe, Essex .	II.

Date.	Name, Description, Place and Emblems, etc.	M.S.
1585	Elizth. Nevell, wid. of T. Eynns, hf-eff. ins., York Cathedral	II.
1598	Dame Mary Darell, wid. of H. Fortescue, ins., Faulkbourne, Essex	III.
1600	Mary, wid. of E. Brooke *alias* Cobbum, ins., Newington-next-Sittingbourne, Kent	V.

17TH CENTURY

1605	Alice Alington, wid. of E. Talkarne, ins., Stoke-by-Clare, Suff.	VI.
1609	Anne Bures, wid. of E. Butts, ins., Redgrave, Suff.	I.
1611	Kath. Awdley, Morton-on-the-Hill, Norf.	I.
1622	Marie Boscawen, wid. of P. Coffin, ins., St. Michael Penkevil, Cornw.	IV.

CHILDREN (FEMALE)

1442	Margt. Grene and Margt. Sumercotes, ins., Hadley, Middx.	I.
1479	Anne Boleyn aet. 3 years, ins., Blickling, Norf.	VI.
c. 1480	5 daus. From the Nichols Collection. In 1894 in possession of the late E. Cleghorn, of Plumstead.	
c. 1490	8 daus., kng., Redbourn, Herts.	I.
1500	5 daus. (Pekham), kng. ins., Wrotham, Kent	III.
c. 1500	7 daus. Said to be from Landwade, Cambs.	
1512	2 daus. (Fogg), ins., Ashford, Kent	IV.
c. 1520	15 daus. (Aldriche), ins., Burnham, Bucks.	II.
c. 1520	3 daus. (Smith), Clavering, Essex	II.
c. 1530	7 daus., Over, Cambs.	I.
1557	3 daus. (Nayle), ins., Abington, Northants	I.
c. 1560	13 daughters. Locality unknown.	
1584	Dorothy Alleine, aet. 3 years, ins., Woodham Mortimer, Essex	I.
c. 1600	Anne Neele, aet. 4 years, Ludgershall, Bucks. (On the brass of A. Englishe.)	I.
1602	Mary Birchemore, aet. 6 years, ins., Hanslope, Bucks.	II.
1607	Elizth. Rowe, aet. 7 years, Pembury, Kent	I.
1615	— Woodyore, ins., Cookham, Berks.	VIII.
c. 1620	One dau. Formerly in possession of Messrs. Warner.	
1630	Dorothy King, aet. 8 months, ins., St. George's Chapel, Windsor. (In cradle.)	IX.
1634	Elizth. Culpeper, aet. 7 years, ins., Ardingly, Suss. PLATE 51	V.
1683	Anne Dunch, aet. 9 months, ins., Little Wittenham, Berks.	XII.

ECCLESIASTICAL COSTUME
ARCHBISHOPS AND BISHOPS IN PONTIFICALS
Archbishops

Date.	Name, Description, Place and Emblems, etc.	M.S.
1315	Wm. de Grenefeld, Archbishop of York, York Minster . .	I.
1397	Robt. de Waldeby, Archbishop of York, ca. ins., Westminster Abbey	V.
1417	Thos. Cranley, Archbishop of Dublin, ca. ins., New Coll., Oxford. PLATE 53	II.

Bishops

1360	John Trilleck, Bishop of Hereford, ca. ins., Hereford Cathedral .	II.
c. 1390	Anon., Adderley, Salop	I.
1395	John de Waltham, Bishop of Salisbury, ca., Westminster Abbey. SS.	III.
1478	John Bowthe, Bishop of Exeter, kng. ins., East Horsley, Surr. .	II.
1496	Rich. Bell, Bishop of Carlisle, ca., Carlisle Cathedral . .	I.
1515	Jas. Stanley, Bishop of Ely, ins., Manchester Cathedral . .	IV.
c. 1525	John Yong, titular Bishop of Callipolis, ins., New Coll., Oxford .	XXI.
1554	Thos. Goodryke, Bishop of Ely, ins., Ely Catherdal . . .	I.
1556	John Bell, Bishop of Worcester, St. James, Clerkenwell, London .	I.
1579	Robt. Pursglove, Suffragan Bishop of Hull, ins., Tideswell, Derb. E.S. PLATE 54	III.

MITRED ABBOTS IN PONTIFICALS

c. 1370	Thos. de la Mare, Abbot of St. Albans, 1349-96, ca. ins., St. Albans Abbey, Herts. E.S. SS. PLATE 52 . . .	I.
1498	John Estney, Abbot of Westminster, ca., Westminster Abbey .	XI.

PRIESTS IN CHASUBLE
14TH CENTURY

c. 1310	Adam de Bacon, ins., Oulton, Suff. Now lost.	
c. 1311	Rich. de Hakebourne, hf-eff., Merton Coll., Oxford . .	I.
c. 1320	Anon. (head only), Ashford, Kent	I.
c. 1330	Nichol de Gore, ins., Woodchurch, Kent. (In the head of a floriated cross.)	I.
1337	Laurence de St. Maur, ca. ins., Higham Ferrers, Northants. L. SS. PLATE 53	I.
c. 1340	Anon., hf-eff. br., Great Brington, Northants . . .	I.
c. 1340	Rich. de Beltoun, hf-eff. ins., Corringham, Essex . . .	I.
c. 1340	John de Grofhurst, ca. ins., Horsmonden, Kent . . .	I.
1347	Thos. de Hop, hf-eff. ins., Kemsing, Kent	I.

Date.	Name, Description, Place and Emblems, etc.	M.S.
1353	Wm. de Herleston, ins., Sparsholt, Berks. (In the head of a cross.)	I.
c. 1360	Esmound de Burnedisshe, ins., Brundish, Suff.	I.
1361	Walter de Annefordhe, hf-eff. ins., Binfield, Berks.	I.
1364	W. Darell, hf-eff. br. ins., Brandesburton, Yorks. (E.R.)	I.
c. 1370	Wm. de Lound, hf-eff. ins., Althorpe, Lincs.	I.
c. 1370	John Seys, ins., West Hanney, Berks.	I.
c. 1370	Robt. Levee, hf-eff. ins., Hayes, Middx.	I.
c. 1370	Anon., br. ca. cha., North Mimms, Herts. SS. PLATE 54	I.
c. 1370	John Verieu, hf-eff. ins., Saltwood, Kent	I.
c. 1370	Anon., ca., Shottesbrooke, Berks.	I.
c. 1370	Anon., Stoke-in-Teignhead, Devon. (Once in a cross, now relaid in a slab with incised inscr. to John Symon, 1497.)	I.
c. 1370	Anon., hf-eff., Wantage, Berks.	I.
1375	Peter de Lacy, ins., Northfleet, Kent	I.
c. 1375	Sir Simon of Wensley, cha., Wensley, Yorks. (N.R.). PLATE 54	I.
1376	Walter Frilende, hf-eff. ins., Ockham, Surr.	I.
1378	Ralph Perchehay, hf-eff. ins., Stifford, Essex	I.
c. 1380	John Aldebourne, hf-eff. ins., Lewknor, Oxon.	I.
c. 1380	Anon., Lidgate, Suff.	I.
1381	Nich. Kaerwent, Crondall, Hants	I.
c. 1385	? John Chervill, Beechamwell St. Mary, Norf.	I.
1388	Alex. Chelseye, hf-eff. cha. ins., Chinnor, Oxon.	V.
1389	Rich. Thaseburgh, ins., Hellesdon, Norf.	II.
c. 1390	Anon., Fulbourn, Cambs.	I.
1391	Wm. Lye, hf-eff., Northfleet, Kent	II.
1395	John de Swynstede, ins., Ashridge House, Bucks., now returned to Edlesborough, Bucks.	I.
1396	Rich. Brey, hf-eff. ins., Barton-in-the-Clay, Beds.	I.
1398	Roger Campdene, hf-eff. ins., Stanford-in-the-Vale, Berks.	I.
1399	Thos. and Rich. Gomfrey, ins., Dronfield, Derb.	I.
c. 1400	Anon., hf-eff., Great Berkhampstead, Herts.	IV.

15TH CENTURY

1404	John Vynter, ins., Clothall, Herts.	I.
1404 ?	John Yop, hf-eff. ins., Worstead, Norf.	I.
1406	John Brown, hf-eff. ins., Hoo St. Werburgh, Kent	I.
1407	Wm. de Thorp, ins., West Wickham, Kent	I.
1408	Britell Avenel, ins., Buxted, Suss. E.S. (In head of a floriated cross.)	I.
1408	Rich. de Thorp, hf-eff. ins., Stanwell, Middx.	I.
1408	John Lumbarde, ins., Stone, Kent. (In head of a floriated cross.)	I.
1410	John Waleys, hf-eff. ins., Houghton Regis, Beds.	I.
c. 1410	John Mordon, ins., Emberton, Bucks.	I.
1412	Rich. Bayly, ins., Hoo St. Werburgh, Kent	II.

Date.	Name, Description, Place and Emblems, etc.	M.S.
1412	Robt. Scarclyf, ins., Shere, Surr.	I.
1413	John Everdon, hf-eff. ins., Twyford, Bucks.	I.
1414	Ralph Strelly, hf-eff. ins., Great Leighs, Essex	II.
c. 1415	John atte Spetyll, Luton, Beds.	I.
1419	John Monemouthe, hf-eff. ins., Harlington, Middx.	I.
1419	Robt. Thresk, hf-eff. ins., Thirsk, Yorks. (Between two angels.)	I.
1420	Wm. Robroke, ins., Chelsfield, Kent	III.
1420	Walter Papley, hf-eff. ins., Marston Mortaine, Beds.	I.
c. 1420	Robt. Fyn, ins., Little Easton, Essex	I.
c. 1420	Anon., Chelsfield, Kent	II.
c. 1420	Anon., Mersham, Kent	I.
c. 1420	Nich. Stafford, ins., Woodford-cum-Membris, Northants	I.
1422	John Henele, hf-eff. ins., Longworth, Berks.	I.
1424	Robt. Willardsey, ins., St. Nicholas, Warwick	I.
1426	Wm. Hewet, ins., Newton Bromshold, Northants	I.
1427	Walter Seller, ins., Iden, Suss.	I.
1427	Adam Babyngton, ins., Milton Keynes, Bucks.	I.
1428	Thos. Nassh, hf-eff. ins., Haddenham, Bucks.	II.
1428	John Ynge, ins., Oxted, Surr.	I.
1430	John Grymston, hf-eff. ins., Beechamwell St. Mary, Norf.	II.
c. 1430	Robt. Clere, ins., Battle, Suss.	II.
c. 1430	Anon., St. John's Coll., Cambridge	II.
c. 1430	Anon., Polstead, Suff.	I.
c. 1430	Anon., Saffron Walden, Essex	I.
1431	Robt. Blundell, Monks Risborough, Bucks.	I.
1431	Edw. Cranford, ins., Puttenham, Surr.	I.
1432	Wm. Byschopton, ca. ins., Great Bromley, Essex	I.
1433	John Heyne, ins., Yelden, Beds.	I.
1433	John Churmond, ins., Little Wittenham, Berks.	I.
1440	John Colt, ins., Tansor, Northants	I.
c. 1440	Anon., Lingfield, Surr.	VI.
1445	John Wyche, hf-eff. ins., Lingfield, Surr.	VII.
1446	Thos. Chaworth, hf-eff. cha., Addington, Kent	V.
1447	John Gerrye, Cobham, Kent	XIV.
c. 1450	Esperaunce Blondell, hf-eff. ins., Arundel, Suss.	V.
c. 1450	? Simon Hert, hf-eff., Great Greenford, Middx.	I.
c. 1450	Anon., Turweston, Bucks.	I.
c. 1450	Wm. Carbrok, hf-eff. ins., Willshamstead, Beds.	I.
1451	Wm. Gysborne, hf-eff. ins., Farningham, Kent	V.
1455	John Baker, Arundel, Suss.	VI.
1455	Roger Gery, cha. ins., Whitchurch, Oxon.	II.
1456	Wm. Moor, ins., Tattershall, Lincs.	II.
1457	John Braydforde, hf-eff. ins., St. Michael, Lewes, Suss.	II.
1458	John Bradstane, hf-eff. ins., Ewelme, Oxon.	III.

Date.	Name, Description, Place and Emblems, etc.	M.S.
1458	Jas. Veldon, hf-eff. ins., Lingfield, Surr.	IX.
c. 1460	John Osteler, hf-eff. ins., Hayes, Kent	I.
c. 1460	? John Spycer, ins., Monkton, Kent.	I.
c. 1460	Walter Davy, hf-eff. ins., Poling, Suss.	I.
1461	Robt. Lond, cha. ins., St. Peter, Bristol. PLATE 54	I.
1462	Reginald Mauser, hf-eff. ins., Slapton, Bucks.	I.
1463	Thos. Mastrupe, cha. ins., Tysoe, Warw.	I.
1465	Rich. Galon, hf-eff. ins., Ash-next-Wrotham, Kent	II.
1465	Robt. Dockyng, ins., Wood Dalling, Norf.	I.
1467	Hen. Morecote, hf-eff. ins., Ewelme, Oxon.	IV.
1468	Wm. Smarte, ins., Chipping Warden, Northants	I.
1469	John Payne, hf-eff. ins., Crowell, Oxon.	I.
1469	John Swetecok, ins., Lingfield, Surr.	XI.
c. 1470	Anon., cha. ins., Broxbourne, Herts.	I.
c. 1470	Anon., Chalfont St. Giles, Bucks.	I.
c. 1470	John Kekilpenny, cha., Laindon, Essex	I.
1471	John Mere, cha. ins., Cholsey, Berks.	III.
1474	Robt. Warde, hf-eff. ins., Arundel, Suss.	VIII.
1475	Geoff. Bysschop, Fulbourn, Cambs. (Holding heart.)	IV.
1477	Stephen Multon, ins., Swanton Abbot, Norf.	I.
1478	Ralph Parsons, cha., Cirencester, Glos.	VIII.
1479	Edm. Kelyng, hf-eff. ins., East Dereham, Norf.	I.
1479	Ralph Fuloflove, ins., West Harling, Norf.	I.
1479	John Andrew, ins., Hayes, Kent	II.
c. 1480	Anon., ins., Childrey, Berks.	III.
1482	Alan Porter, hf-eff. ins., Chislehurst, Kent	I.
1482	Rich. Kegell, ins., Little Ringstead, Norf.	I.
1485	Denis Slon, cha., Buxted, Suss.	IV.
c. 1485	Roger Clerk, St. Ethelred, Norwich	I.
1486	John Botolff, ins., Sharrington, Norf.	II.
1487	Roger Hewet, ins., Newton Bromshold, Northants	II.
1487	Thos. Wheteaker, cha., Radwell, Herts.	I.
c. 1490	Anon., cha., Childrey, Berks.	V.
c. 1490	Anon., Heydon, Essex. Now lost.	
c. 1490	Wm. Mustarder, ins., Sparham, Norf.	I.
1492	Morris Jones, ins., Brightwell Salome, Oxon.	I.
1492	Robt. Morley, cha., Walton-on-Trent, Derb.	I.
1493	Walter Gaynesford, cha., Carshalton, Surr.	III.
1493	Robt. Thursbe, ins., Hughenden, Bucks.	I.
1493	Rich. Blakysley, ins., Lillingstone Dayrell, Bucks.	II.
1494	? Rich. Newland, ins., Chenies, Bucks.	III.
1494	John Taknell, hf-eff. ins., Winchester College	VIII.
1496	John Balam, ins., Blewbury, Berks.	I.
1497	Hen. Sargeaunt, St. John, Stamford, Lincs.	III.

Date.	Name, Description, Place and Emblems, etc.				M.S.
1498	Wm. Branwhait, hf-eff. ins., Ewelme, Oxon.	.	.	.	IX.
1498	Hen. Denton, cha. ins., Higham Ferrers, Northants	.	.		V.
1498	Wm. Goode, ins., Odiham, Hants	.	.	.	II.
1500	Wm. Abell, cha. ins., Coleshill, Warw.	.	.	.	I.
c. 1500	John Marskre, ins., Charlcote, Warw. Now lost.				

16TH CENTURY

1503	Thos. Leddes, cha. ins., Brookland, Kent	.	.	.	I.
1503	John Erton, ins., Long Newton, Wilts.	.	.	.	II.
1504	Philip Eyre, Ashover, Derb.	.	.	.	I.
1504	Alex. Inglisshe, ca. cha. ins., Campsey Ash, Suff.	.	.		I.
1504	Wm. Plewme, ins., Fladbury, Worc.	.	.	.	V.
1505	John Sadler, ins., Faringdon, Berks.	.	.	.	IV.
1506	Wm. Walley, ins., Houghton Regis, Beds.	.	.	.	II.
1507	John Scoffyld, cha. ins., Brightwell, Berks.	.	.	.	I.
1507	John Frye, hf-eff. cha. ins., New Coll., Oxford	.	.	.	XVII.
1508	Hen. Frekylton, ins., Aldbourne, Wilts.	.	.	.	II.
1509	Rich. Ardern, cha. ins., Eton Coll., Bucks.	.	.	.	IV.
1509	Thos. Lyrypyn, hf-eff. ins., Winchester College	.	.		XI.
1510	? Rich. Bladwell, cha., Laindon, Essex	.	.	.	II.
c. 1510	Anon., Bletchingley, Surr.	.	.	.	II.
c. 1510	Anon., cha., Cobham, Surr.	.	.	.	II.
c. 1510	Anon., cha., Littlebury, Essex	.	.	.	II.
c. 1510	John Stokys, cha. ins., Wymington, Beds.	.	.	.	IV.
1511	Walter Elmes, ins., Harpsden, Oxon.	.	.	.	III.
1512	Wm. Bisshop, cha. ins., Wiveton, Norf.	.	.	.	I.
1513	Wm. Mowfurth, ins., Streatham, Surr.	.	.	.	I.
1514	Hugh Parke, hf-eff. ins., Loughton, Bucks.	.	.	.	I.
1514	John Gylbert, hf-eff., Winchester College	.	.	.	XIII.
1514	John Erewaker, hf-eff. ins., Winchester College	.	.	.	XIV.
1515	Philip Metcalf, ins., Ardeley, Herts.	.	.	.	II.
1515	Thos. Cardiff, ins., St. John, Margate	.	.	.	VIII.
1515	John Stokton, West Wickham, Kent	.	.	.	II.
1518	Robt. Beuford, ins., Northiam, Suss. E.S.	.	.	.	I.
1518	Thos. Lawne, ins., St. Cross, Winchester	.	.	.	VI.
1519	John Bloxham, cha. ins., Great Addington, Northants.	E.S.	.	.	I.
1519	John Wryght, cha. ins., Clothall, Herts.	.	.	.	II.
1519	Wm. Estwood, ins., Kingsclere, Hants	.	.	.	II.
1519	Hen. Dodschone, ins., Stanton Harcourt, Oxon.	.	.	.	III.
1519	Wm. Symson, ins., Tattershall, Lincs.	.	.	.	VII.
c. 1520	Anon., cha., Hereford Cathedral	.	.	.	XIX
1521	Rich. Redberd, ins., Bradenham, Bucks.	.	.	.	I.
1521	Thos. Symons, Great Greenford, Middx.	.	.	.	III.
1521	Ralph Babyngton, cha. ins., Hickling, Notts.	.	.	.	II.

Date.	Name, Description, Place and Emblems, etc.	M.S.
1522	Edm. Assheton, cha. ins., Middleton, Lancs.	II.
1523	John Heynys, cha. ins., Birchington, Kent	IV.
1523	Rich. Idon, cha. ins., Clayton, Suss.	II.
1523	John Heygge, ins., Hayes, Kent	III.
1524	Wm. Grey, cha., Evershot, Dorset	I.
1524	John Warwekhyll, cha. ins., Totternhoe, Beds.	II.
1525	Wm. Herun, ins., Bledlow, Bucks.	I.
1525	— Horman, cha. ins., Eton Coll., Bucks.	IX.
1525	Ralph Wulf, ins., Tunstall, Kent	III.
1526	Alex. Anne, cha. ins., Middle Claydon, Bucks.	II.
1527	Wm. Richardson *alias* Byggins, cha. ins., Sawston, Cambs.	V.
1529	Thos. Knyghton, ch. ins., Slapton, Bucks.	III.
c. 1530	Anon., cha., Somersham, Hunts.	I.
1531	John Athowe, cha. ins., Brisley, Norf.	III.
1531	John Redborne, cha., Faversham, Kent	XI.
1531	Rich. Bennet, cha. ins., Whitnash, Warw.	II.
1533	Wm. Wardysworth, cha. ins., Betchworth, Surr. PLATE 54	I.
1535	Thos. Westeley, cha. ins., Wivenhoe, Essex	II.
1536	Wm. Styrlay, cha., Rauceby, Lincs.	I.
1543	Rich. Huntyngdon, cha. ins., Waddesdon, Bucks.	II.
1545	Robt. Hanson, ins., Chalfont St. Peter, Bucks. (Appropriated effigy, with inscr. added.)	VI.

PRIESTS IN COPE
14TH CENTURY

1361	Wm. de Rothewelle, ins., Rothwell, Northants	I.
c. 1370	? John Brigenhall, Watton-at-Stone, Herts.	II.
c. 1380	Anon., St. Andrew, Auckland, Durham	I.
1382?	Sir Adam Ertham, hf-eff., Arundel, Suss.	I.
1382	John de Campeden, ins., St. Cross, Winchester. H.T.	I.
1383	Nich. de Luda (Louth), ca. ins., Cottingham, Yorks.	I.
1386	Rich. de la Barre, Hereford Cathedral. (In the head of a cross.) PLATE 56	III.
1391	Wm. de Fulburne, ca. ins., Fulbourn, Cambs.	II.
1400	Matthew de Asscheton, ins., Shillington, Beds.	I.
c. 1400	? John Strangsill, Boston, Lincs. SS.	II.
c. 1400	? John Felbrigg, hf.-eff., South Creake, Norf.	I.

15TH CENTURY

1401	John Sleford, ca. ins., Balsham, Cambs. B.V. H.T. E.S. SS. PLATE 55	I.
1401	Wm. Ermyn, Castle Ashby, Northants. SS. PLATE 56	I.

Date.	Name, Description, Place and Emblems, etc.	M.S.
1402	Reginald de Cobham, br. ca., Cobham, Kent	VIII.
1403	Rich. Malford, New Coll., Oxford	I.
1404	Hen. de Codyngtoun, ca. ins., Bottesford, Leic. SS. PLATE 56	I.
1409	Thos. de Busshbury, Ashbury, Berks.	II.
1411	Thos. Clerke, Horsham, Suss. (With amice, alb and crossed stole.)	I.
1413	Wm. Langeton, kng. ins., Exeter Cathedral	II.
1413	Thos. Aileward, Havant, Hants	I.
1414	John Oudeby, ins., Flamstead, Herts.	I.
1414	Simon Bache, ins., Knebworth, Herts. SS.	I.
1416	Robt. London, ins., Chartham, Kent	II.
1416	John Prophete, ca., Ringwood, Hants. SS.	I.
1418	Thos. Pattesle, ca., Great Shelford, Cambs.	I.
1419	John Desford, hf-eff. ins., New Coll., Oxford . . .	III.
1420	Robt. Wyntryngham, br. ca. ins., Cotterstock, Northants. E.S. .	I.
c. 1420	Anon., Bennington, Herts. (With garter (?) badge.) . . .	I.
c. 1420	Anon., Haddenham, Bucks.	I.
1423	Thos. Harlyng, ca. ins., Pulborough, Suss.	I.
1425	John Mershden, ca. ins., Thurcaston, Leic. E.S. . . .	I.
1428	Hen. Keys, Fakenham, Norf.	I.
1428	Edm. Ryall, Hereford Cathedral	VI.
c. 1430	? Wm. Mowbray, ca., Upwell, Norf.	I.
1432	John Mapilton, ca. ins., Broadwater, Suss.	II.
1432	John Wyllynghale, hf-eff. ins., Winchester College. (With amice, alb and crossed stole.)	II.
1435	Hen. Martyn, ins., Upwell, Norf. (With amice, alb and crossed stole.)	II.
1436	Wm. Prestwyk, ca. ins., Warbleton, Suss. E.S. . . .	I.
1438	John Lovelle, ins., St. George, Canterbury	I.
c. 1440	John Freman, ins., Bottesford, Leic.	II.
1442	Simon Marcheford, Harrow, Middx.	III.
1445	Nich. North, hf-eff. ins., Winchester College	IV.
1448	Wm. Skelton, ins., Ashbury, Berks.	III.
1450	Robt. Thurberne, Winchester College	V.
c. 1450	John Gladwyn, ins., Cobham, Kent	XV.
1454	Robt. Arthur, ins., Chartham, Kent	III.
1456	John Tubney, hf-eff. ins., Southfleet, Kent	IV.
1458	Thos. Mordon, hf-eff. ins., Fladbury, Worc.	II.
1458	Wm. Kirkaby, Theydon Gernon, Essex	I.
c. 1460	Anon., Temple Church, Bristol, Glos.	II.
c. 1460	Anon., Wells Cathedral, Som.	I.
1461	Philip Polton, kng. ins., All Souls Coll., Oxford . . .	I.
1462	John Blodwell, ca. ins., Balsham, Cambs. SS. PLATE 55 .	II.
1464	John Heth, hf-eff. ins., Tintinhull, Som.	II.

Date.	Name, Description, Place and Emblems, etc.	M.S.
1465	Thos. Cod, hf-eff. ins., St. Margaret, Rochester. (In cassock, surplice, amice and cope ; on rev. a similar eff. but wearing almuce.) .	I.
1468	John Byrkhed, ca. ins., Harrow, Middx.	V.
c. 1470	Rich. Warriner, ins., Little Hadham, Herts.	I.
1471	Hen. Sever, ca. ins., Merton Coll., Oxford. SS.	V.
1472	Thos. Tonge, ins., Beeford, Yorks. (E.R.). PLATE 56	I.
1473	Edw. Tacham, hf-eff., Winchester College	VII.
1476	Thos. Key, ins., Charlton-on-Otmoor, Oxon.	I.
1477	Rich. Bole, ca. ins., Wilburton, Cambs.	I.
1478	Wm. Langley, cha. ins., Buckland, Herts.	II.
1480	Wm. Thornbury, Faversham, Kent	III.
1480	Wm. Tibarde, ins., Magdalen Coll., Oxford	III.
c. 1480	Anon., ins., Queen's Coll., Cambridge	I.
1485	John Spence, ins., Quainton, Bucks.	III.
1485	Thos. Portyngton, Shillington, Beds.	II.
1487	John Perch, ins., Magdalen Coll., Oxford	VIII.
1490	Thos. Chawndiler, Hereford Cathedral	XVI.
c. 1490	Anon., Fiskerton, Lincs.	I.
c. 1490	Thos. Sutton, ins., West Tanfield, Yorks.	II.
1492	Wm. Malster, Girton, Cambs.	I.
1494	Walter Hyll, ins., New Coll., Oxford.	XVI.
1497	Wm. Stevyn, ins., Girton, Cambs.	II.
1498	John Sprotte, ins., Cobham, Kent	XVII.
1498	Jas. Hert, Hitchin, Herts.	XIII.
1500	Robt. Halcot, ins., Bampton, Oxon.	II.
c. 1500	Stephen Hellard, ins., Stevenage, Herts.	I.

16TH CENTURY

1501	Thos. Worsley, ins., Wimpole, Cambs. B.V.	I.
1508	Hen. Wykes, ins., All Saints, Stamford, Lincs.	VII.
1509	John Norton, ins., South Creake, Norf.	II.
c. 1510	Walter Hewke, ins., Trinity Hall, Cambridge. SS.	I.
c. 1510	? John Gygur, Tattershall, Lincs. SS.	VI.
1511	Thos. Wilkynson, ins., Orpington, Kent	II.
1512	Gabriel Silvester, ins., Croydon, Surr.	III.
1517	Wm. Lichefeld, Willesden, Middx.	III.
c. 1518	Robt. Langton, Queen's Coll., Oxford	III.
1519	Thos. Swayn, ins., Wooburn, Bucks.	III.
c. 1520	Anon., Dowdeswell, Glos. PLATE 56	I.
1521	Christ. Urswick, ins., Hackney, London	I.
1521	John Rede, ins., New Coll., Oxford	XX.
1522	Wm. Boutrod, ins., Eton Coll., Bucks.	VII.
1523 ?	Rich. Wylleys, ins., Higham Ferrers, Northants	IX.

Date.	Name, Description, Place and Emblems, etc.	M.S.
1529	Edm. Frowsetoure, ca. ins., Hereford Cathedral. SS.	XXII.
1530	Adam Grafton, ins., Withington, Salop	II.
c. 1535	Thos. Dalyson, Clothall, Herts.	III.
1545	Thos. Capp, ins., St. Stephen, Norwich	X.
c. 1548	John White, Winchester College	XX.
1550	Thos. Magnus, ins., Sessay, Yorks.	I.

PRIESTS IN ALMUCE

15TH CENTURY

1418	Wm. Tannere, hf-eff. ins., Cobham, Kent	XII.
1419	Wm. Whyte, Arundel, Suss.	II.
c. 1480	Thos. Teylar, ins., Byfleet, Surr. PLATE 58	I.
c. 1490	Thos. Tylson, ins., Aylsham, Norf.	I.
1493	Rich. Harward, St. Cross, Winchester	IV.
1494	Thos. Buttler, ins., Great Haseley, Oxon.	II.

16TH CENTURY

1501	Thos. Parker, ins., Dean, Beds.	I.
1508	Robt. Sheffelde, ins., Chartham, Kent	IV.
1514	John Fynexs, ins., St. Mary, Bury St. Edmunds, Suff.	II.
1515	Wm. Goberd, ins., Magdalen Coll., Oxford	XIV.
c. 1515	Edw. Sheffeld, ins., Luton, Beds.	XI.
1518	John Aberfeld, Great Cressingham, Norf.	III.
c. 1520	John Laurence, Benedictine Abbot of Ramsey, ca., Burwell, Cambs. (Effigy originally in mass vestments; after the Dissolution altered to almuce.)	I.
1521	Wm. Fordmell, ins., Borden, Kent	II.
1522	Rich. Adams, cha. ins., East Malling, Kent. PLATE 58	II.
1528	Robt. Hacombleyn, King's Coll., Cambridge. E.S. PLATE 58	III.
1528	Robt. Sutton, kng., St. Patrick's Cathedral, Dublin	I.
1537	Geoff. Fyche, kng. ins., St. Patrick's Cathedral, Dublin. (With representation of Our Lady in Pity.)	II.
1557	Jas. Coorthopp, ins., Christ Church Cathedral, Oxford	III.
1558	Robt. Brassie, ins., King's Coll., Cambridge	IV.

PRIEST IN AMICE, ALB AND CROSSED STOLE

1415	John West, Sudborough, Northants	I.

PRIESTS IN CASSOCK

1422	John Lewys, kng. ins., Quainton, Bucks.	II.
c. 1480	Anon., Cirencester, Glos.	IX.

I

Date.	Name, Description, Place and Emblems, etc.	M.S.
1510	Wm. Smyght, ins., Ashby St. Legers, Northants	VII.
1512	Wm. Geddyng, Wantage, Berks.	IV.
1518	Rich. Bethell, ins., Shorwell, Isle of Wight	I.
c. 1520	John Yslyngeton, D.D., cha. ins., Cley-next-the-Sea, Norf.	VI.
c. 1530	Wm. Lawnder, kng. ins., Northleach, Glos. H.T.	IX.

PRIEST IN SURPLICE

1567	Wm. Dye, ins., Westerham, Kent	IX.

PRIESTS IN MANTLE OF THE ORDER OF THE GARTER

1363 ?	Roger Parkers, hf-eff. ins., North Stoke, Oxon.	I.
1540	Roger Lupton, Provost of Eton, ins., Eton Coll., Bucks. PLATE 58	XI.
1558	Arthur Cole, ins., Magdalen Coll., Oxford	XVII.

MONASTIC COSTUME
MALE

1433	Thos. Nelond, Cluniac Prior of Lewes, ca. ins., Cowfold, Suss. B.V. H.T. SS. PLATE 59	I.
1437	Geoff. Langeley, Benedictine Prior of St. Faith, Horsham, br. ins., St. Laurence, Norwich	VII.
c. 1440	A friar, Great Amwell, Herts.	I.
c. 1440	Bro. William Jernemu (Yarmouth), hf-eff. ins., Halvergate, Norf. (Palimpsest : on obverse Alice Swane, 1540.)	II.
c. 1450	? Reginald Bernewelt, Benedictine monk, St. Albans Abbey, Herts.	IV.
c. 1460	Robt. Beauner, Benedictine monk, ins., St. Albans Abbey, Herts. (Holding a bleeding heart.)	VI.
c. 1460	Martin Forester, hf-eff. ins., Yeovil, Som.	I.
c. 1470	A Benedictine monk, hf-eff., St. Albans Abbey, Herts.	X.
1502	John Stodeley, Augustinian Canon of St. Frideswide's, Oxford, ins., Over Winchendon, Bucks.	I.
c. 1510	Rich. Bewfforeste, Augustinian Abbot of Dorchester, Dorchester, Oxon. PLATE 56	V.
1521	Thos. Rutlond, Benedictine Sub-Prior, St. Albans Abbey, Herts.	XVI.

FEMALE

1436	Dame Mary Gore, Prioress of Amesbury, Nether Wallop, Hants .	I.
c. 1520	Dame Elizth. Herwy, Benedictine Abbess of Elstow, Elstow, Beds. (With crozier.)	II.
c. 1540	Dame Agnes Jordan, Abbess of Syon, Denham, Bucks.	II.
1546	Eel Buttry, Prioress of Campesse, St. Stephen, Norwich	I.

Date.	Name, Description, Place and Emblems, etc.	M.S.
1561	Margt. Dely, Treasurer of Syon, ins., Isleworth, Middx. . .	III.
1577	Anne Boroeghe, kng. ins., Dingley, Northants . . .	I.

ORDER OF VOWESSES

(Widows who have vowed never to remarry)

1430	Dame Joan Besford, wid. of Sir W. Clopton, ca. ins., Quinton, Glos.	I.
c. 1500	Dame Julian Anyell, Witton (Blofield), Norf. . . .	I.
1519	Dame Joan Braham, ins., Frenze, Norf.	III.
1540	Dame Susan Fetyplace, wid. of J. Kyngeston, ins., Shalston, Bucks.	I.

POST-REFORMATION ECCLESIASTICS

BISHOPS

1578	Edm. Guest, Bishop of Rochester, ins., Salisbury Cathedral. (In rochet, chimere, lawn-sleeves and scarf.) PLATE 58 . .	II.
1616	Hen. Robinson, Bishop of Carlisle, kng. ins., Queen's Coll., Oxford. (In rochet, chimere, lawn-sleeves and scarf.) .	IV.
1631	Samuel Harsnett, Archbishop of York, ins., Chigwell, Essex. E.S. (In rochet, chimere and cope.) PLATE 57 . . .	II.

RECTORS, VICARS, Etc.

1561	Wm. Bill, Dean of Westminster, ins., Westminster Abbey . .	XIV.
1566	John Fenton, ins., Coleshill, Warw.	III.
1581	Hen. Helme, ins., Sturminster Marshall, Dorset . . .	II.
1582	Nich. Asheton, B.D., Whichford, Warw.	I.
1587	Rich. Woddomes, w. ch. ins., Ufton, Warw.	I.
1588	Patrick Fearne, kng. ins., Sandon, Essex	II.
1589	John Garbrand, kng. ins., Crawley, Bucks.	II.
1589	Edw. Leeds, ins., Croxton, Cambs.	I.
1591	Hen. Wilsha, ins., Storrington, Suss.	I.
1595	Thos. Reve, kng. ins., Monewden, Suff.	II.
1602	Wm. Lucas, ins., Clothall, Herts. E.S.	V.
1606	John Metcalfe, ins., Stonham Aspall, Suff.	I.
1608	John Burton, kng., Burgh St. Margaret, Norf. . . .	I.
1608	Thos. Rogerson, w. and dau. Agnes Bigge, ins., Ingoldisthorpe, Norf.	I.
1610	Isaiah Bures, kng. ins., Northolt, Middx. . . .	III.
1610	Peter Winder, ins., Whitchurch, Oxon.	IV.
c. 1610	Anon. In the possession of Mr. Philip Nelson, F.S.A., and on loan to the Victoria and Albert Museum. . . .	IX.
1613	Vincent Huffam, ins., St. James, Dover, Kent . . .	I.

Date.	Name, Description, Place and Emblems, etc.	M.S.
1614	Umphry Tindall, ins., Ely Cathedral	III.
1615	John Wythines, ins., Battle, Suss.	VI.
1616	Hen. Airay, D.D., ins., Queen's Coll., Oxford	IV.
1617	Thos. Browne, ins., Piddlehinton, Dorset	III.
1617	Wm. Lee, ins., Stapleford, Cambs.	II.
1617	Thos. Barker, kng. ins., Yelden, Beds.	II.
1618	Hugh Johnson, hf-eff. (in pulpit), ins., Hackney, London	IV.
1618	Wm. Palke, w. ins., High Halstow, Kent	II.
1619	Hen. Mason, ins., Eyke, Suff.	II.
1621	Andrew Willet, ins., Barley, Herts.	II.
1622	John Newman, ins., Remenham, Berks.	II.
1625	Rich. Lightfoot, Stoke Bruerne, Northants	I.
1627	Thos. Stones, hf-eff. ins., Acle, Norf.	IV.
1627	Wm. Procter, ins., Boddington, Northants	II.
1631	Maurice Hughes, ins., Abergavenny, Mon.	V.

See also Academical Costume.

ACADEMICAL COSTUME

14TH CENTURY

1361	John Hotham, D.D., Provost of Queen's Coll., Oxford, hf-eff. ins., Chinnor, Oxon.	II.
1370	Anon., Merton Coll., Oxford. (In the head of a cross.)	II.

15TH CENTURY

1405	John Strete, D.D., br. kng. ins., Upper Hardres, Kent. SS. PLATE 60	I.
c. 1410	Wm. Calwe, kng. ins., Ledbury, Hereford	I.
1414	Eudo de la Zouch, Juris Civilis Doctor, Chancellor of the University, ca., St. John's Coll., Cambridge. PLATE 60	I.
1420	John Motesfont, LL.B., ins., Lydd, Kent	I.
c. 1420	John Bloxham, B.D., and John Whytton, br. ca. ins., Merton Coll., Oxford. PLATE 59	III.
1421	Wm. Taveram, ca., Royston, Herts.	I.
1427	John Lowthe, Juris Civilis Doctor, ins., New Coll., Oxford	V.
c. 1430	John Kent, scholar of Winchester, ins., Headbourne-Worthy, Hants. PLATE 60	I.
c. 1430	Anon., ca., Melton, Suff. (On brass of parents.)	I.
1436	John Holbrook, Master of Peterhouse, ins., St. Mary-the-less, Cambridge	I.
1441	Wm. Hautryve, Juris Canonici Doctor, ins., New Coll., Oxford	VII.
1442	Rich. Billingford, D.D., Master of Benet Coll., kng., St. Benedict, Cambridge	I.

Date.	Name, Description, Place and Emblems, etc.	M.S.
1445	John Kyllyngworth, M.A., hf-eff. ins., Merton Coll., Oxford	IV.
1447	Geoff. Hargreve, S.T.S., Fellow, ins., New Coll., Oxford	VIII.
c. 1450	John Darley, B.D., ins., Herne, Kent. E.S.	II.
c. 1450	Anon., M.A., Thaxted, Essex	I.
1451	Wm. Snell, M.A., Boxley, Kent	I.
1451	Walter Wake, S.T.S., Fellow, hf-eff. ins., New Coll., Oxford	IX.
1451	Rich. Folcard, M.A., hf-eff. ins., Pakefield, Suff.	II.
1456	Rich. Drax, "in utroque jure Baculari," ins., Brauncepeth, Durham	II.
1460	John Alnwick, M.A., ins., Surlingham, Norf.	I.
c. 1460	Anon., hf-eff., Harrow, Middx.	IV.
1468	Thos. Hylle, D.D., ins., New Coll., Oxford. PLATE 60	XII.
1472	Thos. Mareys, ins., Stourmouth, Kent	I.
1474	John Child, Cheriton, Kent	I.
1478	Ralph Vawdrey, M.A., hf-eff. ins., Magdalen Coll., Oxford	I.
1478	Thos. Sondes, S.T.S., ins., Magdalen Coll., Oxford	II.
1478	Rich. Wyard, LL.B., ins., New Coll., Oxford	XIV.
1479	John Palmer, B.A., ins., New Coll., Oxford	XV.
c. 1480	Anon., cha., Barking, Essex	I.
c. 1480	Anon., kng., Fulbourn, Cambs.	IV.
c. 1480	Anon., M.A., Magdalen Coll., Oxford	IV.
c. 1480	Anon., Little Shelford, Cambs.	III.
c. 1480	Anon., Strethall, Essex	I.
1482	Nich. Wotton, LL.B., St. Helen, Bishopsgate. From St. Martin Outwich	III.
1487	Hen. Upnore, ins., Great Horwood, Bucks.	I.
1490	Rich. Spekyngton, LL.B., ins., All Souls Coll., Oxford	II.
c. 1490	? Thos. Freer, Magdalen Coll., Oxford	V.
1496	Wm. Towyn, D.D., ins., King's Coll., Cambridge	I.
1499	Wm. Goche, ins., Barningham, Suff.	I.
c. 1500	Anon., D.D., St. Mary-the-less, Cambridge	II.
c. 1500	Geo. Rede, kng. ins., Fovant, Wilts. A.	I.
c. 1500	Anon., D.D., St. Helen, Bishopsgate, London. From St. Martin Outwich	VI.
c. 1500	Geo. Lassy, M.A., hf-eff. ins., Magdalen Coll., Oxford	IX.
c. 1500	? John Crosse, Turvey, Beds.	II.
c. 1500	Anon. In the possession of Mr. Philip Nelson, F.S.A., and on loan to the Victoria and Albert Museum	V.

16TH CENTURY

1501	Wm. Herward, D.D., ins., Abingdon, Berks.	II.
1501	Thos. Mason, M.A., ins., Magdalen Coll., Oxford	XI.
1506	Thos. Gerard, ins., Stokesby, Norf.	III.
1507	John Argentein, D.D., M.D., Provost, ins., King's Coll., Cambridge	II

Date.	Name, Description, Place and Emblems, etc.	M.S.
1508	John London, M.A., S.T.S., ins., New Coll., Oxford . . . XVIII.
1510	David Lloyde, LL.B., and Thos. Baker, hf-eff. ins., All Souls Coll.,
	Oxford. (T. Baker wearing civil dress with scholar's gown.)	III.
c. 1510	Anon., ins., Broxbourne, Herts. E.S. . . . . . III.
1512	John Stonor, ins., Wraysbury, Bucks. (Schoolboy.) PLATE 60 .	II.
1515	John Trembras, M.A., ins., St. Michael Penkevil, Cornw. . . II.
1517	John Spence, B.D., ins., Ewelme, Oxon. . . . . XI.
1518	Thos. Coly, M.A., cha. ins., Bredgar, Kent . . . . II.
1519	John Bowke, M.A., hf-eff. cha., Merton Coll., Oxford . . VII.
1521	Wm. Blakwey, M.A., kng., Little Wilbraham, Cambs. . . I.
1522	Robt. Godfrey, LL.B., ins., East Rainham, Norf. . . . II.
1523	Robt. Gosebourne, ins., St. Alphege, Canterbury . . . II.
1523	Nich. Goldwell, M.A., ins., Magdalen Coll., Oxford . . XVI.
1524	John Barratte, B.A., kng. ins., Winchester College . . . XVIII.
1525	Walter Smith, M.A., Eton Coll., Bucks. . . . . VIII.
1530	Hugh Humphray, M.A., ins., Barcheston, Warw. . . . I.
c. 1530	Anon., Trinity Hall, Cambridge . . . . . II.
c. 1530	Wm. Taylard, LL.D., kng., Offard Darcy, Hunts. . . . II.
1534	Thos. Leman, kng. ins., Southacre, Norf. B.V. . . . III.
c. 1535	Anon., Queen's Coll., Cambridge . . . . . II.
c. 1540	Anon., D.D., Christ's Coll., Cambridge. PLATE 60 . . II.
1545	Thos. Edgcomb, hf-eff. ins., Eton Coll., Bucks. . . . XII.
1571	Robt. Harte, kng. ins., St. John's Coll., Oxford . . . I.
1578	Hen. Dow, kng. ins., Christ Church Cathedral, Oxford . . VI.
1578	John Glover, M.A., kng. ins., St. John's Coll., Oxford . . IV.
1580	Wm. Smith, M.A., kng. ins., St. Mary Magdalen, Oxford . II.
1587	Stephen Lence, M.A., hf-eff. ins., Christ Church Cathedral, Oxford	VIII.
1598	Thos. Prestone, LL.D., ins., Trinity Hall, Cambridge . . IV.

17TH CENTURY

1601	Hugh Lloyd, Juris Civilis Doctor, kng. ins., New Coll., Oxford .	XXIII.
1613	Thos. Thornton, M.A., kng. ins., Christ Church Cathedral,
	Oxford . . . . XI.
1619	Anth. Aylworth, Regius Professor of Medicine, ins., New Coll.,
	Oxford . . . . XXV.
1631	Jerome Keyt, LL.B., kng. ins., Woodstock, Oxon. . . II.
1637	Nich. Roope, B.A., kng. ins., St. Aldate, Oxford . . . III.

LEGAL COSTUME

14TH CENTURY

| 1400 | Sir John Cassy, Chief Baron of the Exchequer, w. ca. ins., Deer- |
| | hurst, Glos. PLATE 61 . . . . I. |

15TH CENTURY

Date.	Name, Description, Place and Emblems, etc.	M.S.
1415	Sir Hugh de Holes, Justice of the King's Bench, Watford, Herts.	I.
1419	Wm. de Lodyngton, Justice of the Common Pleas to Hen. v., ca. ins., Gunby, Lincs.	II.
1420	Rich. Norton, Chief Justice of the King's Bench, w., Wath, Yorks. (N.R.)	I.
c. 1430	John Staverton, Baron of the Exchequer, w., Eyke, Suff.	I.
1436	John Martyn, Justice of the Common Pleas, w. ca. ins., Graveney, Kent	IV.
1439	John Cottusmore, Chief Justice of the Common Pleas, w. kng. ins., and the same persons with 5 sons and 13 daus. standing under canopy, Brightwell Baldwin, Oxon.	II, III.
1439	Sir John Juyn, Recorder of Bristol, Chief Justice of the King's Bench, ins., St. Mary Redcliffe, Bristol. PLATE 61	I.
1440	Thos. Rolf, serjeant-at-law, ins., Gosfield, Essex	I.
1467	Sir Peter Arderne, Chief Baron of the Exchequer, w., Latton, Essex	I.
1472	Sir Wm. Yelverton, Justice of the King's Bench, w., Rougham, Norf. (Robes worn over armour.)	I.
1475	Sir Wm. Laken, Justice of the King's Bench, ins., Bray, Berks. PLATE 61	IV.
1476	Sir Rich. Byngham, Justice of the King's Bench, wid. ins., Middleton, Warw.	I.
1479	Sir Thos. Urswyk, Recorder of London, Chief Baron of the Exchequer, w. ch., Dagenham, Essex	I.
1479	Sir Thos. Billyng, Chief Justice of the Common Pleas, w. ins., Wappenham, Northants	II.
1494	Brian Roucliff, Baron of the Exchequer, w. ins., Cowthorpe, Yorks. (W.R.) (Holding a church.)	I.

16TH CENTURY

Date.	Name, Description, Place and Emblems, etc.	M.S.
1513	Wm. Greville, Justice of the Common Pleas, w. ch. ins., Cheltenham, Glos.	I.
1522	John Brook, serjeant-at-law to Hen. VIII., Justice of Assize in the west of England, Chief Steward of the Monastery of Glastonbury, w. ins., St. Mary Redcliffe, Bristol	V.
1538	Sir Anth. Fitzherbert, Justice of the Common Pleas, w. ins., Norbury, Derb. Armf. R.	II.
1544	Sir Walter Luke, Justice of the Common Pleas, w. kng. ins., Cople, Beds. Armf.	V.
1545	Thos. Holte, Justice of North Wales, w. ch. ins., Aston, Warw. E.S.	I.

Date.	Name, Description, Place and Emblems, etc.	M.S.
1545	Sir John Spelman, Recorder of Norwich, Secondary Justice of the King's Bench, w. kng. ins., Narborough, Norf. Armf. R. PLATE 61	IV.
1553	Wm. Coke, Justice of the Common Pleas, w. ch. ins., Milton, Cambs. E.S.	I.
1563	Nich. Luke, Baron of the Exchequer, w. ch. kng. ins., Cople, Beds.	VIII.

SHROUDS AND SKELETONS

SHROUDED EFFIGIES

15TH CENTURY

1431	Joan Mareys, hf-eff. ins., Sheldwich, Kent	III.
1454	John Brigge, ins., Sall, Norf.	V.
1455	John Manfeld, ins., Taplow, Bucks.	II.
1468	Robt. Brampton, w. ins., Brampton, Norf. B.V. . .	I.
1472	Thos. Flemyng, ins., New Coll., Oxford . . .	XIII.
1472	Agnes Bulstrode, kng., Upton, Bucks. . · . . .	I.
1477	Joan Walrond, w. of Robt. Strangbon, ins., Childrey, Berks. H.T.	VI.
1477	Margery Beel, ch., Hitchin, Herts.	V.
c. 1480	Anon. (priest), Stifford, Essex	II.
1484	Wm. Robert, w. ins., Digswell, Herts. PLATE 62 . .	III.
1484	John Leventhorpe, w. ins., Sawbridgeworth, Herts. . .	IV.
1485	Elizth. Mattock, Hitchin, Herts.	IX.
1485	Tomesin Sydney, w. of W. Tendryng, ch. ins., Yoxford, Suff. .	IV.
1486	Thos. Spryng, kng. ins., Lavenham, Suff. . . .	I.
c. 1490	? John Wisebeard, Hitchin, Herts.	X.
c. 1490	Anon., Hitchin, Herts.	XI.
1495	Margt. Shelley, ins., Hunsdon, Herts. H.T. . .	I.
1497	Wm. Leynthall, ins., Great Haseley, Oxon. . . .	III.
1500	Rich. Yate, w. ins., Longworth, Berks. · . .	II.
c. 1500	John Reynes, w., Clifton Reynes, Bucks. . . .	II.
c. 1500	Cecily Legge, Great Fransham, Norf. . . .	II.
c. 1500	Robt. Lockton, w. ch., Sawston, Cambs. . . .	IV.

16TH CENTURY

1501	Thos. Chylton, ins., Newington-next-Hythe, Kent . .	II.
1501	Wm. Gibson, w., Watlington, Oxon.	II.
1505	Thos. Tyard, ins., Bawburgh, Norf.	IV.
1505	Wm. Dussyng, w. ins., Kirby Bedon, Norf. . . .	III.
1506	Wm. Lenthorpe, ins., Marston Mortaine, Beds. Now lost.	
1507	Thos. Wymer, ins., Aylsham, Norf.	V.

Date.	Name, Description, Place and Emblems, etc.	M.S.
c. 1510	John Hampton, w. ch. ins., Minchinhampton, Glos. (One son a monk, one daughter a nun.)	II.
c. 1510	Anon., w., West Molesey, Surr. Now lost.	
1512	John Symondes, w. ins., Cley-next-the-Sea, Norf.	V.
1513	Wm. Wetherden, ins., Bodyam, Suss.	III.
c. 1514	Wm. Fyssher, ins., Wigston's Hospital, Leicester	I.
1515	Hen. Scolows, w., St. Michael Coslany, Norwich. E.S.	III.
1516	Wm. Feteplace, w. ins., Childrey, Berks. (Rising from tombs.)	VIII.
1516	Hen. Fayrey, w., Victoria and Albert Museum. (From Dunstable, Beds.)	V.
1518	Robt. Alee, w., Victoria and Albert Museum. (From Dunstable, Beds.)	VI.
1519	Sir Lionel Dymoke, ins., Horncastle, Lincs.	II.
1520	Kath. Incent, ins., Great Berkhampstead, Herts.	VII.
c. 1520	Anon., Fincham, Norf.	I.
c. 1520	Thos. Hobson, ins., Frenze, Norf.	IV.
c. 1520	Christ. Grantham, ins., Wooburn, Bucks. H.T.	IV.
1529	Margt. Hornebolt, hf-eff. ins., Fulham, London. PLATE 62	I.
1533	Francis Younge, w., Edgmond, Salop	I.
1540	Elizth. Rok, ins., Penn, Bucks.	I.
1546	John Blomeville, w. ins., Loddon, Norf.	VII.
1547	Lucas Goodyere, ins., Aldenham, Herts.	XI.
1548	Elizth. Horne, ins., Shipton-under-Wychwood, Oxon.	I.
1548	Hugh Brystowe, ins., Waddesdon, Bucks.	III.
1567	Alex. Belsyre, ins., Handborough, Oxon.	II.
c. 1580	Anon., Leigh, Kent. PLATE 62	II.
1590	Thos. Nele, ins., Cassington, Oxon.	II.

17TH CENTURY

1638	Mary Howard, ins., West Firle, Suss.	VII.
1660	Philip Tenison, Bawburgh, Norf.	VI.

SHROUDED SKELETONS

1499	Rich. Howard, w. ins., Aylsham, Norf..	III.
c. 1500	Anon., Lowestoft, Suff.	II.
c. 1500	Anon., Sedgefield, Durham	IV.
c. 1510	Ralph Hamsterley, ins., Oddington, Oxon.	I.
1518	John Goodryngton, ins., Appleton, Berks.	I.
c. 1530	Anon., Hildersham, Cambs.	IV.
c. 1530	John Claimond, ins., Corpus Christi Coll., Oxford	I.
c. 1540	Anon., Wiveton, Norf.	II.
c. 1560 ?	Anth.(?) Cave, ins., Chicheley, Bucks.	II.

SKELETONS

Date.	Name, Description, Place and Emblems, etc.	M.S.
1446	Rich. Notfelde, ins., St. John, Margate .	VI.
1452	Thos. Childes, St. Laurence, Norwich .	VIII.
1585	Jone Furnace, ins., Church Brampton, Northants	I.
1598	Rich. Ballett, ins., Ufford, Suff. .	II.
1605	John Maunsell, ins., Haversham, Bucks. .	II.
1612	On brass to Margt. Myssenden, ins., Whaddon, Bucks.	II.
1641	John Eager, ins., Crondall, Hants	III.
1694	Dorothy Williams, ins., Pimperne, Dorset	I.

INFANTS IN SWADDLING CLOTHES

15TH CENTURY

1467	6 sons and 4 daus. (Astley), formerly Standon, Herts. (In shrouds.)	
1492	Thos. Greville, ins., Stanford Rivers, Essex .	I.

16TH CENTURY

1509	On brass to Robt. Heyward, Teynham, Kent .	II.
1510	John and Roger Yelverton, ca. ins., Rougham, Norf. .	IV.
1512	On brass to Anne Asteley, Blickling, Norf. .	XIX.
1516	Elyn Bray, ins., Stoke d'Abernon, Surr. (Chrysom.) .	V.
c. 1520	Benedict Lee, Chesham Bois, Bucks. (Chrysom.) .	II.
c. 1520	On brass to a civilian, Cranbrook, Kent .	I.
c. 1520	John Skevington, ins., Hornsey, Middx.⋅ (Chrysom.) .	II.
c. 1520	Thos. Cowrll, ins., Southfleet, Kent. (In shroud.) .	VI.
c. 1530	John Colvyle, Ketteringham, Norf. .	IV.
1533	On brass to Margt. Cryppys, Birchington, Kent. (Chrysom.) .	VI.
1580	Anne Bedingfield, ins., Pinner, Middx. .	I.
1581	On brass to Constance Bownell, Heston, Middx. L. .	I.
1583	Elizth. Bacon, ins., Aveley, Essex .	III.
1584	On brass to John Daye, Little Bradley, Suff. .	III.
1587	On brass to Ed. Greneville, ins., Wotton Underwood, Bucks. .	I.
1590	On brass to Wm. Butler, Coates-by-Stow, Lincs. .	II.
1590	On brass to Margt. Tuke, Tilty, Essex .	IV.
1596	On brass to John Tedcastell, Barking, Essex .	V.
1600	John Howard, Great Chesterford, Essex. (Chrysom.) .	II.

17TH CENTURY

1606	Anne Consant, St. Leonard, Deal, Kent. (Chrysom.) .	III.
1607	On brass to John Bannister, Netteswell, Essex .	II.
1610	On brass to Dorcas Musgrave, ins., Cressing, Essex. .	I.
1624	On brass to Rich. Martin, Long Melford, Suff. .	X.

Date.	Name, Description, Place and Emblems, etc.	M.S.
1631	Clopton Dewes, ins., Lavenham, Suff. (Chrysom.) . . .	III.
1636	Margt. Pye, ins., Odiham, Hants . . .	VII.
1637	On brass to Margt. Robertes, Abergavenny, Mon. . . .	VII.
1638	Ann Tyrell, ins., Stowmarket, Suff. (In shroud.) . . .	I.

SACRED SUBJECTS

THE HOLY TRINITY

1462	Sir Sampson Meverell, ins., Tideswell, Derb. E.S. . . .	I.
1499	Rich. Ardern, ins., Leigh, Surr.	III.
c. 1545	Myghell Fox, ins., Chacombe, Northants	I.

See also entries marked " H.T." in lists of Costume.

THE RESURRECTION

c. 1500	Anon., All Hallows, Barking, London	VII.
1503	Robt. Harding, ins., Cranleigh, Surr.	I.

See also entries marked " R." in lists of Costume.

THE BLESSED VIRGIN

1417	Robt. de Brun, ins., Chelsfield, Kent	I.
c. 1500	The Blessed Virgin kneeling at a desk. British Museum.	

See also entries marked " B.V." in lists of Costume.

THE ADORATION OF THE SHEPHERDS

c. 1500	Anon., Cobham, Surr.	I.

ST. CHRISTOPHER

1498	Wm. Complyn, ins., Weeke, Hants. PLATE 62 . . .	I.

See also entries marked " C." in lists of Costume.

ANGELS

c. 1430	Walter Beauchamp, Checkendon, Oxon. (A soul borne by angels.)	III.
1496	Dame Anne Muston, Saltwood, Kent. (An angel holding a heart.)	III.
1509	Jas. Seyntleger, ins., Monkleigh, Devon. (Angels holding scroll.)	I.

EVANGELISTIC SYMBOLS

c. 1470	Anon., Beeston Regis, Norf.	I.
1482	Thos. Clerk, All Saints, North St., York	I.

Date.	Name, Description, Place and Emblems, etc.	M.S.
1483	Thos. Hagham, ins., Sall, Norf.	X.
1516	Robt. Burght, St. Stephen, Norwich	VIII.

See also entries marked " E.S." in lists of Costume.

CROSSES

NOTE.—*All crosses are floriated unless otherwise stated.*

c. 1320	Anon., Chinnor, Oxon. (With head of priest.) . . .	I.
c. 1380	Anon., Grainthorpe, Lincs.	I.
1400	Thos. Chichele, ins., Higham Ferrers, Northants. L. E.S. (Plain cross.) PLATE 62	II.
c. 1400	? John Cheney, Hanbury, Staffs. Now lost.	
1414	Roger Cheyne, ins., Cassington, Oxon.	I.
1416	Wm. Baron, ins., St. Mary, Reading, Berks.	I.
c. 1420	Roger Trewythynnyk, ins., Sithney, Cornw.	I.
1425	Margt. Oliver, ins., Beddington, Surr.	II.
1445	Rich. Tooner, ins., Broadwater, Suss.	III.
1469	Wm. Horn, ins., St. Mary-le-Wigford, Lincoln. (Plain cross.) .	I.
c. 1500	Anon., Royston, Herts. (Plain cross, with the Five Wounds.) .	II.
1502	Rich. Pendilton, ins., Eversley, Hants. (Plain cross.) . .	I.
1516	Thos. Burgoyn, ins., Sutton, Beds.	I.
c. 1520	Thos. Bwllayen, ins., Penshurst, Kent. (Plain cross.) .	III.
1527	Sir Wm. Constable, ins., Rudstone, Yorks. (Plain cross.) . .	I.
1537	Alyce Wyrley, ins., Floore, Northants	III.
1581	Fridesmond Giffard, w. of W. Barnes, ins., St. Andrew, Auckland, Durham	III.
n. d.	Anon., formerly Ringwould, Kent. Now lost.	
n. d.	Anon. Locality unknown.	

For crosses with effigies, see lists of Costume.

CHALICES

1460	Peter Johnson, ins., Bishop Burton, Yorks.	I.
1466	Wm. Langton, ins., St. Michael Spurriergate, York . . .	I.
1469	Thos. Clarell, ins., St. Peter, Leeds, Yorks.	III.
1499	John Smyth, ins., St. Giles, Norwich	IV.
1502	Hen. Alikok, ins., Colney, Norf.	I.
1502	Rich. Grene, ins., Hedenham, Norf.	III.
1504	John Robertson, ins., Guestwick, Norf.	I.
1508	John Feelde, ins., Belaugh, Norf.	II.
1508	Robt. Northen, ins., Buxton, Norf.	III.
1510	Thos. Hoont, ins., Bintry, Norf.	I.
1510	Edw. Warcop, ins., Wood Dalling, Norf.	IX.

Date.	Name, Description, Place and Emblems, etc.	M.S.
1513	Rich. Louhawkys, ins., Surlingham, Norf.	II.
1515	Robt. Wodehouse, ins., Holwell, Beds. (With two wild men.)	I.
1515	John Thorp, ins., Taverham, Norf.	III.
1519	Robt. Sevyr, ins., Salthouse, Norf.	I.
1519	Thos. Elys, ins., Shorne, Kent	V.
c. 1520	Anon., Old Buckenham, Norf.	II.
c. 1520	Nich. Wethyrley, ins., Scottow, Norf.	I.
c. 1520	Wm. Weststow, ins., Little Walsingham, Norf. (In hand issuing from clouds.)	XIII.
c. 1520	Robt. Wythe, ins., North Walsham, Norf.	VI.
1523	Thos. Kyng, ins., Rendham, Suff.	I.
c. 1525	Geo. Cunynggam, ins., Attlebridge, Norf.	V.
c. 1530	Anon., Gazeley, Suff.	I.
1531	Wm. Richers, ins., Bawburgh, Norf. (In hands issuing from clouds.)	V.
1540	Wm. Curtes, ins., South Burlingham, Norf.	I.

For effigies with chalices, see Ecclesiastical and Academical Costume.

SECULAR SUBJECTS

INSCRIPTIONS

(Inscriptions are in English or Latin unless otherwise stated)

1333	Inscription relating to the foundation of Bisham Abbey. Palimpsest : on rev. of inscr. to Wm. Hyde, 1562, Denchworth, Berks. PLATE 63	III.
	Edward roy Danglet'e qe fist le siege deuant la cite de Berewyk et cōquyst la bataille illeoqz et la dite cite la veille seinte Margarete lan de g'ce MCCCXXXIII mist ceste pere a la requeste Sire William de Mountagu foundour de ceste mesoun.	
1349	Philip de Lee, Barton-in-the Clay, Beds. PLATE 63	I.
1349	Sir Esmonde Illeye, Holme Hale, Norf. (French.)	I.
1349	Wm. de Haukesworth, St. Mary-the-Virgin, Oxford	I.
c. 1360	Phelipe and Isobel de Louthe, Hertingfordbury, Herts. (French.)	
1361	John Barfoot, Cholsey, Berks. (French.)	I.
1361	Sir Robt. de Bilhemore, Lower Gravenhurst, Beds. (French.)	I.
1362	Robt. le Wale, Tolleshunt Darcy, Essex. (Palimpsest : on rev. of inscr. to Anth. Darcy, 1540.)	IV.
1368	Rauf Fallywolle, Ivinghoe, Bucks. (French.)	I.
c. 1370	John the Smith, Brightwell Baldwin, Oxon.	I.
1375	Hen. de Aldryngton, Goring, Oxon. (French.)	I.

Date.	Name, Description, Place and Emblems, etc.	M.S.
1399	John de Cobham, Hever, Kent. (French.)	I.
c. 1400	Adam Ramseye, Chinnor, Oxon. (French.)	VIII.
c. 1400	John Cristemas, Chinnor, Oxon. (French.)	IX.
c. 1400	John and Margt. Waltham, parents of John, Bishop of Salisbury, Waltham, Lincs.	I.
1403	Godithe de Stathum, Morley, Derb. PLATE 63	I.
1407	Thos. Chanu, Leigh, Kent	I.
1409	Jas. Donet, Rainham, Kent	I.
1410	Rich. Lenton, Faringdon, Berks.	I.
1411	Geo. Felbrygge of Tutyngton, Felbrigg, Norf.	II.
1415	John Corby, Broadwater, Suss.	I.
1418	Ralph de Stathum, Morley, Derb.	II.
c. 1420	Rich. Ruggenale, Hornsey (old church), Middx. PLATE 64	I.
c. 1420-30	Fragment of marginal inscription, St. Laurence, Norwich	II.
1430	Thos. Salmon, usher of the chamber to Hen. v., Arundel, Suss.	IV.
1432	Wm. Hotale, Hereford Cathedral	VII.
1433	Wm. Clyff, Winchester College	III.
1440	John Spicer, Worstead, Norf.	II.
1441	Dame Agnes, w. of John Fynderne, Childrey, Berks.	I.
1446	Robt. Clere, Great Ormesby, Norf. (Three scrolls with text from Job xix. 25.)	III.
1447	Robt. Whitecoumbe, Newark, Notts.	II.
1452	John Newles, St. Cross, Winchester	II.
1454 ?	Thos. Attelude, Bray, Berks.	III.
1455	Wm. Cotton, Landwade, Cambs.	I.
1460	Isabel, w. of Reginald Cobham, Lingfield, Surr. PLATE 64	X.
1460	Roger Merlawe, Wantage, Berks.	III.
1463	Sir John Popham, " dñs de Turney in Normandia et dñs de Charde-ford de Dene ac de Alvynton et alibi in Anglia," St. Laurence, Reading. (Palimpsest : on rev. of inscr. to Walter Barton, 1538.)	III.
1464	Wm. Saundres, St. Cross, Winchester	III.
1470	Margery, w. of Sir — Conyers, Sockburn, Durham	IV.
1475	John Chapman " quondam " Barker, Sibton, Suff.	I.
1479	Rich. Fastolf, Nacton, Suff.	I.
c. 1480	Wm. and John Tendryng, Yoxford, Suff.	III.
1490	John Playstow, vicar. Locality unknown.	
c. 1490	Anon., Lowestoft, Suff. (Two scrolls.)	I.
1492	Elizabeth Noon, w. of Robt. Dynne, Heydon, Norf.	IV.
1493	Edm. Ryghtwys, Bawburgh, Norf.	I.
1495	Thos. Amys, Barton Turf, Norf.	II.
1495	Alys, w. of John Thomas, Long Sutton, Lincs.	I.
1497	John Idewyn, Barton Turf, Norf.	IV.
1497	Rich. Betteson, Fakenham, Norf.	IV.

Date.	Name, Description, Place and Emblems, etc.	M.S.
1497	Anne Huggefford, w. of Gerard Danet, Weston-under-Weatherley, Warw.	I.
1499	John Aylyff, Biddenham, Beds.	II.
1499	John Swafham, Rougham, Norf.	II.
1500	James Pekham, Wrotham, Kent	III.
c. 1500	Thos. Amys, Barton Turf, Norf.	III.
c. 1500	Hen. Barn[aby ?], Cley, Norf.	III.
c. 1500	Wm. Garard, Darsham, Suff.	I.
c. 1500	Marion Reve, Darsham, Suff. PLATE 64 . . .	II.
c. 1500	Hen. Berd, Horstead, Norf. PLATE 64 . . .	I.
c. 1500	John Bischop, Southwold, Suff.	I.
c. 1500	Isabel Cossale, St. Mary Cray, Kent	I.
c. 1500	Katharine Pays, Theberton, Suff.	I.
c. 1500	Anne, w. of John Caly, Thelnetham, Suff. . . .	I.
c. 1500	Alice Sampson. East Anglian school. Formerly in possession of J. B. Nichols.	
1501	Rich. Ferror, St. Michael Coslany, Norwich . . .	II.
1501	Edm. Chapman, Sibton, Suff.	II.
1502	Walter Charyls, M.A., Magdalen Coll., Oxford . .	XII.
1502	John Wayte, St. Cross, Winchester	V.
1503	Robt. Wellyngton, Gilling, Yorks.	I.
1504	Five fragments of marginal inscription to Sir Thos. Rotherham, Luton, Beds.	VI.
1505	John Symondis, Cley, Norf.	IV.
1506	Robt. Ware, Burham (old church), Kent . . .	I.
1506	Thos. Rawlyn, Mepshall, Beds.	III.
1507	Christ. Peyton, Isleham, Cambs.	IV.
1507	Walter Darnowll, Penshurst, Kent	I.
1510	Wm. Bysse, Merton Coll., Oxford	VI.
c. 1510	Roger Wells, Adderbury, Oxon.	III.
1511	John Skottow, Yoxford, Suff.	V.
1512	Wm. Fyske, Halesworth, Suff.	II.
1513	John Kyppyng. Formerly in possession of Geldart and Son, Norwich.	
1514	Rich. Skynner, Winchester College	XV.
c. 1515	Thos. Coke, St. Michael Coslany, Norwich . . .	IV.
1518	Margt. Dawtrey, w. of Sir John Ernele. In possession of the Society of Antiquaries	VII.
1520	Sir Marmaduke Constable, Flamborough, Yorks. . .	I.
c. 1520	Robt. Incent, Great Berkhampstead, Herts. . . .	VI.
c. 1520	John Bukkenham, Isleham, Cambs.	VII.
c. 1520	Thos. Hervy, St. Giles, Norwich	V.
1521	Nich. Purvey, Dunstable, Beds.	VI.
1521	John Pynnoke, Stoke d'Abernon, Surr.	VI.

Date.	Name, Description, Place and Emblems, etc.	M.S.
1522	Thos. Halsey and Gavan Dowglas, Savoy Chapel, London	I.
1522	John Coke, Yoxford, Suff.	VI.
1525	Christ. Gray, Bisham, Berks.	III.
1525	John Jobson, "ffychmonger," St. Mary-le-Wigford, Lincoln. (With knife and cleaver.) PLATE 64	II.
1526	Thos. Themylthorpe, Foulsham, Norf.	I.
1527	Aubrey Goodwyn, Necton, Norf.	IV.
1527	Ralph Eyer, Sulhampsted Abbots, Berks.	I.
1530	Helen and Elizabeth Godfrey, St. Michael Coslany, Norwich	V.
1530	Alys Feteplas, Swinbrook, Oxon.	III.
c. 1530	John Dew, Stone, Kent	III.
c. 1530	Symond Feteplas, Swinbrook, Oxon.	IV.
1531	Wm. Lyveryche, John Tanner and Thos. Benet, Chipping Norton, Oxon.	VIII.
1531	Sir Thos. Blenerhaysette, Frenze, Norf.	VI.
1531	Rich. Bennet, Whitnash, Warwick	II.
1532	John Moore, Sibstone, Leic.	I.
1533	John Crugge, Harefield, Middx.	VII.
1537	Elsabeth, w. of Wm. Cornwaleys, Thrandeston, Suff.	I.
1542	Sir Thomas Nevell, Mereworth, Kent	III.
1543	Wm. Lukyn, Isleham, Cambs.	
1544	Wm. Chase, serjeant to Hen. VIII., Isleworth, Middx.	II.
1546	Rich. Poly, Boxstead, Suff.	I.
1551	John Burnell, West Drayton, Middx.	IV.
1551	Elizth. Wroughton, St. Cross, Winchester	VII.
1558	Elinor Cheseman, w. of John Palmer, Chipping Barnet, Herts.	I.
1562	Geo. Robertes, Brenchley, Kent	III.
1562	Wm. Hyde and w. Margery Cater, Denchworth, Berks.	III.
1566	Thos. Morley, St. Olave, Hart Street, London	II.
1566	Joyce Tomer, Weston-under-Weatherley, Warw.	III.
1567	Eustace Mascoll, Farnham Royal, Bucks.	I.
1568	John Stokes, Queen's Coll., Cambridge	III.
c. 1570	Emme Fox, Aldeburgh, Suff.	III.
1571	Edw. Glemham, Benhall, Suff.	I.
1571	John Thompson, St. George's Chapel, Windsor	VI.
1577	Anth. Russhe, St. George's Chapel, Windsor	VII.
1578	Robt. Tayllar, Cley, Norf.	VII.
1581	John Bredgman, Hythe, Kent	I.
1581	John Spelman, Narborough, Norf.	VII.
1583	John Sharp, Northiam, Suss.	IV.
1585	John Hersant, Dennington, Suff.	I.
1585	Anne, w. of Augustin Curteis, Honington, Suff. PLATE 65	I.
1586	Edm. Gresham, Thorpe Market, Norf. PLATE 65	II.
1586	Thos. Lovett, Wappenham, Northants	VI.

Date.	Name, Description, Place and Emblems, etc.	M.S.
1587	Mychaell Webbe, St. Peter, Thanet	IV.
1588	Rich. Rayle, Cley, Norf.	VIII.
1588	Sir Hen. Terrell, Downham, Essex	III.
1588	George Multon, Ightham, Kent	III.
1592	Geo. Amhurst, Yalding, Kent. (2 shields and inscr. added 1870.)	I.
1593	Clement Kelke, Bray, Berks.	VII.
1593	Martha Glascocke, w. of Edm. Aleyn, Hatfield Peverell, Essex .	IV.
1593	Robt. Rivett, Yoxford, Suff.	VII.
1594	Joyce Baker, w. of John Tyrell, Downham, Essex . . .	IV.
1594	Anne Harte, w. of Edw. Hall, Lullingstone, Kent . . .	V.
1594	Robt. Edgar, Sotterley, Suff.	IX.
1595	Thos. Copland, Sibton, Suff.	V.
1596	Zacheus Metcalfe, Great Missenden, Bucks.	III.
1599	William Clift, Steeple Ashton, Wilts.	
1600	Wm. Houghton, Gayton, Northants	I.
16th cent.	Two Latin vv. to 3 infant brothers, Ightham, Kent . . .	IV.
16th cent.	Four Latin vv. to a maiden, Ightham, Kent	V.
1601	Joan Hytchcocke, w. of Hen. Moncke, Iver, Bucks. . .	III.
1601	Hen. Baldwyn, Watford, Herts.	III.
1603	Alice Bruce, w. of T. Wingfelde, Parham, Suff. . . .	I.
1603	Rich. Brooke, Whitchurch, Hants	I.
1604	Thos. Cleeve, Margate, Kent	XIII.
1605	Rich. Manning, St. Mary Cray, Kent	IV.
1605	John Yonge, D.D., Bishop of Rochester, Bromley, Kent . .	V.
1605	Rich. Boys, Hawkhurst, Kent	III.
1605	Alex. Norwood, Margate, Kent	XIV.
1606	John Thruston, Hoxne, Suff.	I.
1607	Francis Hynson, w. of Robt. Southwell, Barham, Suff. . .	II.
1607	Sefton Bromwich, Bratton, Wilts.	I.
1608	Joan Emptage, St. Nicholas-at-Wade, Thanet . . .	IV.
1609	Kath. Mulcaster, Stanford Rivers, Essex	VI.
1610	Constance Castell, East Hatley, Cambs.	II.
1611	Robt. Chapman *alias* Barker, Sibton, Suff.	VI.
1611	Mary Blofeld, Sustead, Norf.	III.
1612	Edw. Seymour, Lord Beauchamp, Great Bedwyn, Wilts. . .	III.
1612	Francis Foxe, Yoxford, Suff.	VIII.
1613	Elizth. Wright, w. of E. Barker, Dennington, Suff. . . .	II.
1613	Hugh Whistler, Goring, Oxon.	IV.
1614	Mary Reed, w. of Hen. Bulstrode, Upton, Bucks. . . .	IV.
1616	Jane Stebbing, Brandeston, Suff.	I.
1616	Robt. Lukyn, Isleham, Cambs.	XII.
1618	Geo. Multon, Ightham, Kent.	VI.
1618	Margery Gilberde, w. of John Drury, St. Laurence, Ipswich .	III.
1618	John Haughfen, Tunstall, Suff.	I.

Date.	Name, Description, Place and Emblems, etc.	M.S.
1618	Francis le Neve, Great Witchingham, Norf.	IV.
1619	Hen. Edgar, Dennington, Suff.	III.
1620	John Denny, Beccles, Suff.	II.
1620	John Dobyn, Finningham, Suff.	I.
1620	Rose Robertson, w. of John Glover, Shottisham, Suff.	I.
1621	Elizth. Stebbing, Brandeston, Suff.	II.
1621	Alice Lukin, Isleham, Cambs.	XIII.
1621	Rich. Keterich, South Mimms, Middx.	V.
1621	Margt. Wegge, Swanton Abbott, Norf. PLATE 65	III.
1623	Anne Hathaway, w. of Wm. Shakespeare, Stratford-on-Avon, Warw.	I.
1624	Wm. Riches, Stalham, Norf.	III.
1624	John Riches, Stalham, Norf.	IV.
1624	Thos. Darce, Tolleshunt Darcy, Essex	VI.
1626	Wm. Jackson, St. Andrew, Norwich	IX.
1626	Christ. Yonges, Southwold, Suff.	II.
1627	Anne Dunch, Little Wittenham, Berks.	XI.
1628	Helen Brokeman, w. of John Strout, Newington-next-Hythe, Kent	X.
1629	Francis Waldegrave, w. of Thos. Laier, Costessey, Norf.	IV.
1629	John Andrewe, Wadenhoe, Northants	I.
1631	Mary Brockman, Newington-next-Hythe, Kent	XII.
1631	Thos. Parmenter, Witton (Tunstead), Norf.	III.
1633	John Brownejohn, Burghclere, Hants	II.
1634	An Cory, St. Michael-at-Plea, Norwich	VII.
1636	Mark Trowts, Faversham, Kent	XXII.
1636	Mary, w. of Donsany Southwell, Morton-on-the-Hill, Norf. PLATE 65	II.
1637	John Cayworth, Suffield, Norf.	II.
1637	Thos. Boteler, Watlington, Norf.	I.
1637	Joseph Fletcher, Wilby, Suff.	V.
1638	Audrey Richars, wid. of Geo. Multon, Ightham, Kent	IX.
1638	Hen. Fyrmage, St. Andrew, Norwich	X.
1638	Peter Ashton, D.D., Shillington, Beds.	III.
1638	Sir Thos. Playters, Sotterley, Suff.	XII.
1641	Dame Dorothy Bonham, w. of Sir Wm. Selby, ins., Ightham, Kent	X.
1641	Elizth. Wegge, w. of Philip Knolles, Swanton Abbott, Norf.	IV.
1642	John Chissull, Dunton, Beds.	I.
1642	6 English vv. from br. to Arthur, son of Philip, Lord Wharton, Wooburn, Bucks.	VII.
1645	Joan Crosse and Mary Keble, Halesworth, Suff.	IV.
1652	Mary Carpenter, Steeple Ashton, Wilts.	II.
1654	Mary Potts, Darley, Derb.	I.
1656	Thos. Manock, Fornham All Saints, Suff.	VI.
c. 1656	Mary Manock, Fornham All Saints, Suff.	V.
1657	Susanna Farrar, w. of John Collet, Little Gidding, Hunts.	III.

Date.	Name, Description, Place and Emblems, etc.	M.S.
1660	Thos. Higgins, Deddington, Oxon.	VI.
1660	Edw. Osborne, West Wittering, Suss.	I.
1662	Anne Hungerford, w. of Roger Markes, Steeple Ashton, Wilts.	III.
1670	John Gawdry, Chesham, Bucks.	I.
1671	Elizth. Wingfield, w. of Thos. Chybnale, Orlingbury, Northants	IV.
1671	Thos. Flower, Steeple Ashton, Wilts.	IV.
1677	Elizth. Taylor, West Wittering, Suss.	II.
1684	Thos. Symonds, Suffield, Norf.	III.
1685	Wm. Budd, LL.B., Alton Barnes, Wilts.	I.
1689	Rich. Sherlock, D.D., Winwick, Lancs.	IV.
1694	Mary Chamberlin, w. of Sir Hen. Goring, Burton, Wilts.	VI.
1702	Ann Brook, w. of John Farrer, Little Gidding, Hunts.	IV.
1705	Ann Michell, Milton Lilbourne, Wilts.	
1713	John and Cornelius Melchior, St. John Maddermarket, Norwich	XIII.
1730	Edward Watton, Devizes, Wilts.	
1744	Mary Eyles, Devizes, Wilts.	
1747	Ann Wilkins (1691) and Jane Rogers, Steeple Ashton, Wilts.	
1771	Robert Foulkes, Steeple Ashton, Wilts.	
1776	Geo. Greenwood, St. Mary Cray, Kent	VII.
1783	Wm. Goodday, Strelley, Notts.	

SHIELDS OF ARMS

Date.	Name, Description, Place and Emblems, etc.	M.S.
1361	Sir John de Rokesle, ins., Lullingstone, Kent	I.
1375	Wm. Holyngbroke, ins., New Romney, Kent	I.
c. 1380	Alice d'Adeleigh, w. of Thos. Tyrell, ins., Downham, Essex	II.
1389	Wm. Tonge, ins., All Hallows, Barking, London	I.
1399	John de Cobham, of Devonshire, ins., Hever, Kent	I.
c. 1400	John Mauntell, ins., Nether Heyford, Northants	I.
1403	Elizth. Aske, w. of Thos. Fitzwilliam, ins., Mablethorpe, Lincs.	II.
1405	John Colkyn, ins., Boughton-under-Blean, Kent	I.
1411	Geo. Felbrygge, ins., Felbrigg, Norf.	II.
1412	John de Burgh and w. Kath. Aske, ins., Catterick, Yorks.	I.
1423	Elizth. Bradston, w. of Sir Walter Pole, ins., Sawston, Cambs.	II.
1439	Wm. Gulby, ins., Orpington, Kent	I.
1440	Wm. Dyer, ins., Bray, Berks.	II.
1443	Rich. Burton, chief cook to the King, ins., Twickenham, Middx.	I.
1452	Thos. Borgeys, ins., Graveney, Kent	V.
1468	Thos. Prude, ins., St. Alphege, Canterbury	I.
1471	Sir Humph. Bourgchier, ins., Westminster Abbey	IX.
1471	Elizth. Hopton, w. of Thos. Knyvet, ins., Yoxford, Suff.	II.
1475	Thos. Scargile, Hornchurch, Essex	II.
1476 ?	Dame Elenor Mullens, w. of Sir Robt. Hungerforde and Sir Oliver Manyngham, ins., Stoke Poges, Bucks.	II.

Date.	Name, Description, Place and Emblems, etc.	M.S.
1485	Hen. le Strawnge, and w. Kath. Drury, ins., Hunstanton, Norf.	II.
c. 1500	Edm. Coket, ins., Ampton, Suff.	V.
c. 1500	Anon., Langley Marsh, Bucks.	IV.
c. 1500	John Brounyng and Wm. Brounyng, ins., Melbury Sampford, Dorset	III.
c. 1500	Wm. Chauncy, ins., Sawbridgeworth, Herts.	V.
c. 1500	Wingfield imp. Wentworth, Stowlangtoft, Suff.	I.
c. 1500	John Damme, ins., Sustead, Norf.	I.
15th cent.	Drury and impalements, Hawstead, Suff.	
1503	John Calthorp, and w. Alice Astley, ins., Blakeney, Norf.	IV.
1509	Garard Borell, ins., Cuckfield, Suss.	I.
c. 1510	— Lathum, and Goldsmiths' Co., Sandon, Essex	I.
1511	Edw. Risley, Great Shelford, Cambs.	II.
1516	Wm. Feteplace, and w. Elizth. Waring, ins., Childrey, Berks.	IX.
1517	Herry Dynne, ins., Heydon, Norf.	VII.
c. 1520	— Apsley, Thakeham, Suss.	III.
1529	Edw. Norrys, ins., Ewelme, Oxon.	XIII.
c. 1530	— Carew, St. Mary, Bury St. Edmunds, Suff.	V.
1534	Edm. Stoktun, Cookham, Berks.	VI.
1536	John Berney, Reedham, Norf.	III.
1540	Anth. Heyham, ins., Goldhanger, Essex	II.
1541	John Underwood, ins., St. Andrew, Norwich	VII.
1541	Wm. Tilgham, ins., Snodland, Kent	V.
1543	John Boys, ins., Denton, Kent	I.
1543	John Manning, and w. Agnes Petle, ins., Downe, Kent	III.
1544	Sir John Cornwallis, Great Berkhamstead, Herts.	VIII.
1547	Dame Elizth. Throkmerton, ins., Coughton, Warw.	II.
1547	John Poyntz, ins., North Ockendon, Essex	III.
1549	Wm. Pulter, ins., Hitchin, Herts.	XVI.
1550	Robt. Bulkeley, ins., Cople, Beds.	VI.
1550	Sir Robt. Peyton, ins., Isleham, Cambs.	X.
c. 1550	John Pulter, ins., Hitchin, Herts.	XVII.
1552	Rich. Waller, ins., Stoke Charity, Hants	III.
1553	Elionor Sea, w. of Thos. Hawkins, ins. Locality unknown.	
1554	John Croke, ins., Chilton, Bucks.	I.
1556	Robert Bulkeley, ins., Cople, Beds.	VII.
1556	Wm. Harris, ins., Southminster, Essex	I.
1558	Margt. Sydney, ins., Penshurst, Kent	VI.
1559	John Stokys, ins., King's Coll., Cambridge	V.
1559	Lady Kath. Blount, w. of Sir Mores Barkeley, ins., Datchet, Bucks.	I.
1561	John Marsh, Mcht. Adventurers, Mercers' Co., Hillingdon, Middx.	IV.
1561	Dame Elizth. Hobby, w. of Wm. Walsh, ins., Wraysbury, Bucks.	III.

Date.	Name, Description, Place and Emblems, etc.	M.S.
1562	Thos. de Grey, and w. Temperance Carewe, Merton, Norf.	VI.
1563	Margery Englefield, w. of Sir W. Saunders, ins., Weston-under-Weatherley, Warw.	II.
1567	Thos. Little, Bray, Berks.	VI.
1568	John Dudley, Duke of Northumberland, Royal Arms, and Arms of Coventry, ins., St. Mary's Hall, Coventry. (Lease of Cheylesmore Park.)	
1568	Geo. Gyll, ins., Wyddiall, Herts.	III.
1569	Nich. Chowne, ins., Aldenham, Herts.	XII.
c. 1570	Sir John Glemham, ins., Little Glemham, Suff.	I.
c. 1570	Christ. Glemham, ins., Little Glemham, Suff.	II.
1571	Thos. Glemham, ins., Little Glemham, Suff.	III.
1574	John Beer, ins., Dartford, Kent	VII.
1574	Robt. Chapman, ins., Stone, Kent	IV.
1575	Edm. Lucas, ins., St. Mary, Bury St. Edmunds, Suff.	VIII.
1575	Anne Goodyere, w. of T. Walkeden, ins., Hadley, Middx.	VI.
1576	John Shakbrugh, ins., Naseby, Northants	II.
1578	Butler imp. Wogan, Coates-by-Stow, Lincs.	I.
1579	Barth. Fromoundes, ins., Cheam, Surr.	VIII.
1580	Sir John Throkmorton, ins., Coughton, Warw.	III.
1580	Thos. Parker, ins., Willingdon, Suss.	II.
c. 1580	Sir John Kingsmill, and w. Constance Goring, Kingsclere, Hants	—
c. 1580	— Mordaunt, Turvey, Beds.	III.
1582	John Brooke, ins., Ash-next-Sandwich, Kent	IV.
1583	Ancestors of Sir Thos. Fane, Mereworth, Kent	IV.
1583	Geo. Rawe, ins., St. Clement, Sandwich, Kent	II.
1584	Chas. Barett, ins., Aveley, Essex	IV.
1584	Thos. Jones, ins., Taplow, Bucks.	X.
1584	Wm. Playters, ins., Sotterley, Suff.	VIII.
1584	Martin Harlakinden, ins., Woodchurch, Kent	IV.
1585	Edw. Barette, ins., Aveley, Essex	V.
1585	Anne Froste, ins., Ewelme, Oxon.	XIV.
1585	Gilbert Salstonstall, ins., South Ockendon, Essex	II.
1586	Thos. Lovett, Wappenham, Northants	VI.
1587	Mary Blenerhaiset, w. of F. Bacon, ins., Frenze, Norf.	X.
1587	Wm. Reve, ins., Monewden, Suff.	I.
1590	Peerce Pennaunte, ins., Hornchurch, Essex	VIII.
1590	Edm. Daye, ins., Thurleigh, Beds.	II.
1590	Augustine Parker, ins., St. Mary Quay, Ipswich	IV.
1594	Wm. Smyth, ins., Bray, Berks.	VIII.
1594	Griffith Hampden, and w. Anne Cave, ins., Great Hampden, Bucks.	III.
1595	John Gage, ins., West Firle, Suss.	VI.
1595	Ancestors of F. Fitzherbert, Tissington, Derb.	II.

Date.	Name, Description, Place and Emblems, etc.	M.S.
1595	Hen. Guyldeford, ins., Tunstall, Kent	V.
1597	Wm. Gomersall, ins., Hillingdon, Middx.	VII.
1597	Thos. Gilbert, ins., St. Peter, Sandwich, Kent . . .	I.
1599	Lionel Throkmorton, ins., Bungay, Suff.	II.
1599	Wm. Foorthe, ins., Hadleigh, Suff.	IV.
1599	Hen. Pettit, ins., St. John, Margate, Kent	XI.
1600	Elizth. Rogers, w. of J. Robinson, ins., St. Helen, Bishopsgate, London	X.
c. 1600	— Wilson, Hereford Cathedral	XXIV.
c. 1600	Mary Partridge, w. of T. Godfrey, ins., Lydd, Kent . .	XIII.
16th cent.	Carew imp. a chevron betw. 3 cushions, a bordure engrailed. Fornham All Saints, Suff.	VII.
16th cent.	Sotherton quartering Hethersett, St. John Maddermarket, Norwich.	
1603	Fayth Sutton, ins., Horsell, Surr.	III.
1604	John Estmond, ins., Gressenhall, Norf.	I.
1604	Susan Parker, ins., St. Nicholas, Ipswich	IV.
1605	Wm. Norwood, ins., St. John, Margate, Kent . . .	XIV.
1605	Mary Ferrer, St. Michael-at-Plea, Norwich	II.
1605	John Hill, ins., Woodnesborough, Kent	IV.
1608	Thos. Ellis, ins., Hertingfordbury, Herts.	II.
1608	Thos. Jernegan, ins., Stebbing, Essex	II.
1609	Sarah Estmond, ins., Gressenhall, Norf.	II.
1610	Hen. Estday, ins., Hythe, Kent	II.
1610	Sir Adam Sprakeling, St. Laurence, Thanet . . .	IV.
1610	Christ. Webbes, ins., Tunstall, Kent	VI.
1611	John Cowell, ins., Trinity Hall, Cambridge . . .	V.
1611	Tomizane Browne, ins., Tysoe, Warw.	III.
1612	Anne Gostling, ins., Ellough, Suff.	V.
1613	Wm. Sydnor, and w. Bridgett Jernegan, ins., Blundeston, Suff. .	I.
1613	Humf. Mildmay, ins., Danbury, Essex	I.
1613	Wm. Derehawgh, ins., Orford, Suff.	XII.
1613	Rich. Baispoole, ins., Potter Heigham, Norf. . . .	I.
1614	Wm. Boteler, ins., Eastry, Kent	III.
1614	Sybbill Greene, ins., Hever, Kent	VI.
1614	Wm. Winchcombe, ins., Little Wittenham, Berks. . .	X.
1615	Elizth. Crayford, w. of Wm. Boteler, ins., Higham, Kent .	II.
1615	Adam Sprakeling, ins., St. Laurence, Thanet . . .	V.
1616	John Danvers, ins., Marsh Baldon, Oxon.	I.
1616	John Tynte, ins., Wraxall, Som.	I.
1617	Anne Waferer, w. of Thos. Turner, Clapham, Beds. PLATE 65	I.
1618	John Bridges, ins., Marsh Baldon, Oxon.	II.
1618	Lady Barbara Bradbery, w. of Sir Hen. Cutts, and Wm. Covert, ins., Thurnham, Kent	I.

Date.	Name, Description, Place and Emblems, etc.	M.S.
1619	Sir John Croke, ins., Chilton, Bucks	III.
1619	Debora Whetenhall, w. of Robt. Multon, ins., Ightham, Kent	VII.
1619	Thos. Dade, ins., Tannington, Suff.	II.
1619	Prudence Cuppledicke, w. of J. Harvy, ins., Thrandeston, Suff.	II.
1620	John Barney, ins., St. Peter Permountergate, Norwich. (With skull.)	I.
1620	Susan Clere, w. of Thos. Wyndham, ins., Pentney, Norf.	I.
1620	Joan Walsh, w. of Thos. Bayles, ins., Wilby, Suff.	IV.
c. 1620	Elizth. More, w. of J. Bayles, ins., Wilby, Suff.	III.
1622	Susan Smart, w. of Jas. Barker, Worlingworth, Suff.	II.
1624	Sam. St. Nicholas, ins., Ash-next-Sandwich, Kent	VIII.
1624	Hen. Pettit, ins., Denton, Kent	II.
1624	Mary Wingfield, w. of W. Dade, ins., Tannington, Suff.	III.
1628	Wm. Wythwood, Felmingham, Norf.	X.
1628	Thos. Maydwell, ins., Geddington, Northants	II.
1628	Martha Ewer, ins., South Mimms, Middx.	VI.
1628	George Fitzpen *alias* Phippen, ins., Truro Cathedral, Cornw.	
1629	Mary Appleton, w. of Robt. Ryece, ins., Preston, Suff.	I.
1630	Edw. Paston, ins., Blofield, Norf.	IV.
1630	— Molesworth, Broxbourne, Herts.	V.
1630	Rich. Elcock, ins., Westhorpe, Suff.	I.
1632	Rich. Burgh, and w. Amy Dillington, Stow, Lincs.	I.
1633	Thos. Wight, ins., St. Helen, Bishopsgate, London	XI.
1634	Rich. Cholmley, ins., Crowhurst, Surr.	IV.
1634	Edw. Hales, ins., Faversham, Kent	XX.
1634	Sir Thos. Whorwood, ins., Holton, Oxon.	IV.
1635	Christ. Rous, ins., Wangford-near-Southwold, Suff.	I.
1638	Wm. Barrowe, ins., Borden, Kent	III.
1638	Thos. Aylet, ins., Coggeshall, Essex	VII.
1638	Mary Godefrey, w. of Sir J. Honywood, ins., Elmsted, Kent	III.
1638	Robt. Ryece, ins., Preston, Suff.	II.
1638	Lucy Bayles, ins., Wilby, Suff.	VI.
1639	Geo. Page, ins., Shorne, Kent	VIII.
1639	John Bayles, ins., Wilby, Suff.	VII.
1640	Helen Gulston, w. of J. Joscelyne, ins., Wyddiall, Herts.	VI.
1641	Edw. Gournay, ins., West Barsham, Norf.	II.
1641	Margt. Berney, w. of Edw. Paston, ins., Blofield, Norf.	V.
1641	John Higgins, ins., Deddington, Oxon.	III.
1641	Hen. Ewer, ins., South Mimms, Middx.	VII.
1641	Edw. Stern, ins., Stow-cum-Quy, Cambs.	II.
1642	Edw. Cheseldyn, ins., Braunston, Rutland	II.
1642	Humf. Dethick, ins., Weybridge, Surr.	V.
1644	Sir Robt. de Grey, and w. Elizth. Bridon, ins., Merton, Norf.	VII.
1644	Elizth. Barttelot, w. of Rich. Mille, ins., Stopham, Suss.	IX.

Date.	Name, Description, Place and Emblems, etc.	M.S.
1650	Sir Chas. Gawdy, ins., Debenham, Suff. (Coffin plate.)	II.
1651	Francis Fane, ins., Hunton, Kent	II.
1651	Geo. Snayth, ins., All Hallows, Barking, London	XVII.
1653	Bernard Wells, ins., Bakewell, Derb.	III.
1653	Sir Robt. Howard, K.B., ins., Clun, Salop. (*Lithograph.*)	I.
1654	Sir Hamon le Strange, ins., Hunstanton, Norf.	IV.
1656	Mary Mapletoft, ins., Little Gidding, Hunts.	I.
1656	Robt. Eyre, ins., Hathersage, Derb.	V.
1657	John Farrar, ins., Little Gidding, Hunts.	II.
1658	Lady Penelope, dau. of John, Earl of Bridgewater, w. of Sir R. Napier, Luton, Beds.	XV.
1659	Daniel Darnelly, ins., Trinity Hall, Cambridge	VII.
1661	Sophia Harrison, ins., South Mimms, Middx.	VIII.
1661	Hen. Ferne, D.D., ins., Westminster Abbey	XVI.
1665	Sir Geo. Feilding, K.B., Earl of Desmond, ins., Euston, Suff.	VII.
1666	Hester Talcot, w. of Rich. May, ins. Locality unknown.	
1668	Wm. Pierson, ins., Bessingby, Yorks.	I.
1673	Anth. Butler, ins., Coates-by-Stow, Lincs.	IV.
1676	Jas. Danby, ins., Kirkby Knowle, Yorks. (N.R.)	I.
1678	Thomasin Danby, ins., Kirkby Knowle, Yorks.	II.
1678	Edw. Cowper, ins., Slinfold, Suss.	III.
1681	Elizth. Wiseman, w. of J. Freshwater, ins., Heybridge, Essex	II.
1684	Hen. Broome, Ufford, Suff.	III.
1685	Jas. Wright, ins., Harbury, Warw.	III.
17th cent.	Anon., Stanford Rivers, Essex	VIII.
17th cent.	— Bowden, Stanwell, Middx.	II.
1707	Ursula Rokeby, ins., Kirkby Knowle, Yorks.	
1717	Eleanor Long, w. of Jas. Goddard, ins., Little Gidding, Hunts.	V.
1719	John Ferrar, ins., Little Gidding, Hunts.	VI.
1726	Micah Rokeby, ins., Kirkby Knowle, Yorks.	
1727	Elizth. Ingram, w. of Wm. French, ins., St. Mary, Cheltenham, Glos.	
1741	Joseph Rokeby, ins., Kirkby Knowle, Yorks.	
1758	Ursula Oakley, ins., Kirkby Knowle, Yorks.	
c. 1760	Elizth. Buxton, ins., Kirkby Knowle, Yorks.	
1766	Joseph Buxton, ins., Kirkby Knowle, Yorks.	
n.d.	Anon., Hereford Cathedral. (From the collection of J. G. Nichols.)	XXIX.
n.d.	Anon., Blickling, Norf.	
n.d.	Anon., Burnham, Bucks.	
n.d.	Carewe, Haccombe, Devon	
n.d.	Anon., Odiham, Hants	

CREST AND MANTLING

Date.	Name, Description, Place and Emblems, etc.	M.S.
1436	John Iwardeby, and w. Kath. de Missenden, Great Missenden, Bucks.	I.
1445	Wm. Hoton, ins., Sedgefield, Durham	II.
1536	John Berney, Reedham, Norf.	III.
1635	Sir Peter Legh, ins., Winwick, Lancs.	III.
n.d.	Anon. Locality unknown.	
n.d.	Anon. Locality unknown.	

SHIELDS WITH DEVICES

c. 1425	Robt. Asger, ins., St. Laurence, Norwich. (Mcht. mark.)	III.
c. 1480	John Jay, St. Mary Redcliffe, Bristol. (Mcht. mark and carding comb.)	IV.
c. 1480	John Stebyrd, ins., Sculthorpe, Norf. (Hammer, crown, etc.)	II.
c. 1490	Laurence Marton, Broughton, Hunts. (Sh. with rebus.)	I.
1501	Rich. Ferror, ins., St. Michael Coslany, Norwich. (Mcht. mark.)	II.
1503	John Goose, ins., East Dereham, Norf. (Sh. with rebus.)	III.
1508	John Carman, ins., Worstead, Norf. (Mcht. mark imp. Mercers' Co.)	VI.
1514	Thos. Warryn, ins., St. George Colegate, Norwich. (Mcht. mark.)	II.
c. 1520	Anon., St. Mary, Bury St. Edmunds, Suff. (Tau cross, with scroll.)	IV.
1527	John Holly, ins., St. Andrew, Norwich. (Mcht. mark.)	V.
1641	Elizth. Tawley, w. of F. Furlong, ins., Stoke-in-Teignhead, Devon. (Death's head, hour-glass, etc.)	II.
n.d.	Anon., Hereford Cathedral. (Mcht. mark, with initials N.H.)	XXIX(i).
n.d.	Anon., Hereford Cathedral. (Mcht. mark.)	XXIX(i).

HEARTS, HANDS, Etc.

1433	Thos. Smyth, ins., St. John, Margate	II.
1446	John Merstun, ins., Lillingstone Lovell, Bucks.	I.
c. 1450	Wm. Stapilton, ins., Helhoughton, Norf.	I.
c. 1450	Anon., Kirby Bedon, Norf.	I.
c. 1450	Sir Robt. Kervile, ins., Wiggenhall St. Mary, Norf.	I.
1454	Sir Roger Harsyk, ins., Southacre, Norf.	II.
c. 1460	Anon., Souldern, Oxon.	I.
1462	Denis Willys, ins., Loddon, Norf.	I.
c. 1470	Anon., Fakenham, Norf.	III.
1474	John Sperehawke, Hitchin, Herts.	
1491	John Colard, ins., Lower Halling, Kent. (The Five Wounds.)	I.
c. 1500	Anon., Higham Ferrers, Northants	VII.
1516	Elizth. Peyton, ins., Isleham, Cambs.	V.
c. 1530	Anon., ins., Trunch, Norf.	II.

Date.	Name, Description, Place and Emblems, etc.	M.S.
1633	Grace Barker, w. of Christ. White, Ludham, Norf.	X.
n.d.	Anon. Locality unknown.	

CANOPIES

(This list is of canopies from lost or mutilated effigies.   For other canopies see lists of Costume.)

1405	Wm. Noion, ins., Haddenham, Cambs.	I.
1408	Joan de Feversham, w. of J. Botiler, ins., Graveney, Kent	III.
1414	Seman Tong, ins., Faversham, Kent. H.T.	I.
c. 1425 ?	Sir John Howard, Stoke-by-Nayland, Suff.	III.
1438	Sir Brian de Stapilton, ins., Ingham, Norf.	I.
1448	Nich. Dixon, ins., Cheshunt, Herts.	I.
1451	John Stoke, ins., St. Albans Abbey, Herts.	V.
1497	Thos. Elynbrigge, Carshalton, Surr. B.V.	IV.
1524	Wm. Porter, Hereford Cathedral	XXI.
n. d.	Fragments of canopy work (4), Hereford Cathedral. (From the collection of J. G. Nichols.)	XXIX.

MISCELLANEOUS BRASSES

1412	John Killyngworth, ins., Ashridge House. From Edlesborough, Bucks. (Rose.)	II.
c. 1440	Peter Denot, ins., Fletching, Suss. (Gloves.)	II.
1481	John Rudyng, Biggleswade, Beds. (Figure of Death.)	II.
1500	Rich. Foxwist, Llanbelig, Carnarvon. (Effigy in bed.)	I.
c. 1580	Anon., Leigh, Kent. (Shrouded figure in a tomb, with female effigy summoned by an archangel.)	II.
1581	Constance Bownell, Heston, Middx. L. (A lady in childbed.)	I.
1587	Silvester Dene, w. of Wm. Lambarde, Lower Halling, Kent. (Effigy in bed, with children standing, and infants in cradle.)	II.
1591	Jas. Gray, ins., Hunsdon, Herts. (In hunting dress shooting at a stag while Death strikes him with a dart.)	III.
c. 1600	Alice Ward, w. of T. Harison, ins., Hurst, Berks. (Effigy in bed.)	II.
1615	Roger Morris, St. John, Margate. (A ship in full sail.) PLATE 62	XVIII.
1618	Edm. West, w. ch. ins., Marsworth, Bucks. (Reclining on a tomb, with the figure of Death.)	V.
1620	Robt. Longe, ins., Broughton Gifford, Wilts. (Altar tomb with Death and a herald.)	I.
c. 1620	Wm. Button, ins., Alton Priors, Wilts. (Effigy rising from a tomb at the summons of an archangel.)	II.
1622	Eliza Franklin, ins., St. Cross, Holywell, Oxford. (Effigy in bed.)	I.

Date.	Name, Description, Place and Emblems, etc.	M.S.
1623	Thos. Hopper, ins., New Coll., Oxford. (Figures of Aesculapius and Fortune, circles, triangles, etc.)	XXVI.
1642	Arthur Wharton, Wooburn, Bucks. (A child reclining on an altar tomb.)	VII.
1652	Dan. Evance, ins., Calbourne, Isle of Wight. (Figure of Death.)	III.
1694	Dorothy Williams, Pimperne, Dorset. (Recumbent skeleton.) .	I.

PALIMPSESTS

Lady, with lion at feet, portions of canopy and inscriptions. c. 1325. Perhaps the wife of Sir Theobald de Verdun (d. 1316).

> Reverse only; the obverse to Sir A. Fitzherbert, Norbury, Derb., 1538, is also in the collection.

Part of a civilian. Flemish, c. 1360.

> Reverse only; the obverse to a man in armour, Winestead, Yorks., c. 1540, is not in the collection.

Upper part of man in armour with armorial jupon, head resting on diapered cushion supported by angels; portions of canopy and marginal inscription. Flemish, c. 1375.

> Reverse only; the obverse to Rich. Gerveys, Constantine, Cornw., 1574, is not in the collection.

Portions of canopy with figures of saints, 14th cent., and ach. with the arms of Cleves and La Marke quarterly, with an inescutcheon of Burgundy modern and ancient with Flanders over all, surmounted by a helmet with the crest of the Dukes of Cleves. All Flemish, 15th cent.

> Reverse only; the obverse to R. Holingworth, Stondon Massey, Essex, 1573, is also in the collection.

Civilian under canopy. Flemish, 14th cent.

> Reverse only; the obverse, inscription to Wm. Wolstanton, Great Bowden, Leic., 1403, is not in the collection.

Saint under canopy. Flemish, 14th cent.

> Reverse only; the obverse, inscription to Wm. Chase, Isleworth, Middx., 1544, is also in the collection.

Head of a lady with braided hair on a cushion. Flemish, 14th cent.

> Reverse only; the obverse, inscription to Geoff. Melman, Sall, Norf., c. 1480, is not in the collection.

Part of canopy. Flemish, 14th cent.

> Reverse only; the obverse, inscription to Hen. Lee, Ewelme, Oxon., 1494, is not in the collection.

Part of a cross-legged effigy in mail with surcoat, c. 1300.

> Reverse only; the obverse, to a lady, hf-eff., Clifton Campville, Staffs., c. 1360, is also in the collection.

Part of effigy of St. Margaret under canopy.   English, c. 1420.

> Reverse only ; the obverse, inscription to Edm. Rede, Checkendon, Oxon., 1435, is not in the collection.

Part of priest in chasuble, c. 1490 ; a shield with the royal arms ; part of a lady, c. 1520 ; inscription to Thos. Cobbe, 1516 ; inscription to Margery Chamberlyn, 1431.

> Reverse only ; the obverse, to A. Cole, Magdalen Coll., Oxford, 1558, is also in the collection.

Parts of 3 marginal inscriptions.   Flemish.   (Another fragment of inscription is at Walkerne, Herts., part of the brass to Edward Humbarstone, 1583.   It gives the name Van Lauwr, 1474.)

> Reverse only ; the obverse, inscription to Wm. West, Marsworth, Bucks., 1583, is not in the collection.

Part of a draped figure, 15th cent., on reverse of inscription portion of the border of a large Flemish brass, with shield of ?De Buseve.

> Reverse only ; the obverse to Ales Maynarde, St. James, Colchester, Essex, 1584, is also in the collection.

Part of abbot.   15th cent.

> Reverse only ; the obverse to a civilian, Upminster, Essex, c. 1530, is also in the collection.

Part of border of Flemish brass, with scenes from the Life of Man.   15th cent.

> Reverse only ; the obverse, inscription to Thos. Flütt, St. John, Margate, 1582, is not in the collection.

Parts of canopy, and head, shoulders, and hands of a lady in diapered gown, head resting on cushion supported by angels.   Flemish, 15th cent.

> Reverse only ; the obverse, inscription to Dorothy Frankyshe, Harrow, Middx., 1574, is not in the collection.

Canopy work and censing angel.   (?) French, 15th cent.

> Reverse only ; the obverse to Robt. Fowler, St. Mary Islington, 1540, is also in the collection.

Part of a priest in chasuble.   15th cent.

> Reverse only ; the obverse, inscription to Robt. Moone, Felmingham, Norf., 1591, is not in the collection.

Part of monk, behind grille under canopy.   English, 15th cent.

> Reverse only ; the obverse, to a civilian, St. John Sepulchre, Norwich, c. 1535, is also in the collection.

Part of inscription with mcht. mark.   Flemish, 15th cent.

> Reverse only ; the obverse, inscription to Walter Bownyng, 1473, formerly Trunch, Norf., and now in the British Museum, is not in the collection.

Part of a civilian, 15th cent., and portions of Flemish canopy work.

> Reverse only ; the obverse to Clement Throkmorton, Haseley, Warw., 1573, is also in the collection.

Lower half of abbot or prior, possibly of the order of St. Dominic, in habit, scapular and cloak. English, c. 1500.

> Reverse only ; the obverse, inscription to Wm. Goldynge, Piddlehinton, Dorset, 1562, is not in the collection.

Part of br. to Thomas Humfre of London and wife Joan Bayntum, in shrouds (?), with children, and St. Michael weighing Souls. c. 1500.

> Reverse only ; the obverse, inscription to John Waterhouse, Great Berkhamstead, Herts., 1558, is not in the collection.

Part of a shrouded skeleton. c. 1500.

> Reverse only ; the obverse, inscription to John Crugge, Harefield, Middx., 1533, is also in the collection.

Part of an achievement from a Flemish brass. c. 1500. (For another portion, see the reverse of the inscription to Fraunces Holland, Isleworth, Middx.)

> Reverse only ; the obverse, inscription to Anne Draper, Erith, Kent, 1574, is not in the collection.

Part of an achievement from a Flemish brass. c. 1500. (For another portion, see the reverse of the inscription to Anne Draper, Erith, Kent.)

> Reverse only ; the obverse, inscription to Fraunces Holland, Isleworth, Middx., 1575, is not in the collection.

Head and shoulders of civilian, ornament. Flemish, c. 1500.

> Reverse only ; the obverse, inscription to Rowland Taillor, Hadleigh, Suff., c. 1560, is not in the collection.

The Holy Trinity. English, c. 1520.

> Reverse only ; the obverse, two shields from the brass to Geo. Assheby, Harefield, Middx., 1537, is not in the collection.

Leg of armed effigy wearing the Garter. c. 1520.

> Reverse only ; the obverse, inscription to Hen. Gee, Holy Trinity, Chester, 1545, is not in the collection.

The Resurrection, and fragments of inscription. c. 1530.

> Reverse only ; the obverse to Margt. Bulstrode, 1540, Hedgerley, Bucks., is also in the collection.

Inscription to Pieter Snouc, bailiff of Vinderhoute, and wife Jaquemyne van Steelant, 1554. Flemish.

> Reverse only ; the obverse, inscription to the brass of Lady Dorothy Taylare, Ewell, Surr., 1577, is also in the collection.

Angel holding lozenge of arms, etc. Flemish, 16th cent.

> Reverse only ; the obverse to Sir Robt. Hesketh, Rufford, Lancs., 1543, is not in the collection.

Parts of two Flemish inscriptions. Early 16th cent.

> Reverse only ; the obverse, inscription to Jane Fitzherbert, St. Mary Magdalen, Oxford, 1574, is not in the collection.

Small part of a Flemish brass. 16th cent.

> Reverse only ; the obverse, inscription to John Browne, Halesworth, Suff., 1581, is also in the collection.

Symbol of St. Luke, and part of marginal inscription ; part of a priest in chasuble with chalice.   Both foreign, probably German.

> Reverse only ; the obverse to Nich. West, Marsworth, Bucks., 1586, is also in the collection.

Ornament and part of canopy.   Flemish.

> Reverse only ; the obverse to Raffe More, Cookham, Berks., 1577, is also in the collection.

Part of effigies of a lady and a priest in mass vestments ; scroll work and part of Latin and English inscriptions.

> Reverse only ; the obverse to Wm. Thynne, All Hallows, Barking, London, 1546, is also in the collection.

Part of Flemish inscription.

> Reverse only ; the obverse to Anne Bedingfield, Pinner, Middx., 1580, is also in the collection.

Parts of two unfinished Flemish brasses.

> Reverse only ; the obverse, inscription to Barbara Strickland, Holme-by-the Sea, Norf., 1582, is not in the collection.

Part of priest in chasuble.   c. 1480.

> Reverse only ; the obverse, inscription to E. Goldyngham, Narborough, Norf., 1556, is not in the collection.

Part of lady in mantle, with two daughters.

> Reverse only ; the obverse, inscription to N. Suttherton, St. John Maddermarket, Norwich, 1540, is not in the collection.

Part of inscription in ornamental border.   Foreign.

> Reverse only ; the obverse, inscription to Margt. Dove, St. Giles, Camberwell, 1582, is not in the collection.

BRITISH INCISED SLABS

MILITARY COSTUME

CIVIL COSTUME
MALE

FEMALE

ECCLESIASTICAL COSTUME
EFFIGY IN CHASUBLE

EFFIGY IN ALB, AMICE, STOLE, Etc.

POST-REFORMATION ECCLESIASTIC

CONTINENTAL BRASSES AND INCISED SLABS

Ref.—C.=Creeny, The Rev. W. F.: *A Book of Facsimiles of Monumental Brasses on the Continent of Europe*, 1884; and also *Illustrations of Incised Slabs on the Continent of Europe*, 1891.

Note.—*The Numbers in the column headed* C. *refer to the Plates in the respective books.*

MILITARY COSTUME

13TH CENTURY

Date.	Name, Description, Place and Emblems, etc.	C.
1210	Sir Alars de Chimaix, Vireux Molheim, Belgium. I.S.	
1262	Georges de Niverlée, ca. ins., Niverlée, Belgium. Arm. I.S. PLATE 66	12
1269	Sir Eustace, *called* "li franshoms de Holleliule," ca. ins., St. Peter, Hognoul, Liège. I.S.	16
c. 1270	Sir Brocardus de Charpignie, ins., Hôtel de Cluny, Paris. From Larnaca, Cyprus. I.S.	19
1271	Sir Renier de Rikle, ca. ins., St. Trond Abbey, Limbourg, Belgium. Arm. I.S.	
1273	Gerard de Villers, ca. ins., Villers-le-Temple, Belgium. Arm. I.S. (Habit of the Order of Knights Templars.)	20
1279	Sir Guillaume de Hamale, ca. ins., St. Stephen, St. Heeren Elderen, Limbourg, Belgium. Arm. I.S.	
1296	Sir Nenkin de Gotheim, ca. ins., St. Denys, Gothem, Belgium. I.S.	27
13th cent.	Sire Antoine (?) de Bolzée, ins., from Glain, Liège. I.S. In the Victoria and Albert Museum.	

14TH CENTURY

Date.	Name, Description, Place and Emblems, etc.	C.
1307	Arnold Nenkin de Gothem, ca. ins., St. Denys, Gothem, Belgium. I.S.	33
1312	Sir Lambert, Lord of Abée, w. ca. ins., Abée, Belgium. Arm. I.S.	34
c. 1315	Sir John Dores, of Sumaing, ca. ins., Rhisnes Castle, Belgium. Arm. I.S.	
1318	Sir Raes de Greis, ca. ins., Villers-la-Ville Abbey, Belgium. Arm. I.S.	37
c. 1322	Daniel de Horpale, ws. (2) ins., Horpmael, Belgium. Arm. I.S.	
1325	William Wenemaer, wid., Archæological Museum, Ghent. B. .	12

160

Date.	Name, Description, Place and Emblems, etc.	C.
1328	Birger Peterson, w. ins., Upsala, Sweden. I.S.	39
c. 1330	Sir René de Malève, ca., Museum, Brussels. Arm. From Villers-la-Ville Abbey, Belgium. I.S.	40
1332	John and Gerard de Heere (1398), ca. ins., Museum, Brussels. From Heere, Belgium. B. PLATE 67	20
1343	Sire Druyes, Sire d'Aguyllei, ca. ins. French. Locality unknown. I.S.	
1352	Sir Guillaume du Chastelier, w. ca., St. Sulpice, Moulbaix, Belgium. Arm. I.S.	
1354	Sir Gilles de Hamale, ca. ins., St. Stephen, St. Heeren Elderen, Belgium. Arm. I.S.	
1358	Gerard de Gothem, w. ca. ins., St. Denys, Gothem, Belgium. I.S. PLATE 68	44
1385	Sir Henry de Guydigove, ca. ins., St. Quentin, Guygoven, Belgium.	

15TH CENTURY

1404	Sir Everard de Rayves, ca. ins., Belgium. Locality unknown. Arm. I.S.	
1423	Jacqueme Belle, w. ca. ins., Hospice Belle, Ypres. Arm. I.S.	
1428	Goswin, son of Goswin, Lord of Genoels Elderen, w. ca. ins., St. Martin, Genoels Elderen, Belgium. I.S.	
1441	Gisbert de Heers, ca. ins., Berlingen, Belgium. I.S.	
1452	Martin de Visch, ins., Bruges Cathedral. Arm. E.S. B. . .	28
1462	Eustace de Beyne, w. ca. ins. Formerly St. Foilan, Liège. B.	
1481	John I., Duke of Cleves, w. ca., St. Mary, Cleves. B. NOTE.—*For description of panels round tomb, see Secular Subjects, p.* 168 .	71

16TH CENTURY

1504	Lodewijc Cortewille, w. ins. From Watou, Belgium. AA. Now in the Victoria and Albert Museum. B.	
1518	Jehan de Likerke, w., Bruges Cathedral. AA. B. . . .	72
1521	John II., Duke of Cleves, w. ca. ins., St. Mary, Cleves. E.S., St. John Ev., St. Elizabeth of Hungary. B.	
1522	Rael van Printhaghen, w. ca. ins., Damme, Flanders. I.S.	
1550	Lodowiic van Leefdael, w. ins., St. Margaret, Thielen, Belgium. B.	

CIVIL COSTUME

MALE

13TH CENTURY

c. 1260   Anon., Antoing, Hainaut. I.S.

L

14TH CENTURY

Date	Name, Description, Place and Emblems, etc.	C.
1324	Ystasses d'Oyssen, ca. ins., Gemeppe, Belgium. I.S. . . .	38
c. 1360	Anon. Formerly Bruges Cathedral. Lower portions of three effigies, with panels of figures. B.	
1367	Anon., St. Sepulchre, Nivelles, Belgium. I.S.	
1373	Wouter de Boric, ca. ins. Flemish. Locality unknown. I.S.	
1378	Jean van Hazebrouck, ca. ins., Ypres. I.S.	
1388	Uladislaus, Duke of Poland, ca. ins., St. Benigne, Dijon. I.S.	

15TH CENTURY

1422	Anon., ca. ins., Villers-le-Temple. I.S.	
1440	Simon de Thiennes, ca. ins., Museum, Douai. Arm. From the Church of the Templars, Douai. I.S. (Habit of the Order of St. John of Jerusalem.)	
1450	Anon., wid. ins., Museum, Douai. B.V. I.S.	
c. 1450	Peter Esscheric, w. ins., Notre Dame, Termonde. E.S., St. Peter, St. Margaret. B.	44
1453	John Mouën, w. ch. ins. Formerly Onghena Collection, Ghent. B.V., St. John Ev., St. John Bapt. B.	
1453	Jean de Dours, w. ch. ins., St. Brice, Tournai. H.T., St. John Bapt., St. Catherine. B.	
1457	Raso de Hollegnoule, w. ins., St. Pierre, Hognoul, Liège. I.S. .	55
1461	Henrick van Eluerick, w. ins. Locality unknown. Cx., St. Anthony, St. Catherine. B.	
1477	Jacques de Houchin, St. Omer, France. I.S. Christ walking on the Sea of Galilee.	
1483	John Roos, w. ch. ins. Formerly Museum, Ypres. I.S. B.V.	
1487	Arnoldus de Meroide, ins., Aix-la-Chapelle Cathedral. AA. B.V. B.	45
1499	Gilles de Hertoghe, w. ins. Formerly St. Nicholas, Dixmude. R. (?), St. Aegidius. B.	

16TH CENTURY

1517	Bernardin van den Hove, ecclesiastical notary, ins., Bruges Cathedral. Escutcheons and inscription below to Johannes de Coudenberghe. B. (Commemorating the first members of the confraternity of Notre Dame des Sept Douleurs.) PLATE 69.	
1517	Johan Peer, w. ins. Flemish. Locality unknown. Cx. I.S.	
1519	Augustine Ghisilin, w. ch. ins., St. Nicolas, Dixmude. Cx., St. Augustine, St. Margaret. B.	
1521	Tydeman Berck, w. ins., Lübeck Cathedral. AA. B.	
1529	Michael Beverlant, w. ins., Lisseweghe, Belgium. I.S.	
1538	Willem van den Kerchove, w. ins. Formerly Notre Dame, Nieuport, Belgium. B.	

Date.	Name, Description, Place and Emblems, etc.	C.

1557 Pertsevael Pollet, w. ch. ins., St. Martin, Courtrai. Cx. B.

1560 Bartholomew Penneman, w. ch., Notre Dame, Termonde. B.V.,
St. Bartholomew, St. Bridget of Sweden. B. . . . 66

1567 Vincent Golle, w. ins. Locality unknown. I.S.

1575 Ghysellbrecht van Hoorenbeke, w. ins., Notre Dame, Termonde.
Cx. B.

1577 Francisco de Lapuebla, w. ch. ins., St. Jacques, Bruges. E.S. AA. B. 70

1579 John Localin, w. ins., St. Jacques, Tournai. Cx., St. John Ev., St.
Barbara. B.

c. 1600 Anon., w., Funchal Cathedral, Madeira. B.

17TH CENTURY

1615 Pierre de Valencia, w., St. Jacques, Bruges. B.

1622 Heinrich, Duke of Sachez-Julieh, ins., Freiberg Cathedral. F.n. B.
(*Process print.*)

CIVIL COSTUME

FEMALE

14TH CENTURY

1312 Gertrude, w. of Sir Lambert, Lord of Abée, ca. ins., Abée, Belgium.
I.S. 34

c. 1322 Helvidis and Lorutta, ws. of D. de Horpale, ins., Horpmael, Belgium.
I.S.

1327 Frau Ramborg de Wik, ins., Vester Åker, Sweden. E.S. B. . 6

1328 Ingiburg, w. of Birger Peterson, ins., Upsala, Sweden. I.S. . . 39

1349 Christina de Raet, ca. ins., from Damme, Belgium. Now in the
Victoria and Albert Museum. I.S.

1352 Margriete Sbrunnen, wid. of W. Wenemaer. From Hospice of
St. Laurence. Now the Archæological Museum, Ghent. B.

1352 Anon., w. of Sir Guillaume de Chastelier, ca., St. Sulpice, Moulbaix,
Belgium. I.S.

1358 Elisabeth Bollen, w. of Gerard de Gothem, ca. ins., St. Denys, Gothem,
Belgium. I.S. 44

1373 Marie Albouts, w. of W. de Boric, ca. ins. Flemish. Locality
unknown. I.S.

1397 Marie Cleinwoutres, ins., Notre Dame, Tongres, Limbourg. I.S. . 49

15TH CENTURY

1423 Marie le Blond, w. of Jacqueme Belle, ins., Hospice Belle, Ypres. I.S.

1428 Agnes, w. of Goswin de Genoels Elderen, ca. ins., St. Martin, Genoels
Elderen, Belgium. I.S.

Date.	Name, Description, Place and Emblems, etc.	C.
1450	Anon., ins., Museum, Douai. B.V. I.S.	
c. 1450	Magriete van den Driessche, w. of P. Esscheric, ins., Notre Dame, Termonde. B.V. B.	44
1453	Jehenne le Marie, w. of J. Mouën, ch. ins. Formerly Onghena Collection, Ghent. B.V. B.	
1453	Catherine de Harlebecque, w. of J. de Dours, ch. ins., St. Brice, Tournai. H.T. B.	
1457	Agnes Butoir, w. of R. de Hollegnoule, ins., St. Pierre, Hognoul, Liège. I.S.	55
1460	Kateline d'Aut, ins., St. Jacques, Bruges. AA. B. (Bridal costume.)	
1461	Yda Greuen, w. of H. van Eluerick, ins. Locality unknown. B.	
1462	Anon., w. of E. de Beyne, ca. ins. Formerly St. Foilan, Liège. B.	
c. 1480	Anon., ca. ins., Damme, Flanders. I.S.	
1481	Elizabeth, dau. of John, Duke of Burgundy, w. of John, Duke of Cleves, ca., St. Mary, Cleves. B.	71
1483	Anon., w. of J. Roos, ch. ins. Formerly Museum, Ypres. B.V. I.S.	
1499	Marie Verauen, w. of G. de Hertoghe, ins. Formerly St. Nicholas, Dixmude. B.	

16TH CENTURY

Date.		C.
1500	Lusbette Baers, ins., Damme, Flanders. E.S. I.S.	
1504	Colyne van Caestre, w. of L. Cortewille, ins. Formerly Watou, Belgium. Now in the Victoria and Albert Museum. B.	
1517	Catherine, w. of J. Peer, ins. Flemish. Locality unknown. Cx. I.S.	
1518	Ihane de le Douve, w. of J. de Likerke, Bruges Cathedral. AA. B. .	72
1519	Margriete, w. of A. Ghisilin, ch. ins., St. Nicholas, Dixmude. Cx. B.	
1521	Anon., w. of John II., Duke of Cleves, ca. ins., St. Mary, Cleves. B.V. B.	
1521	Elizabeth, w. of T. Berck, ins., Lübeck Cathedral. AA. B.	
1522	Anon., w. of Rael van Printhaghen, ca. ins., Damme, Flanders. I.S.	
1524	Florentine Wielant, w. of Sir Jacques Vander Vichte, The Hospice, Vichte, Belgium. E.S. AA. B.	62
1529	Anne van den Busche, w. of M. Beverlant, ins., Lisseweghe, Belgium. I.S.	
1538	Josine van der Gracht, w. of W. van den Kerchove, ins. Formerly Notre Dame, Nieuport, Belgium. B.	
1550	Marguerite de Beer, w. of L. de Leefdael, ins., St. Margaret, Thielen, Belgium. B.	
1557	Josine Vanderpoele, w. of P. Pollet, ch. ins., St. Martin, Courtrai. Cx. B.	
1560	Brigitte Meulandts, w. of B. Penneman, ch., Notre Dame, Termonde. B.V. B.	66

Date.	Name, Description, Place and Emblems, etc.	C.

1567   Anne, w. of V. Golle, ins.   Locality unknown.   I.S.

c. 1570   Anon., ins.   Locality unknown.   I.S.

1575   Elisabeth Schoormans, w. of G. van Hoorenbeke, ins., Notre Dame,
Termonde.   Cx.   B.

1577   Marie, dau. of Seigneur Ferry de Marvoorde, w. of F. de Lapuebla,
ch. ins., St. Jacques, Bruges.   E.S.   AA.   B.   .   .   70

1579   Barbe Mallet, w. of J. Localin, ins., St. Jacques, Tournai.   Cx.   B.

c. 1585   Marie and Jeanne de Lannoy, ins., St. Jacques, Tournai.   Cx.   B.V.
St. John Bapt.   B.

c. 1600   Anon., Funchal Cathedral, Madeira.   B.

16th cent. Margareta . . . de Monte Sancti Wiberte, ca. ins., Villers-le-Temple.
I.S.

17TH CENTURY

1601   Anthonine Willebaert, w. of Pieter van der Mase, ch ins., St. Jacques,
Bruges.   B.

1615   Marie de Bailleul, w. of P. de Valencia, St. Jacques, Bruges.   B.

BÉGUINES

1410   Griel van Ruwescuere, ca. ins., Béguinage, Bruges.   B.   .   .   25

1458   Katherine van Voirsselaer, ca. ins., Béguinage, Louvain.   I.S.

1459   Katherine van Nethenen, wid. of Andrew Thomars, ca. ins., Béguinage,
Louvain.   I.S.   PLATE 70   56

1594   Elisabeth van de Voorde, ins., Béguinage, Bruges.   I.S.

ECCLESIASTICAL COSTUME

PRIESTS IN CHASUBLE

1279   Otto de Brunswick, Bishop of Hildesheim, ins., Hildesheim Cathedral.   B.   PLATE 71   1

1283   Theodericus de Aquis, ca. ch. ins., Maestricht.   B.

1292   Edmund von Werth, Bishop of Courland, ca. ins., Chapel of the Order
of Teutonic Knights, Oude Biesen, Belgium.   I.S.

1313   Henry . . . , ca. cha. ins., Houppertingen, Limbourg.   I.S.

1368   Anon., cha. ins., Archæological Museum, Ghent.   B.   (Palimpsest
on inscription to L. van Haute, 1590.)

1394   N. and J. (1402) Dukien, ca. ins., St. Mary Magdalene, Tournai.   I.S.

c. 1430   St. Henry, Bishop of Upsala, ins., Nausis, Finland.   E.S.   AA.   B.

1447   Gilles de Byssenhaye, cha. ca. ins., Canon of St. Paul's, St. Paul, Liège.
E.S.   I.S.

1462   Symon Bocheux, ca. cha. ins., Notre Dame, St. Omer.   I.S.

1510   Wouter de Raet, cha. ins., Bruges Cathedral.   I.S.

Date.   Name, Description, Place and Emblems, etc.   C.

1531 Johannes de Fonte, cha. ins., Hospital of St. Jean, Damme, Belgium.
   B. 62
1545 Jean van den Couteren, ca. cha. ins., Melsele, Belgium. E.S. B. and I.S. 66
1570 F. Q., cha., Museum, Douai. B.
1584 Josse Lambrecht, Hospice of St. Josse, Bruges. E.S. B.
n.d. Joachim Moenius, cha. ins., Belgium. Locality unknown. I.S.

PRIEST IN COPE

1456 John Avantage, Bishop of Amiens, kng. ins., Amiens Cathedral. B.V.
   St. John Ev. B. 31

PRIESTS IN CASSOCK AND SURPLICE

1463 Vincent Breion, ca. ins., St. Omer. E.S. St. Denys. I.S.
1557 Adrian van Pollinchove, kng. ins., St. Basil, Bruges. Cx. I.S.

PRIEST IN ALB, AMICE, STOLE, Etc.

1390 ? Adam Sapientis, ca. ins., Auxerre Cathedral.

MISCELLANEOUS

c. 1380 Head of a bishop or abbot, ca., with soul, saints, etc. Locality unknown.
   British Museum. B.

MONASTIC COSTUME

MALE

1264 Abbas Alardus de Hierges, twenty-second Abbot of Waulsort, ins., Has-
   tière, Namur. I.S. 14
1286 Robert . . . , Béguinage, Maestricht. I.S. .
1294 Wautier de Cortenberg, ca. ins., Béguinage, Maestricht. I.S.
1483 Abbot Adam Hertzogenrade, ca. ins., Brauweilers, Germany. E.S.
   SS. Nicolas and Medard. B. Plate 71.
1560 Abbot Zæchæus Paludanus, cha. ins., Zoetendaele, Belgium. I.S.
1607 Leonard Betten, Abbot of St. Trond, ins., Archæological Museum,
   Ghent. B.

FEMALE

n.d. Marguerite de Scornay, kng. ins., St. Gertrude, Nivelles, Belgium.
   B.V. AA. B. (Guardian angel protecting her from a dragon.)

ACADEMICAL COSTUME

Date.	Name, Description, Place and Emblems, etc.	C.
1483	Jacob Schelewaerts, ins., Bruges Cathedral. B	44
1508	Heinrich von Berchem, cha. ins., St. Maria im Capitol, Cologne. B.V., St. John Ev. B.	
1535	Henry Oskens, kng. ins., St. Mary, Nippes, Cologne. B.V., St. Peter, St. Henry. B. Now in the Victoria and Albert Museum .	64
1540	Sibert van Ryswick, ins., Xanten. E.S. B.	
1554	Herman Blanfort, cha. ins., St. Colomba, Cologne. B.V. B.	

SHROUDS AND SKELETONS

1387	Wouter Copman (head only), Bruges Cathedral. E.S. B.	
1439	Joris de Munter and w. Jakemine van der Brucghe, ins., Bruges Cathedral. E.S. AA. B. PLATE 72	25
1546	Peter Claessoen Palinck and w. Josina van Foreest, w. ins., Alkmaar, Holland. AA. B.	73
1547	Nicolas le Brun, ins., British Museum. The Virgin, St. Mary Magdalen, St. John Ev., St. John Bapt., a nude corpse reclining on a pallet below. From Jeumont, France. B.	
1557	Anon. Formerly St. Pierre, Nieucapelle, Belgium. I.S. (Figure of Death stabbing the child.)	
n.d.	J. de Landas, ins., Locality unknown. I.S. (Figure of Death stabbing the child.)	

SAINTS

c. 1180	Saint Helena, Forêt, Brabant. I.S.	4

SACRED SUBJECTS

1448	H. van Tongheren, ins., St. Dymphna, Gheel, Belgium. B.V., St. Catherine, St. Dymphna. I.S.
1457	Guillaume de Wavre, ins., St. John, Liège. Lamb and cross in cusped medallion. I.S.
1466	Thomas Lambaert, Notre Dame, Nieuport, Belgium. Angel bearing a shield. B.
1468	Jean Clays, ins. Formerly Notre Dame, Nieuport, Belgium. Angel in alb, amice, and stole, bearing a shield. E.S. B.
1505	Gysbert Willemsz de Raet, cha. ins., Rijks Museum, Amsterdam. Angel in cusped trefoil, bearing shields. E.S. B.

SECULAR SUBJECTS

SHIELDS OF ARMS

Date.   Name, Description, Place and Emblems, etc.

1481   John 1., Duke of Cleves, St. Mary, Cleves.   16 panels, each with escutcheon, helmet, mantling, and crest, and an inscription as follows :—

           (1) Die Greyf van Gey.   (2) Celler.   (3) Flanderen.   (4) Cleve Marck.   (5) Burgondien.   (6) Die Hartoch vā den Berge. (7) Franckryck.   (8) Htoch vā Brabant.   (9) Marck.   (10) Die Greyf van Stampus.   (11) Buyrgondien.   (12) Die Hetzych van Cleve.   (13) Behem.   (14) Htoch vā Brabāt. (15) Die Gref vā Fladen.   (16) Brijc.

1506   Thomas de Oiren, ins., St. Peter, Cologne.   B.

c. 1520   Johannes de Coudenberghe, ins.   On the brass of Bernadin van den Hove, Bruges Cathedral.   B.

1530   Pierre Meulenbeke, ins., Hospice St. Jean, Bruges.   B.

1540   Catherine de Loe, ins., St. Maria im Capitol, Cologne.   B.

1559   Willem van Bampoele, ins., St. Blaise, Crombeke, Belgium.   B.

1605   Michael de Corte, ins., St. Martin, Ypres.   B.

n.d.   Anon., Sluyvekenkerke, West Flanders.   I.S.

n.d.   Anon., S. Blaise, Crombeke, West Flanders.   B.

INSCRIPTIONS

1036   Dedication of Church, Rixingen, Belgium.   I.S.

1235   From the tomb of Henry 1., Duke of Brabant, St. Pierre, Louvain.   I.S.

13th cent.   Record of dedication of altar by Heinrich Winterschutze, St. Maria im Capitol, Cologne.

1365   Druda de foro lignario, St. Maria im Capitol, Cologne.   I.S.

1423   Record of foundations by Sir Guillebert de Launoy, Notre Dame, Hal, Belgium.   B.

1424   Record of foundation of Church, St. Pierre, Nieucapelle, Belgium.   I.S.

1430   Record of foundations by Ernoul Wicart, St. Sauveur, Jollain Merlin, Belgium.   B.

1448   Record of foundations by Provost of Nivelles and Gilles d'Escornaix, Notre Dame, Hal, Belgium.   B.

1458   Record of foundations, Hal, Belgium.   B.

1467   Record of dedication of holy-water stoup by Jan Pinnoc, St. Jacques, Louvain.   I.S.

1467   Record of foundations by Pieter Lansaem, St. Mary's Hospital, Ypres.   B.

1473   Record of dedication of holy-water stoup, St. Michel, Louvain.   I.S.

Date.	Name, Description, Place and Emblems, etc.
1480	Adolphus Stakelhusen, St. Peter, Cologne. B.
15th cent.	Inscription from a holy-water stoup, St. Michel, Louvain.
15th cent.	Inscription from a holy-water stoup, St. Jacques, Louvain. I.S.
1506	Johannes Junghe, St. Maria im Capitol, Cologne. B.
c. 1510	" Salve Regina Broderschaff," St. Martin, Cologne. B.
c. 1520	Record of foundations by Jean Losschaert, Bruges. In private possession. B.
c. 1530	Jan de Mersseman and others, Hospice St. Jean, Bruges. Figures of Moses, King David and Job in border. B.
1533	Jan de Deckere (1519), and Jacops de Witte, Bruges Cathedral. I.S.
1546	Hôtel de Ville, Louvain. B.
1563	Charles, Comte de Lalaing, Museum, Douai. B.
1585	Record of foundations by J. Vernimmen, Notre Dame, Termonde. B.
1604	Laurens van Haute, Ghent. B.
1659	Herdt van Lathem, Port de la Hal, Museum, Brussels. B.

ORNAMENT

1317	Burchard de Serken (1317) and John de Mul (1350), ins., Lübeck Cathedral. Part of canopy. B. (Photograph.)
n.d.	Bostoen van Assenede, ins., Belgium. Locality unknown. Part of border. B.
14th cent.	Fragment, St. Gertrude, Nivelles, Belgium. I.S.
n.d.	Portions of canopy, with heads of a man, a woman, and a bishop with the upper part of a crosier. I.S.

INDEX OF NAMES

The first reference, in four figures, is to date ; the second, to page :
i.e. 1454, 118 = *date* 1454, *page* 118.

Atlee, John, 1599, 73.

Attelese : Dennis, 1394, 79 ; Sir Rich., 1394, 37.

Attelude, Thos., 1454, 142.

Aucher : Jas., 1508, 45 ; John, 1502, 44 ; Wm., 1514, 46.

Audeley : Sir T., 1385, 36 ; W. de, 1365, 36. *See also* Audley, Awdeley, *and* Awdley.

Audley, Sir J. Towchet, Lord, c. 1525, 47. *See also* Audeley, Awdeley, *and* Awdley.

Audyan, Steven, 1523, 66.

Aumberdene, N. de, c. 1350, 5, 53.

Austen, Anne, 1609, 114.

Aut, Kateline d', 1460, 164.

Avantage, John, 1456, 166.

Avenel, Britell, 1408, 122.

Avenyng : Alice, c. 1500, 92 ; John, c. 1500, 61.

Avery. *See* Abere *and* Abery.

Awdeley, Anne, 1514, 96. *See also* Audeley, Audley, *and* Awdley.

Awdley, Kath., 1611, 120. *See also* Audeley, Audley, *and* Awdeley.

Awmarle, Thos., c. 1400, 28.

Awnsham, Rich., c. 1490, 60. *See also* Agmondesham, *and* Amondesham.

Awodde : Dyones, 1525, 99 ; John, 1525, 66. *See also* Wode, *and* Wood.

Awsiter, Francis, 1629, 76.

Aylet, Thos., 1638, 151.

Ayleway, Joan, 1609, 114.

Ayliff. *See* Alefe *and* Aylyff.

Aylmer. *See* Ailemer.

Aylward. *See* Aileward.

Aylworth, Ant., 1619, 134.

Aylyff, John, 1499, 143. *See also* Alefe.

Aynesworth : Agnes, 1488, 89 ; Geo., 1488, 59 ; Isabel, 1488, 89 ; Joan, 1488, 89.

Ayscough, Jane, 1578, 107. *See also* Askew, Askowe, *and* Ayscugh.

Ayscugh : Kath., 1610, 114 ; Margery, 1509, 95 ; Sir W., 1509, 45. *See also* Askew, Askowe, *and* Ascough.

Ayshcombe : John, 1592, 72 ; Margery, 1592, 110 ; Martha, 1611, 114 ; Oliver, 1611, 75 ; Rich., 1606, 74.

Babham : —, 1527, 100 ; John, 1458, 57 ; Mary, 1577, 107 ; R., 1527, 47.

Babington, Elizth., 1543, 103. *See also* Babyngton.

Babyngton : Adam, 1427, 123 ; Anne, 1507, 94 ; Ralph, 1521, 125. *See also* Babington.

Bache, Simon, 1414, 127.

Bacon : Sir — de, c. 1320, 14, 35 ; Adam de, c. 1310, 121 ; Elizth., 1580, 108 ; Elizth., 1583, 138 ; Frances, 1580, 70 ; Joan, 1437, 83 ; John, 1437, 55 ; John, 1528, 66 ; Mary, 1580, 108 ; Mary, 1587, 149.

Badby, Thomasyn, 1532, 101.

Badlesmere, Joan de, c. 1335, 78.

Baers, Lusbette, 1500, 164.

Bagot, Sir Wm., 1407, 37 ; Margt., 1407, 80.

Bailey : John, 1601, 73 ; Walter, 1592, 72. *See also* Bayly.

Bailleul, Marie de, 1615, 165.

Baispoole, Rich., 1613, 150.

Baker : Deonys, 1508, 94 ; Eden, 1598, 111 ; John, 1455, 123 ; Joyce, 1594, 145 ; T., 1510, 30 ; Thos., 1508, 63 ; Thos., 1510, 134.

Balam, John, 1496, 124.

Baldiston. *See* Byldysdon.

Baldry : Alys, 1506, 94 ; Thos., 1506, 62.

Baldwyn : Alice, 1533, 102 ; Hen., 1601, 145.

Balgay, Hen., 1685, 8, 77.

Ballard : John, 1463, 57 ; Margt., 1463, 86.

Ballett, Rich., 1598, 138.

Bampfield, Elizth., 1619, 115.

Bampoele, Willem van, 1559, 168.

Bannister : Elizth., 1607, 113 ; John, 1607, 74, 138.

Barantyn : Beatrix, 1446, 84 ; D., 1446, 40 ; Joan, 1446, 84 ; R., 1441, 40. *See also* Barrentyne.

Barbar, Agnes, 1515, 96. *See also* Barbur.

Barbur, G., 1417, 54. *See also* Barbar.

Bardolf : Joan, 1455, 85 ; Lord, 1507, 45 ; Sir Robt., 1395, 37. *See also* Bardolfe.

Bardolfe, Elizth., 1593, 110. *See also* Bardolf.

Baret : Cecily, 1442, 84 ; V., 1442, 40. *See also* Barett, Barette, Barratte, *and* Barret.

Barett, Chas., 1584, 149. *See also* Baret, Barette, Barratte, *and* Barret.

Borell, Garard, 1509, 148. *See also* Borrell, *and* Burrell.

Borgeys, Thos., 1452, 147.

Boric : Marie de, 1373, 163 ; Wouter de, 1373, 162.

Boroeghe, Anne, 1577, 131. *See also* Borrow, Burgh, *and* Burrough.

Borrell, John, 1531, 47. *See also* Borell, *and* Burrell.

Borrow : Alys, 1503, 93 ; R., 1503, 44. *See also* Boroeghe, Burgh, *and* Burrough.

Bosard : Margery, 1490, 89 ; Philip, 1490, 59. *See also* Bozard.

Boscawen : Edw., 1619, 75 ; J., 1634, 52 ; Jane, 1619, 115 ; Marie, 1622, 120.

Boselingthorpe, Sir Rich. de, c. 1310, 35.

Bostocke, Frances, 1612, 114. *See also* Bostok.

Bostok : Hugh, c. 1450, 56 ; Margt., c. 1450, 84. *See also* Bostocke.

Bosworth : Elinor, 1674, 117 ; Isabel, 1674, 117 ; John, 1674, 77.

Boteler : Alice, 1451, 84 ; Elizth., 1441, 84 ; Elizth., 1615, 150 ; Helen, 1639, 117 ; J., 1441, 40 ; Thos., 1637, 146 ; Wm., 1614, 150. *See also* Botiler, Butler, *and* Buttler.

Bothe : Anne, 1481, 88 ; Alice, 1531, 101 ; Douce del, 1460, 85 ; Kath., 1467, 86 ; Margt., 1478, 119 ; R., 1467, 41 ; R., 1478, 42 ; Sir R. del, 1460, 41 ; T., 1531, 47 ; Thos., c. 1495, 60. *See also* Boothe, *and* Bowthe.

Botiler : Anne, 1436, 83 ; Joan, 1408, 154. *See also* Boteler, Butler, *and* Buttler.

Botolff, John, 1486, 124.

Bougins : Alice, 1606, 113 ; John, 1606, 74. *See also* Byggins.

Bourchier : Barth., Lord, c. 1420, 38 ; Hen., Earl of Essex, 1483, 43 ; Iden, c. 1420, 82 ; Isabel, 1483, 88 ; Joan, c. 1470, 119 ; Margt., c. 1420, 82. *See also* Bourgchier.

Bourgchier, Sir Humph., 1471, 147. *See also* Bourchier.

Bourne, Joan, 1496, 91.

Boutrod, Wm., 1522, 128.

Bowden, —, 17th cent., 152.

Bowet, Ele, 1400, 80. *See also* Bowett.

Bowett : Anne, 1490, 90 ; Edith, 1444, 84. *See also* Bowet.

Bowf, Augnes, 1417, 81.

Bowke, John, 1519, 134.

Bowland : Edw., 1609, 74 ; Joan, 1616, 115.

Bowles : Elizth., 1636, 116 ; Margt., 1615, 115.

Bownell, Constance, 1581, 138, 154.

Bowser, John, 1608, 74.

Bowthe, John, 1478, 27, 121. *See also* Boothe, *and* Bothe.

Bowyar : Elizth., 1570, 106 ; J., 1570, 69. *See also* Bowyer.

Bowyer : Elizth., 1601, 112 ; H., 1589, 51 ; H., 1601, 52 ; John, 1521, 66 ; Jone, 1521, 98. *See also* Bowyar.

Box : —, c. 1650, 117 ; G., c. 1650, 77.

Boys : — de, c. 1420, 82 ; Isabel, 1507, 94 ; J. de, c. 1420, 39 ; John, 1543, 148 ; Malin, 1584, 108 ; Mary, 1558, 105 ; Rich., 1605, 145 ; Sara, 1604, 113 ; T., 1562, 50 ; Vyncent, 1558, 69 ; Wm., 1507, 63.

Bozard, Roger, 1505, 62 ; Wm., 1505, 62. *See also* Bosard.

Bozon, Wm., c. 1485, 43.

Brabant, Henry I., Duke of, 1235, 168.

Bradbery, Barbara, 1618, 150. *See also* Bradbuirye.

Bradbridge : Alice, 1592, 110 ; Wm., 1592, 72. *See also* Bradbryge.

Bradbryge : Denys, 1533, 102 ; Rich., 1533, 67. *See also* Bradbridge.

Bradbuirye, Jane, 1578, 107. *See also* Bradbery.

Bradford. *See* Braydforde.

Bradschawe : Alice, 1537, 102 ; Wm., 1537, 68. *See also* Bradshawe.

Bradshawe : Hen., 1598, 73 ; Joan, 1598, 111. *See also* Bradschawe.

Bradstane, John, 1458, 123. *See also* Bradston.

Bradston, Elizth., 1423, 147. *See also* Bradstane.

Bragge, Anne, 1614, 115.

Braham, Joan, 1519, 131.

Bramfeld, Anne, 1578, 107.

Brampton : Anne, 1535, 102 ; Edw., 1622, 75 ; J., 1535, 48 ; Jone, 1622, 115 ; Robt., 1468, 136 ; Thomasseyng, 1535, 102.

Branch. *See* Braunche.

Browning : Agnes, 1455, 85 ; W., c. 1455, 41. *See also* Brounyng.

Bruce, Alice, 1603, 145. *See also* Brewes, *and* Brewys.

Brudenell : —, 1606, 113 ; Agnes, 1584, 108 ; Aubrey, 1584, 108 ; Sir Edm., 1584, 51 ; Eleanor, 1430, 82 ; Elizth., 1586, 109 ; Hen., 1430, 55 ; John, 1606, 52 ; Mary, 1611, 114 ; Sir Thos., 1586, 51.

Bruges, Elizth., 1525, 99. *See also* Bridges, *and* Brugge.

Brugge : Alice, 1523, 99 ; W., 1523, 46. *See also* Bridges, *and* Bruges.

Bruley, Amice, 1439, 83.

Brun, Robt. de, 1417, 139. *See also* Brown, *and* Browne.

Brunham, Alys, c. 1420, 82.

Brunker. *See* Brouncker.

Brunswick, Otto de, 1279, 5, 165.

Bruyn, Sir Ingram, 1400, 37.

Bryan, Alice, 1435, 118. *See also* Bryene.

Bryene, Sir Wm. de, 1395, 37. *See also* Bryan.

Bryghtye, E., 1467, 57.

Brystowe, Hugh, 1548, 137.

Buckfold, Elizth., 1598, 111.

Buckingham. *See* Bokenham, *and* Bukkenham.

Buckton, Isabel, c. 1430, 55, 82.

Budd, Wm., 1685, 147.

Bugge : Edw., 1582, 70 ; Jane, 1582, 108. *See also* Boggis, *and* Bugges.

Bugges : Elizth., 1636, 116 ; Rich., 1636, 52 ; Vahan, 1636, 116. *See also* Boggis, *and* Bugge.

Buggins. *See* Bougins, *and* Byggins.

Bukkenham, John, c. 1520, 143. *See also* Bokenham.

Bulcley, Margt., 1528, 100. *See also* Bulkeley, *and* Bulkley.

Bulkeley, Joan, 1556, 104 ; Robt., 1550, 148 ; Robt., 1556, 49, 149. *See also* Bulcley, *and* Bulkley.

Bulkley : Elizth., c. 1530, 101 ; Rich., c. 1530, 67. *See also* Bulcley, *and* Bulkeley.

Bull, Josias, 1621, 75.

Bullen, Sir Thos., Earl of Wiltshire, 1538, 48. *See also* Boleyn, *and* Bollen.

Bulowe : Frederic and Godfrey de, 1375, 3 ; Hen. and Ludolph de, 1339, 3, 4.

Bulstrode : Agnes, 1472, 136 ; Anne, 1518, 97 ; Cecil, 1599, 112 ; E., 1517, 46 ; Edw., 1599, 52 ; Ellen, 1517, 97 ; Margt., 1517, 97 ; Margt., 1540, 10, 103, 157 ; Mary, 1517, 97 ; Mary, 1614, 145.

Bulwer : Anne, 1607, 159 ; Edw., 1626, 159 ; John, 1518, 65 ; Thos., 1518, 65. *See also* Bolwar.

Bures : Alice de, 1435, 118 ; Anne, 1609, 120 ; Hen., 1528, 47 ; Isaiah, 1610, 131 Sir Robt. de, 1302, 13, 35.

Burgate : Eleanor, 1409, 80 ; Sir Wm. de, 1409, 37.

Burgehill, Rich., 1492, 60.

Burgess. *See* Borgeys.

Burgh : Amy, 1632, 151 ; John de, 1412, 147 ; Kath. de, 1412, 147 ; Rich., 1632, 151. *See also* Boroeghe, Borrow, *and* Burrough.

Burghersh, Maud, 1436, 118.

Burght, Robt., 1516, 140.

Burgoyn : J., 1505, 45 ; John, c. 1500, 62 ; Margt., 1505, 93 ; Thos., 1516, 140.

Burgundy, Elizabeth of, 1481, 164.

Burington, Jane, 1589, 109. *See also* Barrington, Buriton, *and* Buryngton.

Buriton : Joan, 1603, 113 ; Margt., 1605, 113 ; Thos., 1603, 74. *See also* Barrington, Burington, *and* Buryngton.

Burkitt. *See* Byrkhed.

Burlton : Kath., 1496, 91 ; Rich., 1496, 60.

Burnedisshe, Esmound de, c. 1360, 122.

Burnell : John, 1551, 144 ; Sir Nich., 1382, 36.

Burrell, Dorothy, 1648, 117. *See also* Borell, *and* Borrell.

Burrough : Elizth., 1616, 115 ; John, 1616, 75 ; Thos., 1600, 73. *See also* Boroeghe, Borrow, *and* Burgh.

Burton : Anne, 1593, 110 ; Elizth., 1593, 110 ; Joan, 1524, 99 ; John, 1608, 131 ; Margery, c. 1410, 81 ; Rich., 1443, 147 ; Simon, 1593, 72 ; Sir Thos., c. 1410, 38.

Buryngton, Margt., 1570, 105. *See also* Barrington, Buriton, *and* Burington.

Burys, Wm., 1444, 40.

Busche : Joan, 1526, 100 ; Thos., 1526, 66. *See also* Bushe.

Buseve, — de, 15th century, 156.

Carlton : Anne, 1582, 108. *See also* Charlton.
Carlyll : Joan, 1489, 89 ; Rich., 1489, 59.
Carman, John, 1508, 153.
Carpenter, Mary, 1652, 146.
Carr : Anne, 1521, 98 ; Margt., 1608, 114. *See also* Carre.
Carre : —, 1570, 106 ; John, 1570, 9, 69. *See also* Carr.
Carreu, Philipe, 1414, 81. *See also* Carew, Carewe, *and* Carrew.
Carrew, Nich., 1432, 55. *See also* Carew, Carewe, *and* Carreu.
Carter : —, 1588, 109 ; Alice, 1528, 100 ; Alys, 1529, 100 ; Elizth., 1649, 117 ; John, 1588, 71 ; Rich., 1529, 66.
Carthwright, Ann, 1611, 114.
Cartwright. *See* Carthwright.
Casey, Alice, 1400, 80.
Cason, Jane, 1603, 113.
Cassy : Sir John, 1400, 31, 134 ; Lady, 1400, 6.
Castell : Audrey, 1486, 89 ; Constance, 1610, 145.
Castle. *See* Castell.
Cater, Margery, 1562, 105, 144.
Caterall : Elizth., 1515, 96 ; Raffe, 1515, 46.
Catesby : Elizth., 1503, 93 ; Francis, 1556, 68 ; Geo., c. 1500, 44 ; Lettice, 1467, 86 ; Mary, 1508, 94.
Catterall. *See* Caterall.
Caus, Joan *or* Helen, 1506, 94.
Cave : Anne, 1594, 149 ; Anth., 1558, 49 ; Anth., c. 1560, 137 ; Elizth., 1558, 105.
Cavell, Humph., 1558, 68.
Cawsen, Grace, 1591, 110.
Caysyll, John, 1493, 60.
Cayworth, John, 1637, 146.
Cely : Isabel, 1426, 82 ; John, 1426, 39.
Chakbon, Isabel, c. 1430, 83.
Challoner : Jane, 1642, 117 ; Margt., 1532, 101 ; Thos., 1532, 67.
Chamber. *See* Chambre.
Chamberleyn : Aleyn, c. 1325, 78 ; Margery, 1431, 156. *See also* Chamberlin, *and* Chamberlyne.
Chamberlin : Amphelice, 1576, 107 ; Mary, 1694, 147. *See also* Chamberleyn, *and* Chamberlyne.
Chamberlyne, Alyne, c. 1325, 78. *See also* Chamberleyn, *and* Chamberlin.

Chambers, Robt., 1638, 76.
Chambre : Arthur, 1564, 69 ; Margt., 1564, 106.
Chancellor. *See* Cancellor, *and* Chaunceler.
Chandler. *See* Chawndiler.
Chanu, Thos., 1407, 142. *See also* Cheney.
Chapman : Agnes, 1522, 99 ; Anne, 1636, 116 ; Edm., 1574, 69 ; Edm., 1626, 76 ; Edm., 1501, 142 ; John, 1475, 142 ; John, 1582, 70 ; Julyan, 1582, 108 ; Margt., 1574, 107 ; Robt., 1574, 149 ; Robt., 1611, 145 ; Wm., 1636, 76.
Charles, Elizth., 1488, 89. *See also* Charlis, *and* Charyls.
Charlis : Alice, 1409, 80 ; Rich., 1378, 36 ; Rich., 1446, 56 ; Stephen, 1446, 56. *See also* Charles, *and* Charyls.
Charlton : Anne, 1533, 102 ; Joyce, c. 1470, 86 ; Margt., 1564, 106 *See also* Carlton.
Charpignie, Sir Brocardus de, c. 1270, 160.
Charyls, Walter, 1502, 143. *See also* Charles, *and* Charlis.
Chase, Wm., 1544, 144, 155.
Chastelier : —, 1352, 163 ; Sir Guillaume de, 1352, 161.
Chaucer : Maud, 1436, 118 ; Thos., 1436, 40.
Chaucey : Marion, 1524, 99 ; Wm., 1524, 66. *See also* Chauncy.
Chaunceler, Edith, c. 1435, 118. *See also* Canceller.
Chauncy, Wm., c. 1500, 148. *See also* Chaucey.
Chawndiler, Thos., 1490, 128.
Chaworth : Elizth., 1474, 119 ; Thos., 1446, 123.
Chedder : Isabel, c. 1475, 119 ; Sir Thos., 1442, 40.
Cheeseman. *See* Cheseman.
Cheesewright. *See* Cheswryght.
Cheke : Isabel, 1590, 110 ; John, 1590, 71.
Chelry, Elizth., 1444, 84.
Chelseye, Alex., 1388, 122.
Cheney, John, c. 1400, 140. *See also* Chanu.
Cherneys, Jamon de, 1458, 23, 85.
Chernocke, Florence, 1591, 110.
Cherowin, John, 1441, 2, 159.
Chervill, John, c. 1385, 122.
Cheseldyn : Edw., 1642, 151 ; Kenelm, 1596, 72 ; Winefrid, 1596, 111.

Clyfton: Sir Adam de, 1367, 36; Sir Gervis, 1491, 43; Sir Robt., 1478, 42. *See also* Clifton.

Cobbe: Alice, 1522, 99; Alice, 1580, 107; Thos., 1516, 156; Thos., 1522, 66; Wm., 1522, 66.

Cobbum, Mary, 1600, 120. *See also* Cobham, *and* Kobeham.

Cobham: Alice, 1580, 107; Eleanor, 1420, 82; Elizth., 1375, 79; Elizth., 1544, 103; Isabel, 1460, 142; Joan de, c. 1380, 23, 79; Joan, 1433, 83; John de, 1399, 142, 147; Sir John de, 1354, 16, 36; Sir John de, c. 1365, 36; Margaret, 1375, 79; Margt. de, 1395, 79; Maud, 1465, 119; Maude de, 1380, 79; Rauf de, 1402, 37; Reginald de, 1402, 127; Sir Reginald, 1403, 37; Thos., 1465, 41; Sir Thos., 1367, 36. *See also* Cobbum, *and* Kobeham.

Coblegh: Isabel, 1480, 87; Joan, 1480, 87; John, 1480, 58.

Cobyndon, Joan de, 1462, 85.

Cockayne: —, c. 1480, 88; Dorothy, 1538, 103; Edm., 1515, 46; Eliz., 1515, 96; Francis, 1538, 48; John, c. 1430, 39.

Cocke, Wm., 1607, 74. *See also* Cok, *and* Coke.

Cockeram. *See* Cokyram.

Cocket, Jane, 1586, 109. *See also* Coket.

Cod, Thos., 1465, 128.

Codington, Elizth., 1567, 106; Rich., 1567, 69. *See also* Codyngtoun.

Codyngtoun, Hen. de, 1404, 127. *See also* Codington.

Coe: Elizth., 1591, 110; Jas., 1591, 72. *See also* Coo.

Coffin, Marie, 1622, 120.

Cogdell: Alice, 1607, 113; Jane, 1607, 113; Thos., 1607, 74.

Coggeshall: Elizth., 1640, 117; John, 1640, 76; Thos., 1421, 39.

Cok: A., c. 1490, 90; John, c. 1490, 60. *See also* Cocke, *and* Coke.

Coke: Alice, 1553, 104; Elizth., 1606, 113; Ellen, 1454, 85; John, 1522, 144; Thos., c. 1515, 143; Wm., 1553, 136. *See also* Cocke, *and* Cok.

Cokeram. *See* Cokyram.

Coket: —, c. 1480, 58, 87; Edm., c. 1500, 148. *See also* Cocket.

Cokyram, Robt., 1508, 63.

Colard, John, 1491, 153.

Colby: Alice, 1560, 105; John, 1559, 49; John, 1560, 49.

Cole: Arthur, 1558, 130, 156; Margt., 1597, 111; Thos., 1597, 73. *See also* Coles.

Colepeper, Joyce, 1525, 99.

Coles: Eleanor, 1640, 117; Geo., 1640, 21, 25, 76; Sarah, 1640, 117. *See also* Cole.

Coleshill. *See* Colshill.

Colkyn, John, 1405, 147.

Collen, Elizth., 1609, 114.

Collet, Susanna, 1657, 147.

Collingbourne, Joan, 1495, 91.

Collingridge: Alice, 1502, 93; Margery, 1502, 93.

Collys, —, c. 1510, 95.

Colman: Kath., 1506, 94; John, 1506, 62.

Colmer: Margt., 1485, 89; Rich., 1485, 59.

Colshill: Anne, 1524, 99; Robt., 1524, 66.

Colt: Elizth., 1521, 98; John, 1440, 123; John, 1521, 46; Mary, 1521, 98. *See also* Colte.

Colte: Jane, 1605, 113; Joan, 1471, 86; Magdalen, 1576, 107; Thos., 1471, 42; Thos., 1576, 70. *See also* Colt.

Coltrop, Elizth., 1611, 114. *See also* Calthorp, *and* Calthorpe.

Colvyle, John, c. 1530, 138.

Colwell: Agnes, 1533, 102; Rich., 1533, 67.

Coly, Thos., 1518, 134.

Comfort, Elizth., 1590, 109.

Complyn, Wm., 1498, 139.

Compton: — de, c. 1365, 36; —, c. 1500, 44, 92; Joan, 1458, 85; John, 1424, 39; John, 1458, 57; Margery, 1424, 82.

Conquest: Eleanor, 1434, 118; Elizth., 1500, 91; Elizth., 1592, 110; Isabel, 1493, 90; John, 1493, 44; Rich., 1493, 44; Rich., 1500, 44.

Consant, Anne, 1606, 138.

Constable: Sir Marmaduke, 1520, 143; Sir Wm., 1527, 140.

Conyers: Anne, c. 1500, 92; Margt., 1520, 97; Margery, 1470, 142.

Eustace. *See* Ewstes.

Evance, Dan., 1652, 155.

Eveas : —, 1530, 100 ; John, 1488, 43 ; Mildred, 1488, 89.

Evelyn, Mary, 1616, 115.

Everard : Clemence, 1617, 115 ; H., 1524, 47 ; John, 1476, 58 ; Margt., 1524, 99 ; Rich., 1617, 75. *See also* Edvarod.

Everdon, John, 1413, 123.

Evyngar : Andrew, 1533, 3, 9, 21, 67 ; Ellyn, 1533, 102.

Ewer : Hen., 1641, 151 ; Martha, 1628, 151.

Ewstes, Jerem, 1588, 71.

Exeter, John Bowthe, Bishop of, 1478, 27, 121.

Eyer : —, 1581, 108 ; John, 1561, 50 ; Margt., 1561, 105 ; Ralph, 1527, 144 ; Thos., 1581, 70. *See also* Eyr, *and* Eyre.

Eyles, Mary, 1744, 147.

Eynns, Elizth., 1585, 120.

Eyr : Joan, 1463, 86 ; Robt., 1463, 41. *See also* Eyer, *and* Eyre.

Eyre : Sir Arthur, c. 1560, 50 ; Elizth., 1493, 90 ; Elizth., c. 1500, 92 ; Margt., c. 1560, 105 ; Philip, 1504, 125 ; R., 1493, 44 ; R., c. 1500, 44 ; Robt., 1656, 152 ; Wm., 1509, 63. *See also* Eyer, *and* Eyr.

Eyston : John, 1589, 51 ; Jane, 1589, 109.

Faggar, Elizth., 1547, 104.

Fairfax : Agnes, 1521, 98 ; Robt., 1521, 66.

Fairman. *See* Fayreman.

Faldo : Agnes, c. 1490, 90 ; Amphelice, 1576, 107 ; Anne, 1594, 111 ; John, c. 1490, 60 ; Rich., 1576, 51 ; Wm., c. 1490, 60.

Fallywolle, Rauf, 1368, 141.

Fane : Francis, 1651, 152 ; Sir Thos., 1583, 149.

Fare, Habram, 1512, 63.

Farman, Robt., c. 1490, 60.

Farnefold, Elizth., 1633, 116.

Farrar : John, 1657, 152 ; Susanna, 1657, 147. *See also* Farrer, Ferrar, Ferrer, *and* Ferror.

Farrer, Ann, 1702, 147. *See also* Farrar, Ferrar, Ferrer, *and* Ferror.

Farrington : Elizth., 1611, 114 ; Leonard, 1611, 75. *See also* Faryndon, *and* Faryngton.

Faryndon : Margt., 1443, 84 ; T., 1443, 40. *See also* Farrington, *and* Faryngton.

Faryngton, Alice, 1506, 94. *See also* Farrington, *and* Faryndon.

Fastolf, Rich., 1479, 142. *See also* Fastolfe, *and* Fastolff.

Fastolfe, —, c. 1530, 67, 101. *See also* Fastolf, *and* Fastolff.

Fastolff : John, 1478, 42 ; Kath., 1478, 87. *See also* Fastolf, *and* Fastolfe.

Faversham. *See* Feversham.

Fayrey, Hen., 1516, 137.

Fayreman : Alice, 1411, 81 ; Thos., 1411, 54.

Fearne, Patrick, 1588, 131. *See also* Ferne.

Feelde, John, 1508, 140. *See also* Feld, Felde, Field, *and* Fielde.

Feilding, Sir Geo., Earl of Desmond, 1665, 152. *See also* Fildyng.

Felbrig : Alice de, c. 1380, 79 ; Eliz., c. 1380, 79 ; Roger de, c. 1380, 53 ; Sir Geo., 1400, 37 ; Symond de, c. 1380, 36. *See also* Felbrigg, *and* Felbrygge.

Felbrigg, John, c. 1400, 126. *See also* Felbrig, *and* Felbrygge.

Felbrygge : Geo., 1411, 142, 147 ; Margt., 1416, 23, 81 ; Sir Symon, 1416, 17. *See also* Felbrig, *and* Felbrigg.

Feld, John, 1477, 42, 58. *See also* Feelde, Felde, Field, *and* Fielde.

Felde : Elizth. de la, 1455, 85 ; John, 1454, 56. *See also* Feelde, Feld, Field, *and* Fielde.

Felthorp : Cecilie, 1454, 85 ; Roger, 1454, 56.

Felton, Cecily, 1615, 115.

Fenner, Joan, 1558, 105.

Fenton, John, 1566, 131.

Fermer : Anne, 1552, 104 ; R., 1552, 49. *See also* Fermour, *and* Fermoure.

Fermour, Anne, 1586, 109. *See also* Fermer, *and* Fermoure.

Fermoure, Elizth., 1552, 104 ; Wm., 1552, 49. *See also* Fermer, *and* Fermour.

Ferne, Hen., 1661, 152. *See also* Fearne.

Fernley, Aubrey, 1584, 108.

Ferrar, John, 1719, 152. *See also* Farrar, Farrer, Ferrer, *and* Ferror.

Ferrer : Mary, 1605, 150. *See also* Farrar, Farrer, Ferrar, *and* Ferror.

Foreest, Josina van, 1546, 167.

Forester, Martin, c. 1460, 130. *See also* Forster, *and* Foster.

Forster: —, c. 1460, 118; Alice, 1513, 119; Anne, 1572, 106; Anth., 1572, 50; Margt., 1587, 109. *See also* Forester, *and* Foster.

Fortescue: Cecily, 1570, 106; Hen., 1576, 51; John, 1595, 72; Mary, 1598, 120; Owner, 1595, 111.

Fortey: Agnes, 1447, 84; John, 1458, 57; Thos., 1447, 56. *See also* Foorthe.

Fosbroke: —, 1602, 112; John, 1602, 73. *See also* Fossebrok.

Fossebrok: John, 1418, 38; Maud, 1418, 81. *See also* Fosbroke.

Foster: —, c. 1507, 94; Agnes, 1519, 97; Robt., c. 1507, 63. *See also* Forester, *and* Forster.

Foulkes, Robt., 1771, 147.

Fountain. *See* Funteyn.

Fowler: Alice, 1540, 103; Edith., c. 1520, 98; Margt., 1546, 104; Robt., 1540, 48, 156; Thos., c. 1520, 46.

Fox: Emme, c. 1570, 106, 144; Myghell, c. 1545, 139; Rich., c. 1439, 40. *See also* Foxe.

Foxe: Christian, 1618, 115; Francis, 1612, 145; Jane, 1554, 25, 104; Joan, 1495, 90; Wm., 1495, 60; Wm., 1554, 25, 49. *See also* Fox.

Foxle: Joan, 1378, 79; Sir John, 1378, 36; Maud, 1378, 79.

Foxwist, Rich., 1500, 154.

Foys, Elizth., 1513, 95.

Framlingham: John, c. 1425, 39; Margt., c. 1425, 82.

Francis: Barbara, 1570, 106; Margt., 1484, 89; Margery, c. 1480, 88. *See also* Frauncis.

Frankeleyn: John, 1462, 57; Margt., 1462, 85; Sibill, 1485, 89; Wm., 1485, 59. *See also* Frankelin, *and* Franklin.

Frankelin, Frances, 1604, 113. *See also* Frankeleyn, *and* Franklin.

Franklin, Eliza, 1622, 154. *See also* Frankeleyn, *and* Frankelin.

Fransham, Geoff., 1414, 38.

Frauncis: Jane, 1587, 109; Mich., 1587, 71. *See also* Francis.

Freeman, Christ., 1610, 74. *See also* Freman.

Freer, Thos., c. 1490, 133.

Frekylton, Hen., 1508, 125.

Freman, John, c. 1440, 127. *See also* Freeman.

Freme, Wm., 1526, 66.

French, Elizth., 1727, 152.

Freney, William de, c. 1290, 2.

Freshwater: Elizth., 1681, 152; Margt., 1517, 97; Thos., 1517, 64.

Freston: Cecily, 1615, 115; Rich., 1616, 75; Rich., 1634, 76.

Frevile: Clarice de, c. 1410, 23, 81; Margt., 1410, 118; R. de, c. 1410, 38; Thos. de, 1410, 38. *See also* Frevill.

Frevill: Margt., 1476, 119. *See also* Frevile.

Frilende, Walter, 1376, 122.

Frogenhall, John, 1444, 40.

Frognal. *See* Frogenhall.

Fromond: Elizth., 1542, 103; Thos., 1542, 68. *See also* Fromoundes.

Fromoundes, Barth., 1579, 149. *See also* Fromond.

Froste, Anne, 1585, 149.

Frowick: Alice, 1451, 118; Elizth., 1545, 104. *See also* Frowyk.

Frowsetoure, Edm., 1529, 129.

Frowyk, Elizth., 1448, 118. *See also* Frowick.

Froxmere, Elizth., 1528, 100.

Frye, John, 1507, 125.

Fulburne, Wm. de, 1391, 126.

Fuller, John, 1610, 74.

Fulleylove. *See* Fuloflove.

Fulmer: Joan, 1498, 91; Robt., 1498, 61. *See also* Filmer.

Fuloflove, Ralph, 1479, 124.

Funteyn: Alice, 1453, 85; Joan, 1453, 85.

Furlong, Elizth., 1641, 154.

Furnace, John, 1585, 138.

Fyche, Geoff., 1537, 129. *See also* Fitch, *and* Fytche.

Fyge, Wm., c. 1450, 56. *See also* Fige.

Fyn, Robt., c. 1420, 123.

Fynche: Elizth., 1589, 109; Elizth., 1640, 76, 117; Rich., 1640, 8, 76; Thos., 1640, 76. *See also* Finch.

Fyndarne, Thos., 1549, 49. *See also* Fynderne, *and* Fyndorne.

Gille : John, 1546, 68 ; Margt., 1546, 104. *See also* Gyll.

Gisborne. *See* Gysborne.

Gladwin, John, 1615, 75. *See also* Gladwyn.

Gladwyn, John, c. 1450, 127. *See also* Gladwin.

Glanfield : Elizth., 1637, 116 ; Rich., 1637, 76.

Glascock, Elizth., 1584, 109. *See also* Glascocke.

Glascocke, Martha, 1593, 145. *See also* Glascock.

Glemham : Christ., c. 1570, 149 ; Edw., 1571, 144 ; Sir John, c. 1570, 149 ; Thos., 1571, 69, 149.

Glinton, Joan, 1581, 108.

Gloucester, Alianora, Duchess of, 1399, 118.

Glover : John, 1578, 134 ; Rose, 1620, 146.

Glynne, Wm., 1633, 78.

Goberd, Wm., 1515, 129.

Goche, Wm., 1499, 133.

Goddard : Eleanor, 1717, 152 ; Joan, 1517, 97 ; Thos., 1517, 64.

Godefray : Joan, 1430, 82 ; T., 1430, 55. *See also* Godefrey, Godfrey, *and* Godfrye.

Godefrey, Mary, 1638, 151. *See also* Godefray, Godfrey, *and* Godfrye.

Godfrey : Elizth., 1530, 144 ; Helen, 1530, 144 ; John, 1454, 56 ; Margt., 1454, 85 ; Mary, c. 1600, 150 ; Robt., 1522, 134. *See also* Godefray, Godefrey, *and* Godfrye.

Godfrye : Joan, 1566, 106 ; Peter, 1566, 69, *See also* Godefray, Godefrey, *and* Godfrey.

Godolphin, Jane, 1603, 113.

Godwyn, John, 1488, 59. *See also* Goodwyn.

Goldsmiths' Company, c. 1510, 148.

Goldwell : Alice, 1485, 89 ; John, c. 1520, 65 ; Margt., c. 1520, 97 ; Nich., 1523, 134 ; Wm., 1485, 59.

Goldyngton : Margt., c. 1490, 90 ; Wm., c. 1490, 60.

Golle : —, 1567, 164 ; Vincent, 1567, 163.

Gomersall, Wm., 1597, 150.

Gomfrey : Rich., 1399, 122 ; Thos., 1399, 122.

Gondeby, Hugh de, 1411, 54.

Gooch. *See* Goche.

Good : Jas., 1581, 70 ; Joan, 1581, 108. *See also* Goode.

Goodday, Wm., 1783, 147.

Goode, Wm., 1498, 125. *See also* Good.

Goodenouth : Margt., c. 1520, 98 ; Thos., c. 1520, 65.

Goodluck, Geoff., c. 1450, 41.

Goodman : Anne, 1630, 116 ; Ciselye, 1583, 108 ; Edw., 1560, 69 ; Edw., 1583, 70.

Goodnestone, —, 1523, 99.

Goodriche : Alice, 1500, 91 ; Thos., 1500, 61. *See also* Goodryke.

Goodryke, Thos., 1554, 121. *See also* Goodriche.

Goodryngton, John, 1518, 137.

Goodwyn : Aubrey, 1527, 144 ; Mary, 1596, 111 ; Robt., 1532, 67 ; Sabine, 1532, 101. *See also* Godwyn.

Goodyere : Anne, 1575, 149 ; Joan, 1504, 93 ; Joan, 1518, 97 ; John, 1506, 62 ; Lucas, 1547, 137 ; Thos., 1518, 64 ; Thomasyn, 1506, 94.

Goose, John, 1503, 153.

Gore : Mary, 1436, 130 ; Nichol de, c. 1330, 5, 121. *See also* Gower.

Gorges : Sir Arthur, 1625, 52 ; Elizth., 1625, 116.

Goring : Constance, c. 1580, 149 ; John, 1520, 46 ; Mary, 1694, 147. *See also* Goringe.

Goringe, Elizth., 1558, 105. *See also* Goring.

Gosebourne, Robt., 1523, 134.

Gosling. *See* Gostling.

Gostling, Anne, 1612, 150.

Gotheim, Sir Nenkin de, 1295, 160. *See also* Gothem.

Gothem : Arnold Nenkin de, 1307, 160 ; Elisabeth de, 1358, 163 ; Gerard de, 1358, 161. *See also* Gotheim.

Gould, Anne, 1583, 108.

Gournay, Edw., 1641, 151.

Gower, Anne, 1593, 110 ; *See also* Gore.

Gowlshull, Joan, 1607, 113.

Graffton : Joan, 1465, 86 ; Wm., c. 1465, 57. *See also* Grafton.

Grafton, Adam, 1530, 129. *See also* Graffton.

Grantham, Christ., c. 1520, 9, 137.

Gray : Christ., 1525, 144 ; H., 1545, 48 ; Jas., 1591, 154 ; T., c. 1507, 45. *See also* Grey, *and* Greye.

Haddon : —, 1516, 96 ; Kath., 1516, 96.

Hadresham, John, 1417, 38.

Hagham, Thos., 1483, 140. *See also* Heigham, Heyham, *and* Higham.

Haines. *See* Heyne, *and* Heynys.

Haitfeld : Ade, 1409, 81 ; R. de, 1409, 54.

Hakebourne, Rich. de, c. 1311, 121.

Halcot, Robt., 1500, 128.

Hale, —, 1588, 71, 109.

Hales, Edw., 1634, 151.

Hall, Anne, 1594, 145.

Halle : Elizth., c. 1430, 83 ; Peter, c. 1430, 23, 39 ; Thos., 1485, 43.

Halley : Barth., 1468, 41 ; Florens, 1468, 86.

Halliday. *See* Halyday.

Hally, Elizth., 1521, 98.

Halsey : Barth., 1468, 41 ; Florens, 1468, 86 ; Thos., 1522, 144.

Halsham : Sir Hugh, 1441, 40 ; Joyce, 1441, 84 ; Philippe, c. 1440, 83.

Halsted : Alice, 1449, 84 ; Wm., 1449, 56.

Halyday : Edw., 1519, 65 ; Margery, 1519, 97.

Hamale : Sir Gilles de, 1354, 161 ; Sir Guillaume, 1279, 160.

Hammerton, Joan, 1494, 90.

Hammond, Martha, 1604, 113.

Hamon, Thos., 1607, 74.

Hampden : Anne, 1594, 149 ; Elizth., c. 1525, 99 ; Elizth., 1553, 104 ; Griffith, 1594, 149 ; Jane, 1512, 95 ; John, c. 1420, 39 ; John, c. 1525, 47 ; Sir John, 1553, 49 ; Phillipa, 1553, 104 ; Rich., 1512, 63. *See also* Hampdyn.

Hampdyn : Edm., 1577, 70 ; Isabel, 1577, 107. *See also* Hampden.

Hampton, John, c. 1510, 137. *See also* Humpton.

Hamsterley, Ralph, c. 1510, 137.

Hanap, Joan, 1437, 83.

Hanchett, Barbara, 1561, 105.

Hansard : Joan, c. 1410, 81 ; Rich., c. 1410, 38. *See also* Hansart.

Hansart : Anth., 1507, 45 ; Kath., 1507, 94. *See also* Hansard.

Hanson, Robt., 1545, 126.

Harcourt, Maud, 1415, 81. *See also* Harecourt.

Harding, Robt., 1503, 139.

Hardy, Helen, 1486, 89.

Hare : Elizth, 1611, 114 ; Mary, 1611, 114.

Harecourt, Thos., 1460, 57. *See also* Harcourt.

Harewell : Anne, 1505, 93 ; John, 1505, 45.

Harflet : Jane, 1642, 117 ; Walter, 1642, 76. *See also* Harflete.

Harflete, Christ., 1602, 52. *See also* Harflet.

Hargreve, Geoff., 1447, 133.

Harington, Christ., 1614, 75.

Harison, Alice, c. 1600, 154. *See also* Harrison, *and* Haryson.

Harlakinden, Martin, 1584, 149. *See also* Harlakynden.

Harlakynden : Elizth., 1558, 105 ; Margt., 1558, 105 ; Thos., 1558, 49. *See also* Harlakinden.

Harlebecque, Catherine d', 1453, 164.

Harleston : Alice, c. 1480, 88 ; Alice, 1528, 100. *See also* Herleston.

Harley, Margery, 1424, 82.

Harlyng, Thos., 1423, 127.

Harpedon, Sir John, 1438, 40.

Harper : Anne, c. 1490, 90 ; Joan, 1493, 90 ; Margt., 1573, 106 ; Roger, 1493, 60 ; Wm., c. 1490, 43 ; Sir Wm., 1573, 50.

Harrington. *See* Harington.

Harris : Edw., 1597, 73 ; John, 1660, 77 ; Martha, 1660, 117 ; Wm., 1556, 148.

Harrison, Sophia, 1661, 152. *See also* Harison, *and* Haryson.

Harrowden. *See* Harwedon.

Harsick : Isabel, c. 1430, 55, 82 ; Sir John, 1384, 36 ; Kath., 1384, 22, 79. *See also* Harsyk.

Harsnett, Samuel, 1631, 9, 27, 131.

Harsyk, Sir Roger, 1454, 153. *See also* Harsick.

Harte : Anne, 1594, 145 ; Malyn, 1557, 104 ; Robt., 1571, 134 ; Thos., 1557, 68. *See also* Hert.

Harve, Sir Nich., 1532, 47. *See also* Harvey, Harvy, Harvye, Hervy, *and* Herwy.

Harvey : Dorothy, 1638, 117 ; Elizth., 1622, 115 ; J., c. 1420, 39. *See also* Harve, Harvy, Harvye, Hervy, *and* Herwy.

Harvy, Prudence, 1619, 151. *See also* Harve, Harvey, Harvye, Hervy, *and* Herwy.

Hertcombe : John, 1488, 59 ; Kath., 1488, 89.

Hertoghe : Gilles de, 1499, 162 ; Marie de, 1499, 164.

Hertzogenrade, Abbot Adam, 1483, 166.

Herun, Wm., 1525, 126. *See also* Heron.

Hervy, Thos., c. 1520, 143. *See also* Harve, Harvey, Harvy, Harvye, *and* Herwy.

Herward : Anne, 1485, 89 ; R., 1481, 42 ; Wm., 1501, 133. *See also* Harward.

Herwy, Elizth., c. 1520, 29, 130. *See also* Harve, Harvey, Harvy, Harvye, *and* Hervy.

Heth, John, 1464, 127. *See also* Hetht.

Hethersett, —, 16th cent., 150.

Hetht, Francis, 1479, 42. *See also* Heth.

Heveningham : Thos., 1513, 63 ; Thomasin, 1513, 64, 96. *See also* Hevenyngham.

Hevenyngham : Anne, 1499, 91 ; Thos., 1499, 44. *See also* Heveningham.

Hewet : Roger, 1487, 124 ; Wm., 1426, 123.

Hewke, Walter, c. 1510, 128.

Heydock : —, 1608, 114 ; T., 1612, 52. *See also* Haydok.

Heydon, Anne, 1561, 105. *See also* Haydon.

Heygge, John, 1523, 126. *See also* Hay.

Heyham, Ant., 1540, 148. *See also* Hagham, Heigham, *and* Higham.

Heylesdone : Beatrice de, c. 1370, 79 ; R. de, c. 1370, 53.

Heyman, Mary, 1601, 112.

Heyne, John, 1433, 123. *See also* Heynys.

Heynys, John, 1523, 126. *See also* Heyne.

Heyward, Robt., 1509, 63, 138. *See also* Hayward, Haywarde, *and* Heyworth.

Heyworth : Eliz., 1520, 97 ; John, 1520, 65. *See also* Hayward, Haywarde, *and* Heyward.

Hiccheceok : Agnes, 1450, 118 ; Wm., 1450, 56. *See also* Hytchcocke.

Hichman : Cristyen, 1521, 98 ; Walter, 1521, 66.

Hicklott. *See* Hyklott.

Hickman. *See* Hichman.

Hierges, Abbas Alardus de, 1264, 166.

Higate : Elizth., 1576, 107; Thos., 1576, 51.

Higgins : John, 1641, 151 ; Thos., 1660, 147.

Higham : Margt., 1599, 112 ; Robt., 1599, 73. *See also* Hagham, Heigham, *and* Heyham.

Highgate. *See* Higate.

Hildesheim, Otto de Brunswick, Bishop of, 1279, 165.

Hildesley. *See* Hyldesley.

Hill : Elizth., 1611, 114 ; John, 1605, 150 ; Thos., 1628, 76. *See also* Hyll, *and* Hylle.

Hilliard, John, 1621, 78. *See also* Hellard, *and* Hylyarde.

Hinton, Mary, 1594, 111.

Hitchcock. *See* Hiccheceok, *and* Hytchcocke.

Hoare. *See* Hoore.

Hobard : Cesily, 1503, 93. *See also* Hobart.

Hobart : Elizth., 1611, 114 ; Francis, 1609, 114 ; H., 1561, 50 ; Jas., 1609, 74. *See also* Hobard.

Hobby, Elizth., 1561, 148.

Hobson, Thos., c. 1520, 137.

Hodge, Margery, c. 1500, 92. *See also* Hodges.

Hodges : George, c. 1630, 19 ; Wm., 1590, 71. *See also* Hodge.

Holbrok : —, 1581, 108 ; Fraunces, 1581, 70. *See also* Holbrook.

Holbrook, John, 1436, 132. *See also* Holbrok.

Holden, Agnes, c. 1530, 101.

Holes : Sir Hugh de, 1415, 135 ; Margt. de, 1416, 81.

Holingworth : —, 1573, 107 ; Rainold, 1573, 50, 155.

Holl, Thos., 1630, 76.

Hollegnoule : Agnes, 1457, 164 ; Raso de, 1457, 162.

" Holleliule," Sir Eustace, called " Li fran-shoms de," 1269, 160.

Hollingworth. *See* Holingworth.

Holly, John, 1527, 153.

Holme, Joan, 1521, 98.

Holt : —, c. 1420, 82 ; Elizth., 1582, 108 ; Sir John, c. 1420, 38 ; Wm., 1582, 70. *See also* Holte.

Holte : Margt., 1545, 103; Thos., 1545, 135. *See also* Holt.

Holyngbroke, Wm., 1375, 147.

Hone : —, 1604, 113 ; Thos., 1604, 74.

Honewood, Mary, 1558, 105. *See also* Honywood.

Honings, Anne, 1570, 106.

Laken, Sir Wm., 1475, 31, 135.

Lalaing, Charles, Comte de, 1563, 169.

Lamar, John, 1512, 63.

La Marke, 15th cent., 155.

Lambaert, Thos., 1466, 167. *See also* Lambard, Lambarde, Lamberd, Lambert, *and* Lumbarde.

Lambard : Amy, 1487, 89 ; John, 1487, 59. *See also* Lambaert, Lambarde, Lamberd, Lambert, *and* Lumbarde.

Lambarde : Silvester, 1587, 154. *See also* Lambaert, Lambard, Lamberd, Lambert, *and* Lumbarde.

Lambe, Kath., 1514, 96.

Lamberd, Thos., 1510, 63. *See also* Lambaert, Lambard, Lambarde, Lambert, *and* Lumbarde.

Lambert : Elizth., 1597, 111 ; Margt., 1608, 114. *See also* Lambaert, Lambard, Lambarde, Lamberd, *and* Lumbarde.

Lambrecht, Josse, 1584, 166.

Lambton, Alice, 1430, 118.

Landas, J. de, n.d., 167.

Lane : Elizth., 1502, 93 ; Wm., 1502, 62.

Langeley, Geoff., 1437, 29, 130. *See also* Langley.

Langeton, Wm., 1413, 127. *See also* Langton.

Langham, Isabel, 1462, 118.

Langley : Elizth., 1470, 86 ; Wm., 1478, 128. *See also* Langeley.

Langton : Eupheme, 1459, 118 ; Sir John, 1459, 41 ; Robt., c. 1518, 128 ; Wm., 1466, 140. *See also* Langeton.

Lannoy : Jeanne de, c. 1585, 165 ; Marie de, c. 1585, 165.

Lansaem, Pierre, 1467, 168.

Lanyon, Alice, 1602, 113.

Lapuebla : Francisco de, 1577, 163 ; Marie de, 1577, 165.

Lasheford, Kath., 1616, 115.

Lassy, Geo., c. 1500, 133. *See also* Lacy.

Lathe, Thos., 1418, 38.

Lathem, Herdt de, 1659, 169.

Lathum : —, c. 1510, 148 ; Ann, 1627, 116 ; Elizth., 1630, 116 ; Grace, 1626, 116 ; Susan, 1622, 115 ; Wm., 1622, 75.

Latton : —, c. 1515, 46, 96 ; Alice, 1523, 99 ; Anne, 1548, 104 ; John, 1548, 49.

Launceleyn, Anne, 1544, 103. *See also* Launcelyn.

Launcelyn : John, 1435, 40 ; Margt., 1435, 83. *See also* Launceleyn.

Launoy, Sir Guillebert de, 1423, 168.

Laurence : Alice, 1522, 99 ; Alice, 1531, 101 ; John, c. 1520, 11, 129 ; Thos., 1522, 66. *See also* Lawrence.

Lauwr, — van, 1474, 156.

Law, John, c. 1450, 158.

Lawerd : Agnes, 1517, 97 ; Wm., 1517, 64.

Lawnder, Wm., c. 1530, 130.

Lawne, Thos., 1518, 125.

Lawrence, John, 1531, 47. *See also* Laurence.

Laxham, Agnes, 1484, 89.

Lea. *See* Lee, Legh, *and* Leigh.

Leake, Kath., 1529, 100. *See also* Leek, *and* Leyke.

Le Blond, Marie, 1423, 163.

Le Brun, Nicolas, 1547, 167.

Leddes, Thos., 1503, 125. *See also* Leeds.

Ledewich, Alice, 1430, 82.

Lee : —, 1528, 100 ; Alice, 1486, 89 ; Benedict, c. 1520, 138 ; Joan, 1564, 106 ; Philip de, 1349, 141 ; Wm., of Morton, 1486, 59 ; Wm., 1617, 132. *See also* Legh, *and* Leigh.

Leeder, Margt., 1573, 106.

Leeds, Edw., 1589, 131. *See also* Leddes.

Leefdael : Lodowiic de, 1550, 161 ; Marguerite de, 1550, 164.

Leek, Anne, 1471, 86 ; Mary, 1442, 84. *See also* Leake, *and* Leyke.

Legge, Cecily, c. 1500, 136.

Legh : Ellen, 1527, 100 ; Sir Peter, 1527, 47 ; Sir Peter, 1635, 153 ; Roger, 1506, 62. *See also* Lee, *and* Leigh.

Le Hunt : J., 1605, 74 ; Jane, 1605, 113. *See also* Hoont, Hunt, *and* Lehunte.

Lehunte, Als, 1584, 108. *See also* Hoont, Hunt, *and* Le Hunt.

Leigh : Elizth., 1619, 115 ; Gertrude, 1619, 115 ; Isabel, 1544, 103 ; John, 1544, 68. *See also* Lee, *and* Legh.

Leman, Thos., 1534, 134.

Lence, Stephen, 1587, 134.

Le Marie, Jehenne, 1453, 164.

Le Neve. *See* Neve.

Lenthall. *See* Leynthall.

Lenthorpe, Wm., 1506, 136. *See also* Leventhorp, *and* Leventhorpe.

Lenton, Rich., 1410, 142.

Ludlow, Elizth., 1501, 92.

Luke : Anne, 1544, 103 ; Cecyle, 1563, 106 ; Nich., 1563, 136 ; Sir Walter, 1544, 135.

Lukin, Alice, 1621, 146. *See also* Lukyn.

Lukyn : Robt., 1616, 145 ; Wm., 1543, 144. *See also* Lukin.

Lumbarde, John, 1408, 122. *See also* Lambaert.

Lupton, Roger, 1540, 28, 130.

Lutterell. *See* Loutterell.

Lye, Wm., 1391, 122.

Lyfelde : Fraunces, 1592, 110 ; Thos., 1592, 72.

Lyford, John, 1610, 74.

Lygon, Elizth., 1598, 111.

Lymsey : John, 1545, 48 ; Margt., 1545, 104.

Lyndewode : Alice, 1419, 81 ; John, 1419, 54 ; John, 1421, 55.

Lyne, Elizth., 1582, 108.

Lyrypyn, Thos., 1509, 125.

Lyon : —, 1592, 110 ; John, 1592, 72.

Lysle, Sir John, c. 1425, 39.

Lytcot, Sir Christ., 1599, 52. *See also* Lytkott.

Lytkott : Kath., 1554, 104 ; Christ., 1554, 49. *See also* Lytcot.

Lytleburye : Elizth., 1560, 105 ; R., c. 1560, 50.

Lytton : Anne, 1582, 108 ; Isabel, c. 1500, 92 ; Margt., 1582, 108 ; Robt., c. 1500, 61 ; Roland, 1582, 51.

Lyveryche, Wm., 1631, 144.

Maghull, Eleanor, 1568, 106.

Magnus, Thos., 1550, 129.

Maidstone. *See* Maydestone.

Maidwell. *See* Maydwell.

Main. *See* Mayne.

Mainwaring. *See* Manwarynge, *and* Maynwaryng.

Makepeace : Dorothy, 1584, 108 ; Rich., 1584, 71.

Makynges, Rich., 1596, 73.

Malemayns, Rich., 1440, 40.

Malève, Sir René de, c. 1330, 161.

Malford, Rich., 1403, 127.

Malin. *See* Malyn, *and* Malyns.

Mallet : Agnes, 1516, 96 ; Barbe, 1579, 165.

Malory, Simon, 1580, 51.

Malster, Wm., 1492, 128.

Maltoun, John, 1447, 40.

Malyn : Elizth., 1536, 102 ; Thos., 1536, 68. *See also* Malyns.

Malyns —, c. 1385, 79 ; —, c. 1390, 79 ; Sir E., c. 1385, 36 ; Isabel de, c. 1385, 79 ; R., 1430, 39 ; Sir R. de, 1385, 22, 23, 36. *See also* Malyn.

Manfeld : Agnes, 1540, 103 ; Isabel, 1455, 56, 85 ; John, 1455, 7, 56, 136 ; Kath., 1540, 103 ; Rich., 1455, 7, 20, 56 ; Thos., 1540, 48.

Manley, Laur., c. 1590, 71.

Manning : Agnes, 1543, 148 ; John, 1543, 148 ; Rachel, 1604, 113 ; Rich., 1604, 74 ; Rich., 1605, 145.

Manningham, Kath., 1420, 82. *See also* Manyngham.

Mannock : Dorothy, 1632, 116 ; Eleanor, 1624, 116. *See also* Mannok, Manock, *and* Monox.

Mannok, —, 1590, 78. *See also* Mannock, Manock, *and* Monox.

Manock : Mary, c. 1656, 146 ; Thos., 1656, 146. *See also* Mannock, Mannok, *and* Monox.

Manston, Joan, 1493, 90 ; Nich., 1444, 40.

Manwarynge : Joan, 1598, 111 ; Wm., 1598, 73. *See also* Maynwaryng.

Manyngham : Elenor, 1476, 147 ; Sir Oliver, 1476, 147. *See also* Manningham.

Mapilton, John, 1432, 127.

Mapletoft, Mary, 1656, 152.

Marcheford, Simon, 1442, 127.

Mare. *See* Delamare.

Mareys : Joan, 1431, 136 ; Thos., 1472, 133 ; Wm., 1459, 41.

Mariott : —, 1584, 108 ; Robt., 1584, 71. *See also* Maryet.

Markeby : Alice, 1439, 83 ; Wm., 1439, 55.

Markes, Anne, 1662, 147.

Marlow. *See* Merlawe.

Marnay : Brygete, 1549, 104 ; John, Lord, 1549, 49. *See also* Marney.

Marner, Philip, 1587, 71.

Marney, Anne, 1476, 119. *See also* Marnay.

Marriott. *See* Mariott, *and* Maryet.

Marrowe : Dorothy, 1538, 103 ; Elizth., 1601, 112.

Marsh, John, 1561, 148.

Mirfin. *See* Myrfin.

Missenden, Kath. de, 1436, 153. *See also* Myssenden.

Mitchell. *See* Michell.

Mitford, Margt., 1483, 88.

Moenius, Joachim, n.d., 166.

Mohun : Anne, 1612, 114 ; M., 1612, 52 ; Margt., 1603, 113 ; Robt., 1603, 52 ; Thos. de, c. 1440, 40. *See also* Moüen.

Molesworth, —, 1630, 151.

Molineux : Elizth., c. 1570, 106 ; Jane, c. 1570, 106 ; Sir Wm., c. 1570, 50. *See also* Molyneux.

Molyneux : Agnes, 1484, 89 ; Eleanor, 1568, 106 ; E., 1484, 43 ; Margt., 1528, 100 ; Sir R., 1568, 50. *See also* Molineux.

Molyngton, Agnes, 1454, 118.

Molyns : Kath., c. 1535, 102 ; Margery, 1425, 118 ; Sir Wm., 1425, 39.

Moncke, Joan, 1601, 145.

Monckton. *See* Monkeden.

Monde, Wm., 1488, 59. *See also* Mawnde.

Monemouth, John, 1419, 123.

Moneslee : Isabel, 1412, 81 ; Walter, 1412, 54.

Monkeden : John, 1503, 62 ; Margt., 1503, 93.

Monmouth. *See* Monemouth.

Monox : Ann, 1543, 103 ; Sir Geo., 1543, 8, 68. *See also* Mannock, Mannok, *and* Manock.

Montague, Jas., c. 1450, 41. *See also* Mountagu.

Monte Sancti Wiberte, Margarete de, 16th cent., 165.

Montford. *See* Mundeford, *and* Mundford.

Montgomery, Isabel, 1558, 105.

Moor, Wm., 1456, 123. *See also* Moore, *and* More.

Moore, John, 1532, 144. *See also* Moor, *and* More.

Mordaunt : —, c. 1580, 149 ; Margt., 1540, 103 ; Wm., 1518, 64.

Mordon : John, c. 1410, 122 ; Thos., 1458, 127.

More : Elizth., c. 1620, 151 ; Gauwyn, 1469, 57 ; Gwen, 1504, 93 ; Isabel, 1469, 86 ; Mary, 1577, 107 ; Raffe, 1577, 70, 158 ; Wm. at, c. 1580, 70. *See also* Moor, *and* Moore.

Morecote, Hen., 1467, 124.

Mores, Elizth., 1514, 96. *See also* Morris *and* Morys.

Moreton, Wenllan, 1427, 82.

Morewood : Grace, 1647, 117 ; John, 1647, 77.

Morflett, Elizth., 1578, 107.

Morland, Kath., 1516, 96.

Morle : Robt., 1410, 38 ; Robt., 1415, 38. *See also* Morley.

Morley : Robt., 1492, 124 ; Thos., 1566, 144. *See also* Morle.

Morrey, Thos., 1584, 71.

Morris, Roger, 1615, 154. *See also* Mores, *and* Morys.

Mortimer, Elizth., 1419, 81.

Morys : Joan, c. 1510, 95 ; Wm., 1509, 63. *See also* Mores, *and* Morris.

Mosley : Alice, 1607, 113 ; Anne, 1630, 116 ; Anth., 1607, 74 ; Oswald, 1630, 76.

Mostyn, Mary, 1658, 117.

Motesfont, John, 1420, 132.

Mottisfont. *See* Motesfont.

Moüen, Jehenne, 1453, 164 ; John, 1453, 162. *See also* Mohun.

Mountagu : Agnes, 1517, 97 ; Thos., 1517, 64 ; Thos., 1630, 77. *See also* Montague.

Mountney, Mary, 1526, 100.

Mowbray, Wm., c. 1430, 127.

Mowfurth, Wm., 1513, 125.

Moyne : Mary, 1404, 80 ; Sir Wm., 1404, 37.

Mul, John de, 1317, 4, 169.

Mulcaster, Kath., 1609, 145.

Mullens, Elenor, 1476, 147.

Mulsho : John, 1400, 54 ; Joan, 1400, 80.

Multon : Audrey, 1638, 146 ; Debora, 1619, 151 ; Geo., 1588, 145 ; Geo., 1618, 145 ; Stephen, 1477, 124.

Mundeford, Elizth., 1474, 87. *See also* Mundford.

Mundford, Margt., 1520, 97. *See also* Mundeford.

Munter : Jakemine, 1439, 7, 167 ; Joris, 1439, 7, 167.

Muscote : Alice, 1512, 95 ; John, 1512, 63.

Musgrave, Dorcas, 1610, 114, 138.

Mustarder, Wm., c. 1490, 124.

Muston, Anne, 1496, 139.

Van den Kerchove: Josine, 1538, 164; Willem, 1538, 162.

Van der Brucghe, Jakemine, 1439, 7, 167.

Van der Gracht, Josine, 1538, 164.

Van der Mase, Anthonine, 1601, 165.

Vanderpoele, Josine, 1557, 164.

Vander Vichte, Florentine, 1524, 164.

Van de Voorde, Elisabeth, 1594, 165.

Vaughan, Sir Thos., 1483, 43.

Vause, Kath., 1535, 102. *See also* Vaux.

Vaux, Elizth., 1601, 112. *See also* Vause.

Vawdrey, Ralph, 1478, 133.

Veer, Constance, 1499, 91.

Veldon, Jas., 1458, 124.

Venables, Douce, 1460, 85.

Verauen, Marie, 1499, 164.

Verdun, — de, c. 1325, 155.

Vere: Elizth. de, 1537, 24, 102; John de, Earl of Oxford, 1537, 24.

Verieu, John, c. 1370, 122.

Verimmen, J., 1585, 169.

Verney: Anne, 1523, 99; Anne, 1526, 100; Elizth., 1547, 104; Geo., c. 1630, 52; Margery, 1509, 95; Rich., 1526, 47; Sir Ralph, 1547, 49.

Vernon: Margt., 1467, 119; Sir Wm., 1467, 41.

Verzelini: Elizth., 1607, 113; Jacob, 1607, 74.

Villers, Gerard de, 1273, 160.

Vipont, Margt. de, 1458, 85.

Vir, Barth de, 1158, 2.

Visch, Martin de, 1452, 161.

Voirsselaer, Kath. van, 1458, 165.

Vynter: John, 1404, 122; Margt., c. 1420, 82; Wm., c. 1420, 55. *See also* Winter, *and* Wynter.

Vyzsdelou, Eleanor, 1409, 80.

Waddoms. *See* Woddomes.

Wade: Alice, 1599, 112; Guy, 1557, 49.

Waferer, Anne, 1617, 150.

Waite. *See* Wayte.

Wake: Elizth., 1503, 93; Roger, 1503, 44; Walter, 1451, 133.

Wakehurst: Elizth., c. 1500, 91; Margt., 1504, 93; Rich., c. 1500, 61; Eliz., 1510, 95.

Waldeby, Robt. de, 1397, 121.

Waldegrave: Anne, 1570, 106; Francis, 1629, 146.

Walden: —, 1496, 77; Emme, 1471, 86; J. de, c. 1360, 53.

Wale, Robt. le, 1362, 141.

Waleys: Alice, 1503, 93; Elizth., c. 1430, 83; John, 1410, 122.

Waliston: Isabel, 1469, 86; Joan, 1469, 86; John, 1469, 57.

Walkeden, Anne, 1575, 149.

Walker: Alis, 1584, 108; Annes, 1590, 109.

Waller, Rich., 1552, 148.

Walley, Wm., 1506, 125.

Wallis. *See* Waleys.

Walrond: Alice, c. 1520, 98; Elizth., c. 1480, 88; Joan, 1477, 136; Wm., c. 1480, 58. *See also* Wolrond.

Walsch: Kath., 1393, 79; Sir Thos., 1393, 37. *See also* Walsche, Walsh, Walsshe, *and* Walysch.

Walsche, Wenllan, 1427, 82. *See also* Walsch, Walsh, Walsshe, *and* Walysch.

Walsh: Elizth., 1561, 148; Joan, 1620, 151. *See also* Walsch, Walsche, Walsshe, *and* Walysch.

Walsingham: Elenor, c. 1590, 110; John, c. 1590, 51.

Walsokne: Adam de, 1349, 3, 4, 22, 53; Margt., 1349, 78.

Walsshe, Elizth., 1441, 118. *See also* Walsch, Walsche, Walsh, *and* Walysch.

Waltham: —, 1420, 55; Joan, 1420, 82; John de, 1395, 121; John, c. 1400, 142; Margt., c. 1400, 142.

Walton, Parnell, 1462, 85. *See also* Waulton, *and* Wautone.

Walworth, Margt., 1513, 95.

Walwyn, Alice, c. 1500, 92.

Walysch: —, c. 1420, 82; Thos., c. 1420, 39. *See also* Walsch, Walsche, Walsh, *and* Walsshe.

Wantele, John, 1424, 18, 39.

Wanton, Agnes, 1411, 81.

Warbulton, Ellen, 1454, 85.

Warburton, Anne, 1579, 107.

Warcop, Edw., 1510, 140.

Ward: Alice, c. 1600, 154. *See also* Warde.

Warde: Joan, 1541, 103; Robt., 1474, 124; Thos., 1541, 68. *See also* Ward.

INDEX OF PLACES

The first reference, in four figures, is to date ; the second, to page :
i.e. 1454, 118=date 1454, page 118.

Ashby St. Legers (Northants), 1416, 54, 81 ; c. 1500, 44 ; 1510, 130.

Ashen (Essex), c. 1440, 40, 83.

Ashford (Kent), c. 1320, 121 ; 1375, 79 ; 1499, 44 ; 1512, 120.

Ash-next-Sandwich (Kent), 1455, 24, 85, 118 ; 1525, 66, 99 ; 1582, 149 ; 1602, 52, 112 ; 1624, 117, 151 ; 1642, 76.

Ash-next-Wrotham (Kent), 1465, 124.

Ashover (Derb.), 1504, 125 ; 1507, 45, 94.

Ashridge House (Bucks.), 1395, 122 ; 1412, 154.

Ashton (Northants), 1584, 71, 108.

Aspenden (Herts.), 1500, 61, 91 ; 1508, 45, 94.

Aspley Guise (Beds.), c. 1501, 44.

Assington (Suff.), c. 1500, 44, 92.

Astley (Warw.), c. 1400, 80.

Aston (Warw.), 1545, 103, 135.

Aston Rowant (Oxon.), 1445, 56, 84 ; c. 1470, 86 ; 1508, 94.

Atherington (Devon), 1539, 48, 103.

Attlebridge (Norf.), c. 1525, 141.

Auckland St. Andrew (Durh.), c. 1380, 126 ; 1581, 140.

Audley (Staffs.), 1385, 36.

Aughton (Yorks.), 1466, 41, 119.

Auxerre Cathedral, France, 1390, 166.

Aveley (Essex), 1370, 3, 36 ; c. 1520, 77 ; 1583, 138 ; 1584, 149 ; 1585, 149.

Avenbury (Heref.), c. 1260, 2.

Axbridge (Som.), 1493, 60, 90.

Aylesford (Kent), 1426, 39, 82.

Aylsham (Norf.), c. 1490, 60, 129 ; 1499, 137 ; c. 1500, 61, 92 ; 1507, 136.

Backwell (Som.), 1604, 74, 113.

Baconsthorpe (Norf.), 1561, 105.

Baginton (Warw.), 1407, 37, 80.

Bakewell (Derb.), 1648, 77 ; 1653, 152.

Baldock (Herts.), c. 1410, 81 ; c. 1420, 55, 82 ; c. 1480, 58, 87.

Balsham (Cambs.), 1401, 28, 126 ; 1462, 28, 127 ; c. 1480, 42.

Bampton (Oxon.), 1500, 128 ; 1633, 116.

Bapchild (Kent), 1529, 99.

Barcheston (Warw.), 1530, 134.

Barford St. Martin (Wilts.), 1584, 108.

Barham (Kent), c. 1370, 53 ; c. 1455, 41, 118.

Barham (Suff.), 1514, 64, 96 ; 1607, 145.

Barking (Essex), c. 1480, 133 ; 1493, 60, 90 ; 1596, 72, 111, 138.

Barking (London) : All Hallows. *See* London : All Hallows, Barking.

Barkway (Herts.), 1561, 69, 105.

Barley (Herts.), 1621, 132.

Barnes (Surr.), 1508, 94.

Barnham Broom (Norf.), 1467, 57 ; 1514, 64, 96.

Barningham (Suff.), 1499, 133.

Barningham Norwood (Norf.), 1516, 46.

Barnwell (Northants), 1610, 74.

Barrow (Suff.), 1570, 50, 106.

Barrowby (Lincs.), 1479, 58, 87 ; 1508, 94.

Barsham (Suff.), c. 1415, 38.

Barton (Cambs.), c. 1600, 73, 112.

Barton-in-the-Clay (Beds.), 1349, 141 ; 1396, 122 ; c. 1490, 60.

Barton-on-Humber (Lincs.), c. 1380, 79 ; 1433, 55.

Barton Segrave (Northants), 1616, 115.

Barton Turf (Norf.), 1495, 142 ; 1497, 142 ; c. 1500, 143.

Basildon (Berks.), 1497, 60, 91.

Basingstoke (Hants), 1606, 74, 113 ; 1621, 78.

Bassingbourne (Cambs.), 1683, 77, 117.

Battle (Suss.), 1426, 39 ; c. 1430, 123 ; 1435, 39 ; 1590, 109 ; 1615, 132.

Bawburgh (Norf.), 1493, 142 ; 1500, 61 ; 1505, 136 ; 1531, 141 ; 1660, 137.

Bayford (Herts.), c. 1545, 49, 104 ; c. 1630, 52.

Beaumaris (Anglesea), c. 1530, 67, 101.

Beccles (Suff.), 1620, 146.

Beckenham (Kent), 1563, 105.

Beckington (Som.), 1485, 43, 89.

Beckley (Oxon.), 1619, 115.

Beddington (Surr.), 1414, 81 ; 1425, 140 ; c. 1430, 55, 82 ; 1432, 55, 83 ; 1437, 40 ; 1507, 94, 119 ; 1520, 46.

Bedford : St. Mary, 1627, 76 ; 1663, 117.

„ St. Paul, 1573, 50, 106.

Beechamwell (Norf.) : St. Mary, c. 1385, 122 ; 1430, 128.

Beeford (Yorks.), 1472, 123.

Beeston Regis (Norf.), c. 1470, 139 ; 1527, 66, 100.

Braughing (Herts.), c. 1480, 58, 88 ; c. 1490, 60 ; 1561, 105.

Brauncepeth (Durh.), 1456, 133.

Braunston (Rutl.), 1596, 72, 111 ; 1642, 151.

Brauweilers, Germany, 1483, 166.

Bray (Berks.), 1378, 36, 79 ; 1440, 147 ; 1454, 142 ; 1475, 31, 135 ; c. 1490, 60, 90 ; 1567, 149 ; 1593, 144 ; 1594, 149 ; 1610, 74, 114 ; 1621, 75, 115.

Brede (Suss.), 1493, 90.

Bredfield (Suff.), 1611, 75, 114.

Bredgar (Kent), 1518, 134.

Brenchley (Kent), 1517, 64, 96 ; c. 1540, 68 ; 1562, 144.

Brent Pelham (Herts.), 1627, 116.

Brightlingsea (Essex), 1496, 60, 91 ; 1505, 93 ; 1514, 96 ; 1521, 65 ; 1525, 66, 99 ; 1536, 102, 119 ; 1578, 70.

Brightwalton (Berks.), 1517, 64, 96.

Brightwell (Berks.), 1507, 125 ; 1509, 63, 94 ; 1512, 63, 95.

Brightwell Baldwin (Oxon.), c. 1370, 141 ; 1439, 83, 135.

Brightwell Prior (Oxon.), 1549, 68.

Brightwell Salome (Oxon.), 1492, 124.

Brinckley (Cambs.), 1521, 77.

Brisley (Norf.), 1531, 126.

Bristol (Glos.) : St. John, 1478, 58, 87.
    ,,   ,,   St. Mary Redcliffe, 1439, 31, 135 ; 1475, 42, 87 ; c. 1480, 58, 88, 153 ; 1522, 98, 135.
    ,,   ,,   St. Peter, 1461, 6, 124.
    ,,   ,,   Temple Church, c. 1400, 54 ; c. 1460, 127.
    ,,   ,,   Trinity Almshouse Chapel, 1411, 54 ; c. 1411, 81.

Broad Blunsden (Wilts.), 1608, 114 ; 1612, 52.

Broadwater (Suss.), 1415, 142 ; 1432, 127 ; 1445, 140.

Bromham (Beds.), 1435. 11, 40, 83 ; 1545, 48.

Bromley (Kent), 1600, 73, 112 ; 1605, 144.

Brookland (Kent), 1503, 125.

Broughton (Hunts.), c. 1490, 60, 153.

Broughton (Lincs.), c. 1390, 23, 36, 79.

Broughton (Oxon.), 1414, 81.

Broughton Gifford (Wilts.), 1620, 154.

Broxbourne (Herts.), c. 1470, 124 ; 1473, 42, 87 ; c. 1510, 134 ; 1531, 47 ; 1630, 151.

Bruges, Belgium, c. 1520, 169.
    ,,   ,,   Béguinage, 1410, 165 ; 1594, 165.
    ,,   ,,   Cathedral, c. 1360, 162 ; 1387, 167 ; 1439, 7, 167 ; 1452, 161 ; 1483, 167 ; 1510, 165 ; 1517, 162 ; 1518, 161, 164 ; 1525, 168 ; 1526, 162 ; 1533, 169.
    ,,   ,,   Hospice St. Jean, 1530, 168 ; c. 1530, 169 ; 1584, 166.
    ,,   ,,   St. Basil, 1557, 166.
    ,,   ,,   St. Jacques, 1460, 164 ; 1577, 163, 165 ; 1601, 165 ; 1615, 163, 165.

Bruisyard (Suff.), 1611, 114.

Brundish (Suff.), c. 1360, 122 ; 1559, 49 ; 1560, 49, 105 ; 1571, 69.

Brussels : Museum, c. 1330, 161 ; 1332, 4, 161 ; 1659, 169.

Buckland (Herts.), 1451, 84 ; 1478, 128 ; 1499, 61.

Bungay (Suff.), 1599, 150.

Burford (Oxon.), 1437, 55, 83 ; 1614, 75, 115.

Burgate (Suff.), 1409, 37, 79.

Burghclere (Hants), 1633, 146.

Burghfield (Berks.), 1568, 50, 106.

Burgh St. Margaret (Norf.), 1608, 131.

Burgh Wallis (Yorks.), 1556, 50.

Burham (Kent) : Old Church, 1506, 143.

Burnham (Bucks.), c. 1520, 120 ; 1581, 70, 108 ; n.d., 152.

Burnham Thorpe (Norf.), 1420, 38.

Burnham Westgate (Norf.), 1523, 99.

Burton (Suss.), 1520, 46 ; 1558, 105.

Burton (Wilts.), 1694, 147.

Burton Coggles (Lincs.), 1620, 52, 115.

Burton Pedwardine (Lincs.), 1631, 116.

Burwell (Cambs.), c. 1520, 11, 129.

Bury St. Edmund's (Suff.) : St. Mary, c. 1480, 58, 88 ; 1514, 129 ; c. 1520, 153 ; c. 1530, 148 ; 1575, 149.

Bushley (Worc.), 1500, 61, 91.

Oxford : Merton College, c. 1311, 121 ; 1370, 132 ; c. 1420, 6, 30, 132 ; 1445, 30, 133 ; 1471, 128 ; 1510, 143 ; 1519, 134.

„　　New College, 1403, 127 ; 1417, 27, 121 ; 1419, 127 ; 1427, 30, 132 ; 1441, 132 ; 1447, 133 ; 1451, 133 ; 1468, 30, 133 ; 1472, 136 ; 1478, 133 ; 1479, 133 ; 1494, 128 ; 1507, 125 ; 1508, 134 ; c. 1510, 63 ; 1521, 128 ; c. 1525, 121 ; 1592, 72 ; 1601, 134 ; 1619, 134 ; 1623, 155.

„　　Queen's College, c. 1518, 128 ; 1616, 29, 131, 132.

„　　St. Aldate, 1607, 74 ; 1612, 75 ; 1637, 134.

„　　St. Cross, Holywell, 1622, 154 ; 1625, 116.

„　　St. John's College, 1571, 134 ; 1578, 134.

„　　St. Mary Magdalene, 1580, 134.

„　　St. Mary the Virgin, 1349, 141 ; 1584, 108.

„　　St. Michael, 1578, 70.

„　　St. Peter-in-the-East, 1478, 58, 87 ; 1572, 69, 106 ; 1574, 69, 107 ; 1599, 73

„　　St. Peter-le-Bailey, 1419, 55 ; c. 1420, 82 ; c. 1650, 77, 117.

Oxted (Surr.), 1428, 123 ; 1480, 87 ; 1611, 78.

Pakefield (Suff.), 1417, 81 ; 1451, 133.
Parham (Suff.), 1603, 145.
Paris, France : Hôtel de Cluny, c. 1270, 160.
Paston (Norf.), c. 1570, 69.
Pebmarsh (Essex), c. 1323, 14, 35.
Pembury (Kent), 1607, 120.
Penn (Bucks.), 1540, 137 ; 1597, 52, 111 ; 1638, 53, 117 ; 1640, 117 ; 1641, 53, 117.
Penshurst (Kent), 1507, 77, 143 ; 1514, 64, 96 ; c. 1520, 140 ; 1558, 148.
Pentney (Norf.), 1620, 151.
Perivale (Middx.). See Little Greenford.
Petistree (Suff.), 1580, 70, 108.
Pettaugh (Suff.), c. 1530, 67, 101.
Piddlehinton (Dorset), 1617, 132.

Piddletown (Dorset), 1517, 64.
Pimperne (Dorset), 1694, 138, 155.
Pinchbeck (Lincs.), 1608, 114.
Pinner (Middx.), 1580, 138, 158.
Playford (Suff.), 1400, 37.
Pluckley (Kent), 1440, 40 ; c. 1517, 46 ; 1526, 100 ; c. 1545, 49.
Poddington (Beds.), 1518, 64.
Poling (Suss.), c. 1460, 124.
Polstead (Suff.), c. 1430, 123 ; c. 1490, 60, 90.
Portbury (Som.), 1621, 115.
Potter Heigham (Norf.), 1613, 150.
Potterspury (Northants), 1616, 115.
Preshute (Wilts.), 1518, 65, 97.
Preston (Suff.), 1629, 151 ; 1638, 151.
Preston-by-Faversham (Kent), 1442, 40, 84 ; 1459, 41 ; 1612, 114.
Preston Deanery (Northants), 1622, 52, 115
Probus (Cornw.), 1514, 64, 96.
Pulborough (Suss.), 1423, 127 ; 1452, 56, 84 ; 1478, 58.
Putney (Surr.). See London : Putney.
Puttenham (Surr.), 1431, 123.
Pyrton (Oxon.), 1522, 66, 99.

Quainton (Bucks.), c. 1360, 79 ; 1422, 129 ; 1485, 128 ; 1509, 95 ; 1510, 63 ; 1593, 111.
Queenhill (Worc.), 1584, 159.
Quinton (Glos.), 1430, 131.

Radwell (Herts.), 1487, 59, 89, 124 ; 1516, 64, 96 ; 1602, 113.
Rainham (Essex), c. 1500, 61, 92.
Rainham (Kent), 1409, 142 ; 1514, 46 ; 1529, 66 ; c. 1530, 101 ; c. 1580, 70, 108.
Rauceby (Lincs.), 1536, 126.
Raunds (Northants), c. 1510, 77, 95.
Raveningham (Norf.), 1483, 88.
Rawreth (Essex), 1576, 51, 107.
Rayleigh (Essex), c. 1450, 56, 84.
Reading (Berks) : St. Giles, 1521, 66, 98.
„　　„　　St. Laurence, c. 1415, 54, 81 ; 1463, 142 ; 1538, 68.
„　　„　　St. Mary, 1416, 140.
Redbourn (Herts.), c. 1490, 120 ; 1512, 63 ; 1560, 50, 105.

Sawbridgeworth (Herts.), 1437, 17, 40; 1470, 57, 86; 1484, 136; c. 1500, 148; 1527, 100; c. 1600, 52, 112.

Sawley (Derb.), 1467, 41, 86; 1478, 42, 119.

Sawston (Cambs.), c. 1420, 55; 1423, 147; c. 1480, 42; c. 1500, 136; 1527, 126.

Sawtrey (Hunts.), 1404, 37, 80.

Schwerin (Mecklenburg), 1339, 3; 1375, 4.

Scotter (Lincs.) 1599, 73, 112.

Scottow (Norf.), c. 1520, 141.

Scrivelsby (Lincs.), 1422, 39, 82; 1545, 48.

Sculthorpe (Norf.), 1470, 41; c. 1480, 153; 1521, 66, 98.

Seal (Kent), 1395, 37.

Seclin (Belgium), c. 1142, 2.

Sedgefield (Durh.), 1445, 153; c. 1500, 137.

Sefton (Lancs.), 1528, 100; 1568, 50, 106; c. 1570, 50, 106.

Selling (Kent), 1525, 66.

Send (Surr.), 1521, 66, 98.

Sessay (Yorks.), 1550, 129.

Shalston (Bucks.), 1540, 131.

Sharnbrook (Beds.), 1522, 66, 99.

Sharrington (Norf.), c. 1445, 40; 1486, 124; c. 1520, 98; 1593, 51, 111.

Sheldwich (Kent), 1394, 37, 79; 1426, 39, 82; 1431, 136.

Sherborne St. John (Hants), c. 1360, 53, 79; 1488, 43; 1492, 43, 90; c. 1540, 48.

Shere (Surr.), 1412, 123; 1512, 64; 1516, 64, 96; c. 1525, 47.

Shernbourne (Norf.), 1458, 18, 23, 41, 85.

Sherringham (Norf.), 1513, 64, 95.

Shillingford (Devon), 1516, 46, 96.

Shillington (Beds.), 1400, 126; 1485, 128; 1638, 146.

Shiplake (Oxon.), c. 1540, 68, 103.

Shipton-under-Wychwood (Oxon.), 1548, 137.

Shopland (Essex), 1371, 36.

Shorne (Kent), 1457, 57, 85; c. 1470, 86; 1519, 141; 1583, 108; 1639, 151.

Shorwell (I. of Wight), 1518, 130; 1619, 115.

Shotesham St. Mary (Norf.), 1528, 47, 100.

Shottesbrooke (Berks.), c. 1370, 53, 122; 1401, 80; 1511, 45; 1567, 21, 69, 106.

Shottisham (Suff.), 1620, 146.

Sibton (Suff.), 1475, 142; 1501, 143; 1574, 69, 107; 1582, 70, 108; 1595, 145; 1611, 145; 1626, 76.

Sibstone (Leics.), 1532, 144.

Sithney (Cornw.), c. 1420, 140.

Slapton (Bucks.), 1462, 124; 1519, 65, 97; 1529, 126.

Slaugham (Suss.), 1503, 44; 1547, 49, 104.

Sleaford (Lincs.), 1521, 98.

Slinfold (Suss.), 1533, 67, 102; c. 1600, 112; 1678, 152.

Sluyvekenkerke, W. Flanders, n.d., 168.

Snettisham (Norf.), c. 1560, 105; 1610, 74, 114.

Snodland (Kent), 1441, 56; 1486, 59; 1487, 59, 89; 1541, 148.

Sockburn (Durh.), 1470, 142.

Solihull (Warw.), 1549, 68, 104.

Somersham (Hunts.), c. 1530, 126.

Somerton (Oxon.), 1552, 49, 104.

Sotterley (Suff.), 1479, 42, 87; c. 1480, 42; 1572, 50; 1578, 107; 1584, 149; 1594, 145; c. 1630, 52, 116; 1638, 146.

Soulbury (Bucks.), 1502, 62, 93; 1516, 96.

Souldern (Oxon.), c. 1460, 153.

Southacre (Norf.), 1384, 22, 36, 79; 1454, 153; 1534, 134.

South Burlingham (Burlingham St. Edmund), (Norf.), 1540, 141.

South Creake (Norf.), c. 1400, 126; 1509, 63, 128.

South Elmham (Suff.), c. 1500, 61, 92.

Southfleet (Kent), 1414, 81; 1420, 55, 82; 1456, 127; c. 1520, 65, 98, 138.

South Kelsey (Lincs.), c. 1410, 38, 81.

South Mimms (Middx.), 1448, 118; 1621, 146; 1628, 151; 1641, 151; 1661 152.

Southminster (Essex), 1556, 148; c. 1560, 69, 105; 1634, 76.

South Ockendon (Essex), 1400, 37; 1585, 149; 1602, 113.

South Ormsby (Lincs.), c. 1410, 81.

South Petherton (Som.), 1442, 84.

South Weald (Essex), c. 1460, 85.

PLATES

PLATE I

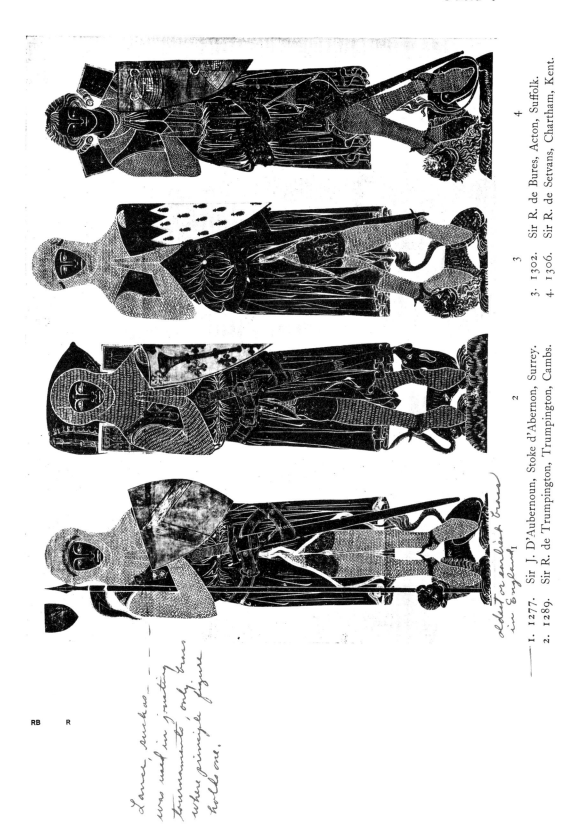

Lances, such as
are used in jousting
tournaments, only brass
where principle figure
holds one.

oldest existant brass
in England.

—— 1. 1277. Sir J. D'Aubernoun, Stoke d'Abernon, Surrey.
2. 1289. Sir R. de Trumpington, Trumpington, Cambs.

3. 1302. Sir R. de Bures, Acton, Suffolk.
4. 1306. Sir R. de Setvans, Chartham, Kent.

1   2   3   4

PLATE 2

c. 1323. Sir Wm. Fitzralph,
Pebmarsh, Essex.

c. 1325. Sir J. de Creke and wife,
Westley Waterless, Cambs.

PLATE 3

c. 1330.　Sir. J. de Northwood and wife,
Minster, Sheppey.

c. 1360.　W. de Aldeburgh,
Aldborough, Yorks.

PLATE 4

The Earl of Warwick

1347. Sir H. Hastyngs,
Elsing, Norfolk.

Lord St. Amand.

panels feature
armed weepers
and religious scenes.

Brass much despoiled.
Marks transition between
two halves of 14th century 1345-1355.

PLATE 5

1

2

3

hic iacet Radulphus de Knetwynton. Obitus
idem die Jouis ante festu sci Nicholai episcopi
anno dni millmo. ccc. lxx. fra dmeat. f.

1. 1327. Sir J. D'Aubernoun, Stoke d'Abernon, Surrey.
2. 1370. Ralph de Knevyngton, Aveley, Essex.
3. 1354. Sir J. de Cobham, Cobham, Kent.

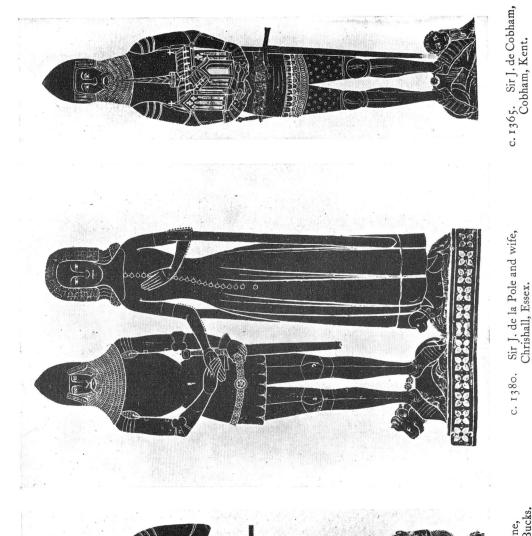

c. 1365. Sir J. de Cobham,
Cobham, Kent.

c. 1380. Sir J. de la Pole and wife,
Chrishall, Essex.

1368. Thos. Cheyne,
Drayton Beauchamp, Bucks.

PLATE 7

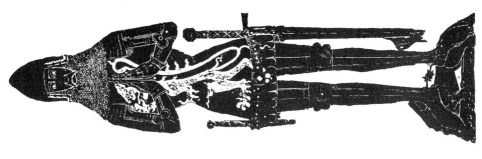

1400. Sir G. Felbrigg,
Playford, Suffolk.

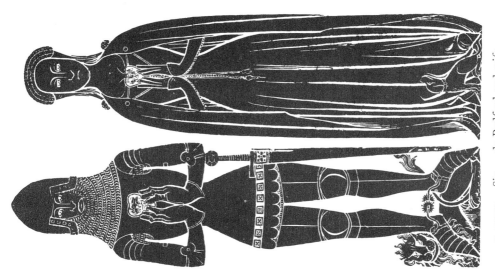

c. 1390. Sir — de Redford and wife,
Broughton, Lincs.

1390. Sir A. Loutterell,
Irnham, Lincs.

PLATE 8

c. 1380.   Sir — Dallingridge and wife,
Fletching, Sussex.

PLATE 9

1384.　Sir J. Harsick and wife,
Southacre, Norfolk.

PLATE 10

1394. Sir R. Attelese and wife, Sheldwich, Kent.

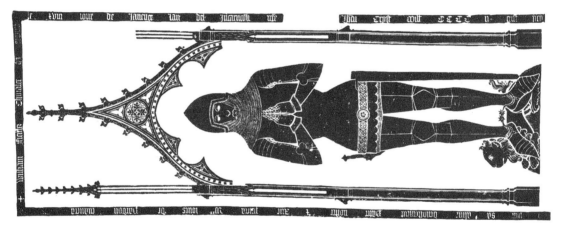

1402. Sir W. Fienlez, Hurstmonceaux, Sussex.

c. 1400. ? — Dalison, Laughton, Lincs.

PLATE 11

c. 1400. Lord Willoughby d'Eresby,
Spilsby, Lincs.

1424. John Wantele,
Amberley, Sussex.

PLATE 12

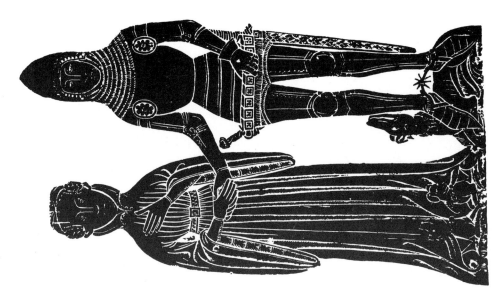

c. 1410. R. de Frevile and wife,
Little Shelford, Cambs.

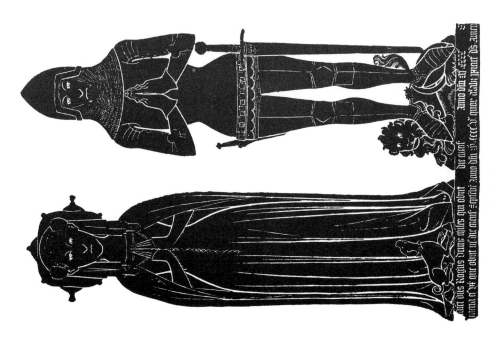

1405. Sir R. Drury and wife,
Rougham, Suffolk.

PLATE 13

1408. Sir W. Tendring,
Stoke-by-Nayland, Suffolk.

1406. The Earl of Warwick and wife,
St. Mary, Warwick.

1401. Sir N. Dagworth,
Blickling, Norfolk.

PLATE 14

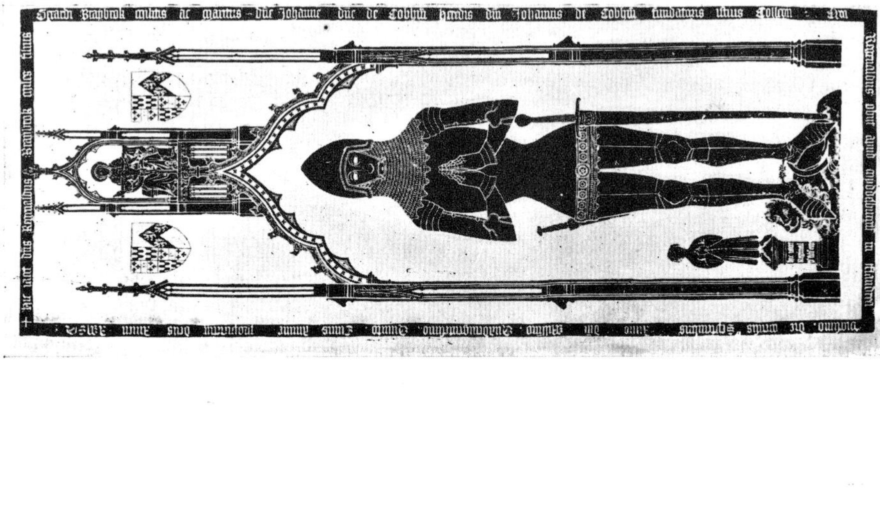

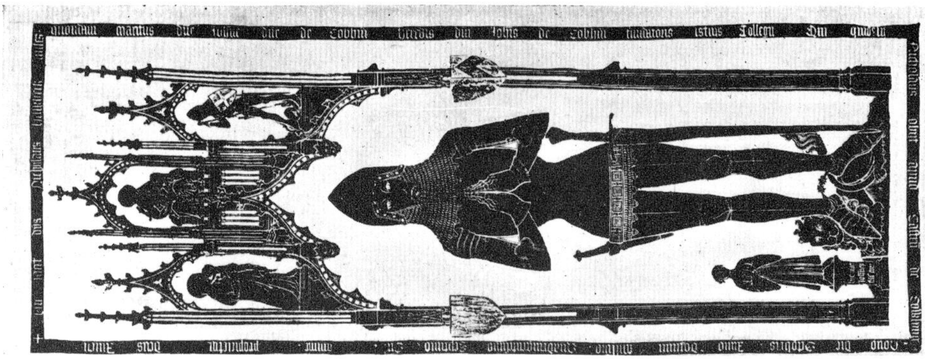

1407. Sir N. Hauberk,
Cobham, Kent.

1408. J. Hauley and two wives,
St. Saviour, Dartmouth.

1405. Sir R. Braybrok,
Cobham, Kent.

PLATE 15

1419. Baron Camoys and wife, Trotton, Sussex.

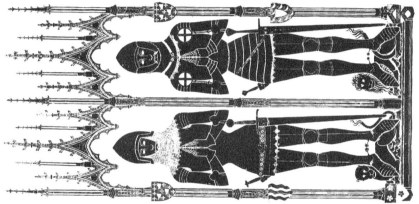

1412. Sir R. Swynborne and son, Little Horkesley, Essex.

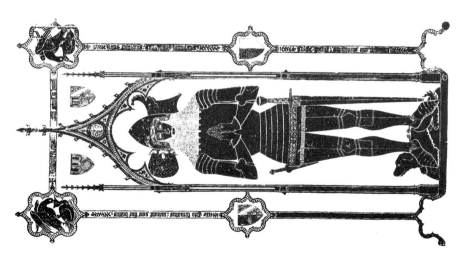

1409. Sir P. Courtenay, Exeter Cathedral.

PLATE 16

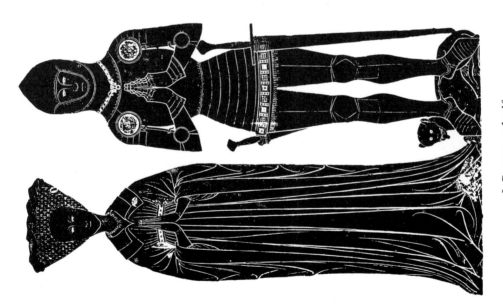

c. 1430. P. Halle and wife,
Herne, Kent.

1415. J. Peryent and wife,
Digswell, Herts.

PLATE 17

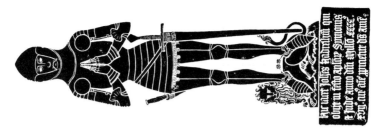

1417. J. Hadresham,
Lingfield, Surrey.

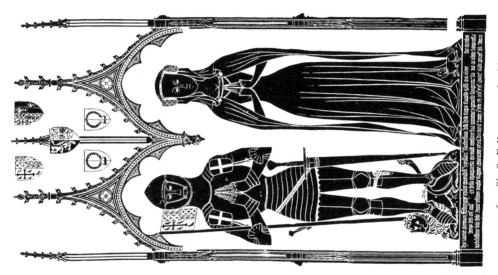

1416. Sir S. Felbrygge and wife,
Felbrigg, Norfolk.

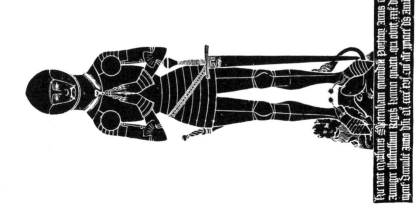

1416. M. Swetenham,
Blakesley, Northants.

RB   S

PLATE 18

1435. Sir J. Dyve, mother, and wife,
Bromham, Beds.

1426. Sir J. de Brewys,
Wiston, Sussex.

PLATE 19

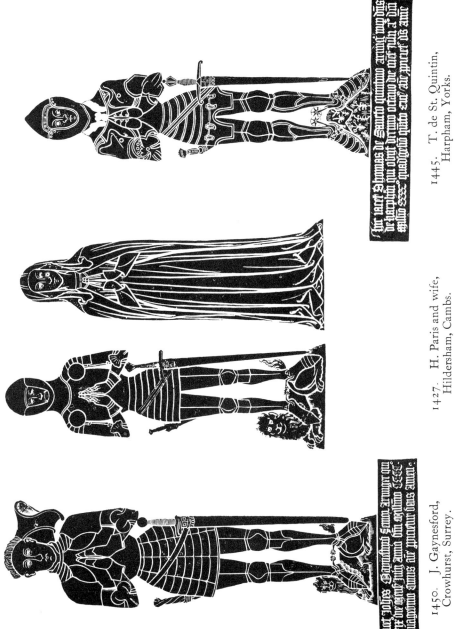

1445. T. de St. Quintin, Harpham, Yorks.

1427. H. Paris and wife, Hildersham, Cambs.

1450. J. Gaynesford, Crowhurst, Surrey.

PLATE 20

1441. Sir H. Halsham and wife,
       W. Grinstead, Sussex.

1444. Sir W. Echyngham, wife, and son,
       Etchingham, Sussex.

PLATE 21

1438. Sir J. Harpeden,
Westminster Abbey.

c. 1460. Anonymous and wife,
Adderbury, Oxon.

1458. R. Staunton,
Castle Donington, Leics.

PLATE 22

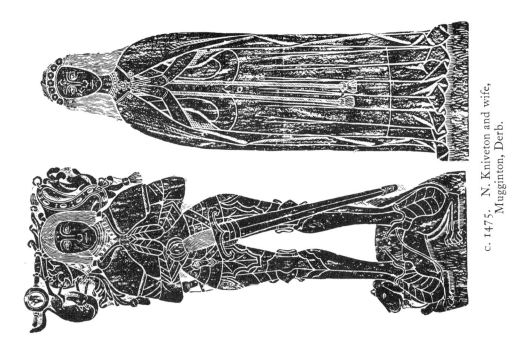

c. 1475. N. Kniveton and wife, Mugginton, Derb.

1458. T. Sherneborne and wife, Shernbourne, Norfolk.

PLATE 23

1470.   R. St. Leger and wife, Ulcombe, Kent.

PLATE 24

1492. P. Gerard, Winwick, Lancs.

PLATE 25

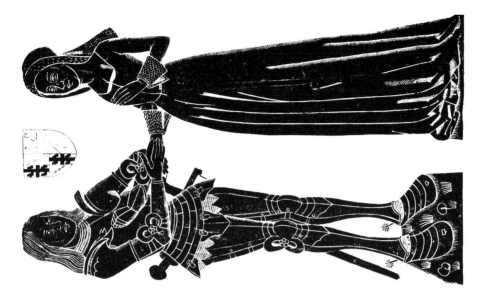

1487. Sir W. Mauntell and wife, Nether Heyford, Northants.

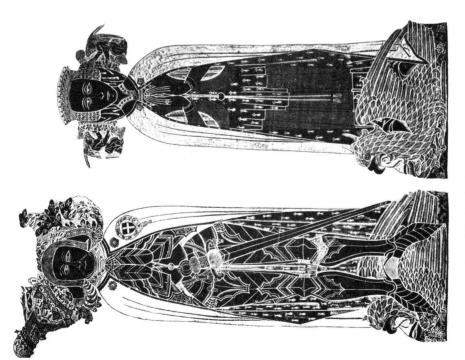

1483. The Earl of Essex and wife, Little Easton, Essex.

PLATE 26

1466. H. Parice,
Hildersham, Cambs.

1509. Lord le Strange and wife,
Hillingdon, Middx.

1480. Sir A. Grey,
St. Albans Abbey.

PLATE 27

2

1

1. 1481. H. Stathum and three wives, Morley, Derb.
2. c. 1500. — Compton and wife, Surrey Archæological Society, Guildford.

PLATE 28

1. c. 1520. Anonymous and wife, Theydon Gernon, Essex.
2. 1528. Sir R. Fitzlewes and four wives, Ingrave, Essex.

PLATE 29

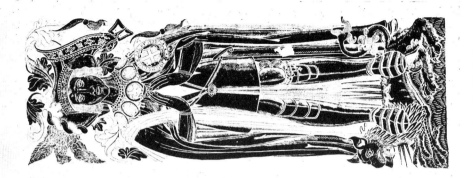

1538. Sir T. Bullen,
Hever, Kent.

1506. Sir R. L'Estrange,
Hunstanton, Norfolk.

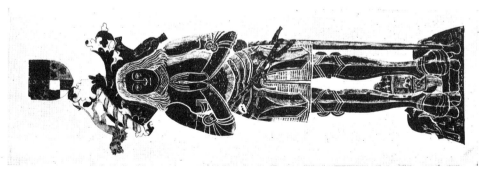

1507. Viscount Beaumont,
Wivenhoe, Essex.

PLATE 30

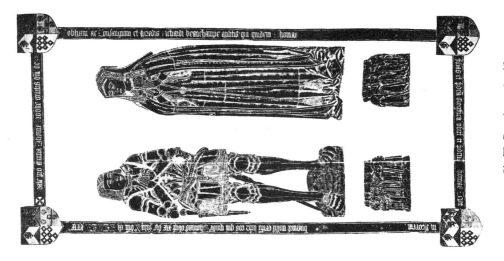

1529. Sir T. Brooke and wife, Cobham, Kent.

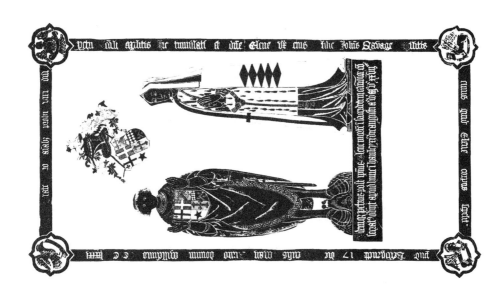

1527. Sir P. Legh and wife, Winwick, Lancs.

PLATE 31

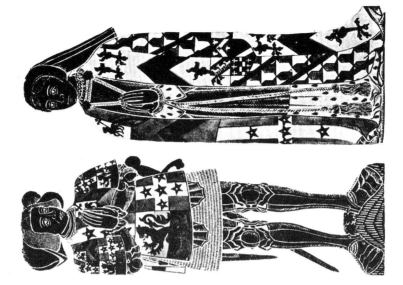

1547. Sir R. Verney and wife, Aldbury, Herts.

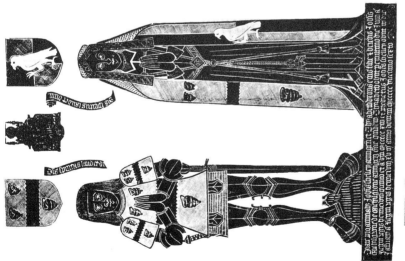

1526. J. Shelley and wife, Clapham, Sussex.

PLATE 32

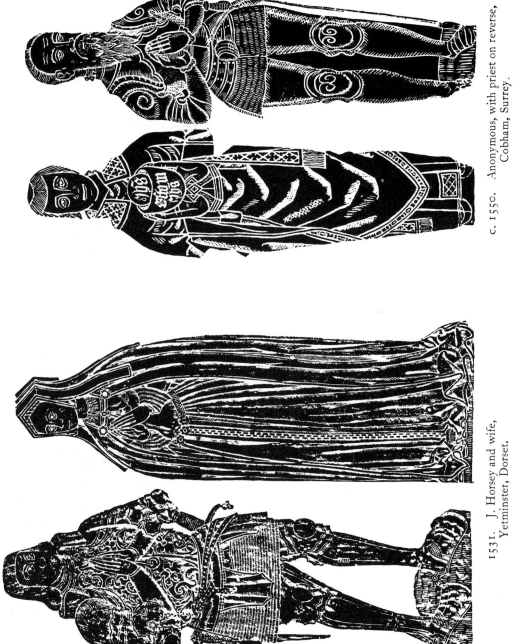

c. 1550. Anonymous, with priest on reverse,
Cobham, Surrey.

1531. J. Horsey and wife,
Yetminster, Dorset.

PLATE 33

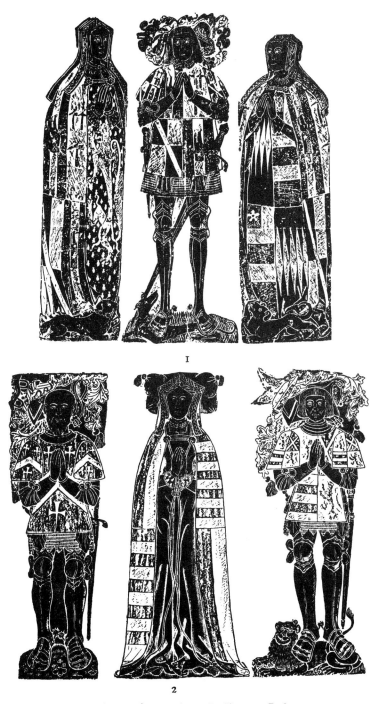

1

2

1. 1540. Sir W. Gascoigne and two wives, Cardington, Beds.
2. 1549. Thos. Fyndarne, and John, Lord Marnay and wife, Little Horkesley, Essex.

PLATE 34

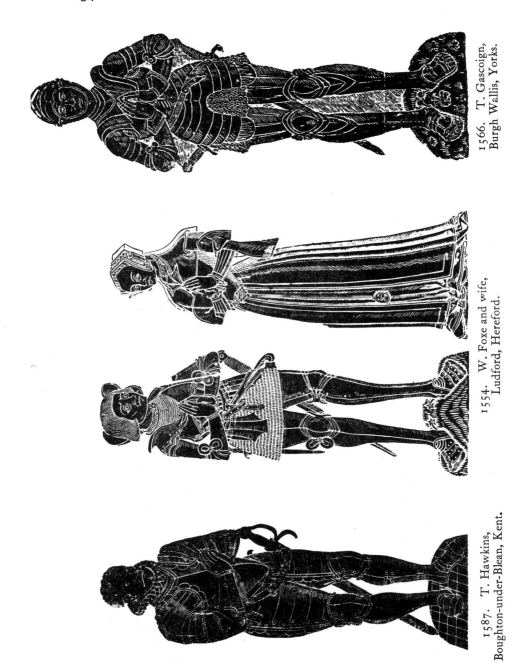

1566. T. Gascoign,
Burgh Wallis, Yorks.

1554. W. Foxe and wife,
Ludford, Hereford.

1587. T. Hawkins,
Boughton-under-Blean, Kent.

PLATE 35

1558. Sir H. Sacheverell and wife, Morley, Derb.

PLATE 36

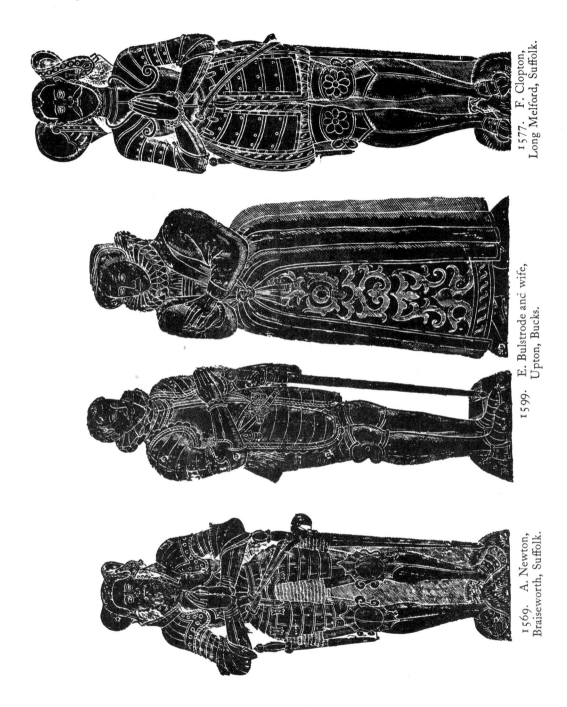

1577. F. Clopton,
Long Melford, Suffolk.

1599. E. Bulstrode and wife,
Upton, Bucks.

1569. A. Newton,
Braiseworth, Suffolk.

PLATE 37

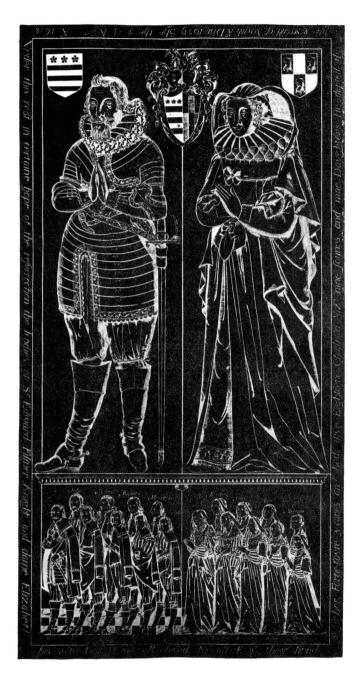

1629. Sir E. Filmer and wife, East Sutton, Kent.

PLATE 38

1

2

1. 1638.   Sir J. Harvye and wife, Cardington, Beds.
2. 1656.   T. Carew and wife, Haccombe, Devon.

PLATE 39

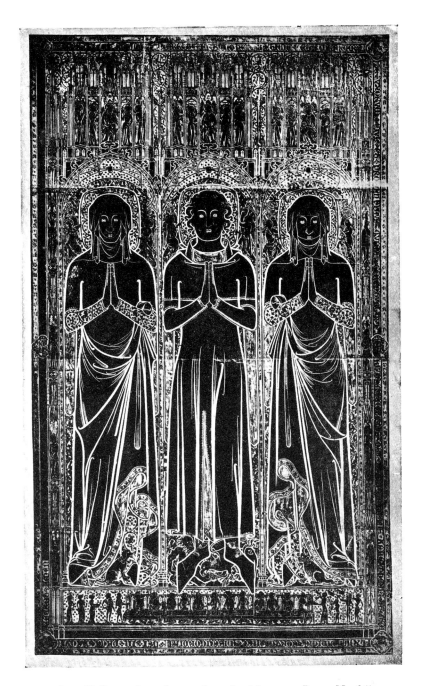

1364. R. Braunche and two wives, St. Margaret, Lynn, Norfolk.

PLATE 40

1402. R. Martyn and wife,
Dartford, Kent.

1408. R. de Paris and wife,
Hildersham, Cambs.

1391. J. Curteys and widow,
Wymington, Beds.

1391. J. Corp and grand-
dau., Stoke Fleming, Devon.

c. 1350. N. de Aumberdene,
Taplow, Bucks.

1356. R. Torryngton and wife,
Gt. Berkhampstead, Herts.

PLATE 41

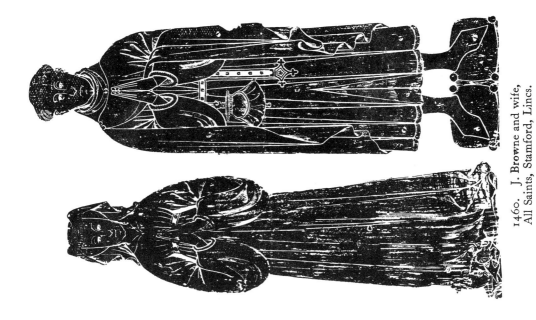

1460. J. Browne and wife,
All Saints, Stamford, Lincs.

1437. Sir T. Brook and wife,
Thorncombe, Devon.

PLATE 42

1. 1455. R. Manfeld and sister, Taplow, Bucks.
2. 1472. W. Norwiche and wife, St. George Colegate, Norwich.
3. 1477. J. Feld and son, Standon, Herts.
4, 5. 1420. J. Urban and wife, Southfleet, Kent.

PLATE 43

1. c. 1475. A Notary, St. Mary-at-Tower, Ipswich.
2. c. 1500. Anonymous and wife, Nayland, Suffolk.
3. 1497. W. Maynwaryng, Ightfield, Salop.

4. 1506. R. Legh, Macclesfield, Ches.
5. 1525. J. Marsham and wife, St. John Maddermarket, Norwich.
6. 1542. Sir T. Nevell, Mereworth, Kent.

PLATE 44

1525. T. Pownder and wife, St. Mary Quay, Ipswich.

PLATE 45

1529. J. Cook and widow,
St. Mary-de-Crypt, Gloucester.

1558. R. Rugge and wife,
St. John Maddermarket, Norwich.

1567. T. Noke and three wives,
Shottesbrooke, Berks.

1513. W. Wyddowsoun and wife,
Mickleham, Surrey.

PLATE 46

1593. T. Beale and family, with ancestors, All Saints, Maidstone, Kent.

1533. A. Evyngar and wife, All Hallows, Barking, London.

1586. T. Inwood and three wives, Weybridge, Surrey.

PLATE 47

c. 1600. Anonymous and wife,
Harrow, Middx.

1591. R. Whalley,
Queen's Coll., Cambridge.

1595. J. Cotrel, York Cathedral.

1596. J. Tedcastell and wife,
Barking, Essex.

PLATE 48

1607.   J. Verzelini and wife,
Downe, Kent.

1640.   G. Coles and two wives,
St. Sepulchre, Northampton.

1604.   J. Sea and two wives,
Herne, Kent.

1613.   H. Dickson, G. Miller and
A. Cooper, Watford, Herts.

PLATE 49

1399   Alianora de Bohun, Duchess of Gloucester,
Westminster Abbey.

PLATE 50

1　　　　　　　　　　　2　　　　　　　　　　　3

4　　　　　　　　　　　5　　　　　　　　　　　6

1. 1435. A. de Bures, wid. of Sir G. Bryan, Acton, Suffolk.
2. 1419. M. Cheyne, Hever, Kent.
3. 1455. J. Keriell, Ash-next-Sandwich, Kent.

4. 1535. Anonymous, St. Helen, Bishopsgate.
5. 1537. Lady Elizth. Scroope, w. of John de Vere, Earl of Oxford, Wivenhoe, Essex.
6. 1535. Lady Howard, St. Mary Lambeth.

PLATE 51

1. 1504.   G. Shelford, Bramley, Hants.
2. 1464.   A. Norbury (widow), Stoke
                d'Abernon, Surrey.
3. 1524.   E. Broughton (spinster), Chenies,
                Bucks.

4. 1596.   M. Rust, Necton, Norfolk.
5. 1634.   E. Culpeper (aet. 7), Ardingly, Sussex.
6. 1543.   E. Perepoynt, W. Malling, Kent.
7. 1632.   D. Mannock, Stoke-by-Nayland,
                Suffolk.

PLATE 52

c. 1370.   T. de la Mare, St. Albans Abbey.

PLATE 53

1337. L. de St. Maur,
Higham Ferrers, Northants.

1417. T. Cranley,
New College, Oxford.

PLATE 54

1461. R. Lond,
St. Peter, Bristol.

c. 1370. Anonymous,
North Mimms, Herts.

1533. W. Wardysworth,
Betchworth, Surrey.

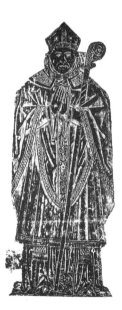

1579. R. Pursglove,
Tideswell, Derb.

c. 1375. Sir Simon of Wensley,
Wensley, Yorks.

c. 1525. J. Yong,
New College, Oxford.

PLATE 55

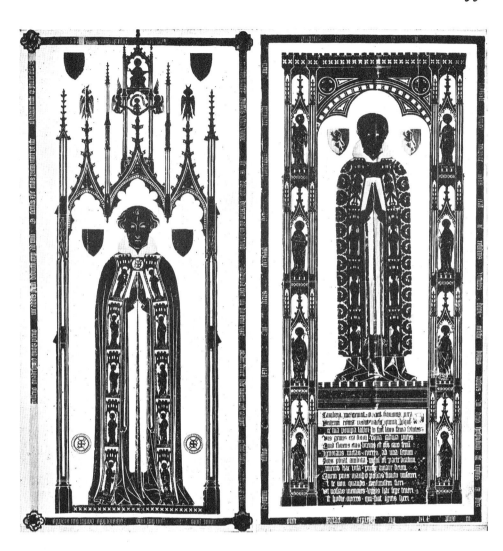

1401. J. Sleford, Balsham, Cambs.　　　1462. J. Blodwell, Balsham, Cambs.

PLATE 56

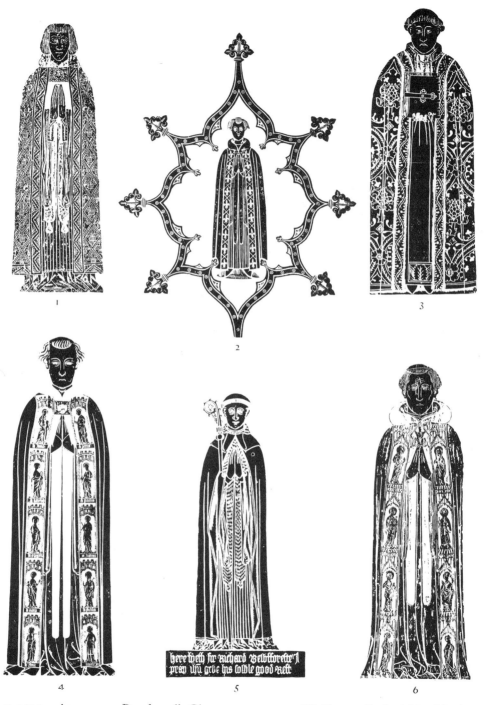

1. c. 1520. Anonymous, Dowdeswell, Glos.
2. 1386. R. de la Barre, Hereford Cathedral.
3. 1472. T. Tonge, Beeford, Yorks.
4. 1401. W. Ermyn, Castle Ashby, Northants.
5. c. 1510. R. Bewfforeste, Dorchester, Oxon.
6. 1404. H. de Codyngtoun, Bottesford, Leic.

PLATE 57

1631. S. Harsnett, Chigwell, Essex.

PLATE 58

1. 1522. R. Adams, East Malling, Kent.
2. c. 1520. E. Herwy, Elstow, Beds.
3. c. 1480. T. Teylar, Byfleet, Surrey.
4. 1528. R. Hacombleyn, King's College, Camb.
5. 1578. E. Guest, Salisbury Cathedral.
6. 1540. R. Lupton, Eton College, Bucks.

PLATE 59

1433. T. Nelond,
Cowfold, Sussex.

c. 1420. J. Bloxham and J. Whytton,
Merton College, Oxford.

PLATE 60

1 2 3 4

1. 1512. J. Stonor (Schoolboy), Wraysbury, Bucks.
2. c. 1540. Anonymous, Christ's College, Cambridge.
3. 1468. T. Hylle, New College, Oxford.
4. c. 1430. J. Kent (Schoolboy), Headbourne Worthy, Hants.

5 7

5. 1414. E. de la Zouch,
St. John's College, Cambridge.

7. 1405. J. Strete,
Upper Hardres, Kent.

PLATE 61

1494.   B. Roucliff and wife,
Cowthorpe, Yorks.

1400.   Sir J. Cassy and wife,
Deerhurst, Glos.

1475.   Sir W. Laken,
Bray, Berks.

1545.   Sir J. Spelman and wife,
Narborough, Norfolk.

1439.   Sir J. Juyn,
St. Mary Redcliffe, Bristol.

PLATE 62

1. 1529. M. Hornebolt, Fulham, London.
2. 1615. R. Morris, St. John, Margate, Kent.
3. 1484. W. Robert, Digswell, Herts.
4. c. 1580. Anonymous, Leigh, Kent.
5. 1498. W. Complyn, Weeke, Hants.
6. 1400. T. Chichele, Higham Ferrers.

PLATE 63

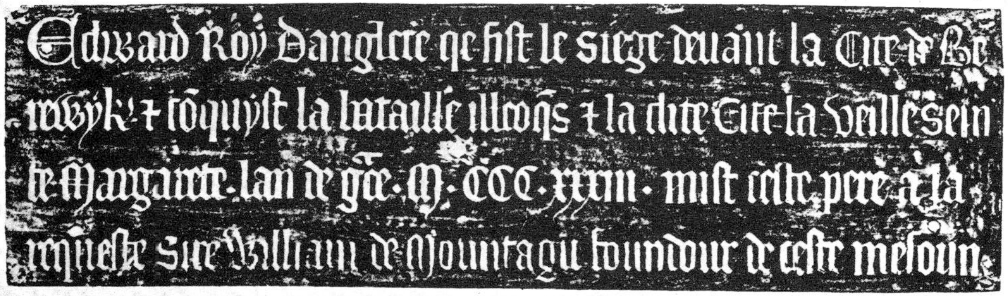

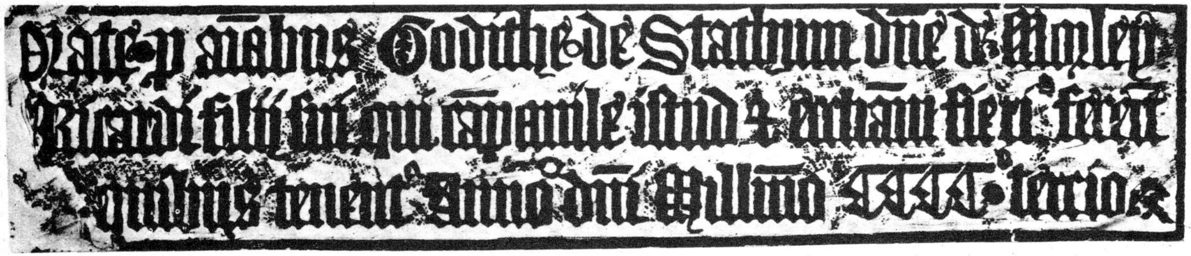

1. 1333. The foundation of Bisham Abbey.
2. 1349. P. de Lee, Barton-in-the-Clay, Beds.
3. 1403. G. de Stathum, Morley, Derb.

PLATE 64

1. c. 1420. R. Ruggenale, Hornsey (old church), Middx. 3. c. 1500. M. Reve, Darsham, Suffolk.
2. 1460. I. Cobham, Lingfield, Surrey. 4. c. 1500. H. Berd, Horstead, Norfolk.
5. 1525. J. Jobson, St. Mary-le-Wigford, Lincoln.

1

2

3, 4

5

PLATE 65

1   HERE LYETH THE BODY OF ANNE CVRTEIS,
THE WYFE OF AVGVSTIN CVRTEIS GENTL:
WHO DECEASED Y.15. DAYE OF FEBR: 1585:

2   Here lyeth buried Edmond Gresham Es-
quyre the sonne of Sir Iohn Gresham
knight, who deceased the last of
August 1586

3   HERE LYETH BVRIED Y BOBYE OF ANNE WAFERER Y
WIFE OF THOMAS TVRNER OF AVDELEVEND IN
ESSEX WHO DECEASED IN CHILDBEDD, THE
VIIJTH DAY OF FEBRVARY ANNO DOMINI 1617

4   HERE RESTH THE BODY OF MARGGET
THE WIFE OF IOHN WEGGE. WHO DIED
THE 4 OF MAY. ANO DOM 1621.

5   Mary Southwell late wife to
Donsany Southwell ESQ Lord of this
Mannor. Departed this life the
29th of May Anno Dñi 1636

1. 1585. A. Curteis, Honington, Suffolk.
2. 1586. E. Gresham, Thorpe Market, Norfolk.
3. 1617. A. Turner, Clapham, Beds.
4. 1621. M. Wegge, Swanton Abbot, Norfolk.
5. 1636. M. Southwell, Morton-on-the-Hill, Norfolk.

PLATE 66

126.   G. de Niverlée, Niverlée, Belgium (I.S.).

PLATE 67

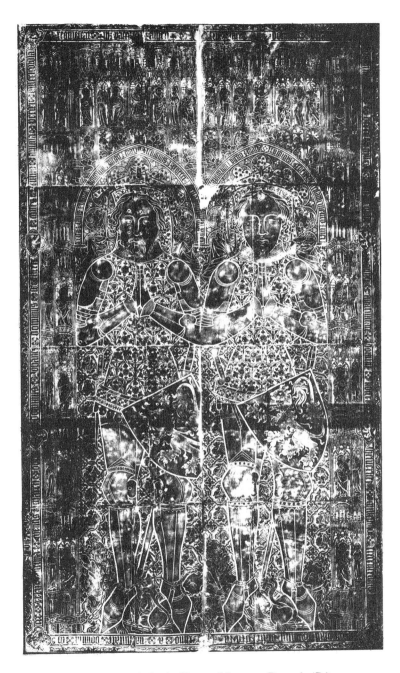

1332.   J. and G. de Heere, Museum, Brussels (B.).

PLATE 68

1358.   G. de Gothem and wife, St. Denys, Gothem, Belgium (I.S.).

PLATE 69

1517.   Bernardin van den Hove, Bruges Cathedral (B.)

PLATE 70

1459.   K. van Nethenen, wid. of A. Thomars,
Béguinage, Louvain (I.S.).

PLATE 71

1483. Abbot Adam Hertzogenrade,
Brauweilers, Germany (B.).

1279. Otto de Brunswick,
Hildesheim Cathedral (B.).

PLATE 72

1439. J. de Munter and wife, Bruges Cathedral (B.).

The Vicar

St. Mary's Vicarage

Church Hill   422-2652

Harrow, on the Hill, Middlesex

Call Miss Harris 422-1922

1.50 for 1
2.00 for 2 brasses

10-1   Tues. only